Limited Edition

Number

55

of

150

Monster. Martyr. Mother.

On Emilia Morris's thirteenth birthday, her mother Rachel moves into a tent at the bottom of their garden. From that day on, she never says another word. Inspired by her vow of silence, other women join her and together they build the Community. Eight years later, Rachel and thousands of her followers around the world burn themselves to death.

In the aftermath of what comes to be known as the Event, the Community's global influence quickly grows. As a result, the whole world has an opinion about Rachel – whether they see her as a callous monster or a heroic martyr – but Emilia has never voiced hers publicly. Until now.

When she publishes her own account of her mother's life in a memoir called *The Silence Project*, Emilia also decides to reveal just how sinister the Community has become. In the process, she steps out of Rachel's shadow once and for all, so that her own voice may finally be heard.

Carole Hailey completed the six-month Guardian/UEA novel writing course taught by Bernardine Evaristo, who imbued Carole with such a love for writing fiction that she abandoned her career in law to undertake an MA in Creative Writing at Goldsmiths, followed by a PhD in Creative Writing at Swansea University. Carole was a London Library Emerging Writer 2020/21. *The Silence Project* is her first published novel and was shortlisted for the Bridport Prize Peggy Chapman-Andrews First Novel Award 2020 and highly commended by the judges. She lives in Wales with her husband and two rescue dogs.

Publicity enquiries
Tel: 020 7269 0246 Fax: 020 7430 0916
Email: publicity@atlantic-books.co.uk

Sales: Natasha Drewett
Tel: 020 7269 0249 Fax: 020 7430 0916
Email: natashadrewett@atlantic-books.co.uk

Atlantic Books, Ormond House,
26–27 Boswell Street, London, WC1N 3JZ
Tel: 020 7269 1610 Fax: 020 7430 0916
Email: enquiries@atlantic-books.co.uk

THE SILENCE PROJECT

CAROLE HAILEY

CORVUS

Published in hardback in Great Britain in 2023 by Corvus,
an imprint of Atlantic Books Ltd.

10 9 8 7 6 5 4 3 2 1

A CIP catalogue record for this book is available from the British Library.

Hardback ISBN: 978 1 83895 606 6
Trade paperback ISBN: 978 1 83895 617 2
E-book ISBN: 978 1 83895 607 3

Printed in Great Britain by Severn, Gloucester

Corvus
An imprint of Atlantic Books Ltd
Ormond House
26–27 Boswell Street
London
WC1N 3JZ

www.corvus-books.co.uk

For Mum and for Pete, with love

Preface to the first edition of
The Silence Project: The Life and Legacy of Rachel Morris
by Emilia Morris

In a fire, you die long before your bones ignite. Skin burns at 40°C. Above 760°C, skin turns to ash. Bones are less flammable because they need to be exposed to 1200°C to burn, although long before that the layer of fat which you carry under your skin will boil. Your internal organs will explode. You will be dead even though your skeleton remains intact.

On 31 October 2011 I watched my mother burn to death. It wasn't an accident. She built her own pyre. She doused it in petrol. She climbed up and stood with her legs apart, bracing herself. I didn't know what she was planning. I assumed it was another publicity stunt, which of course it was, just not in the way that I was expecting.

Mum was wearing a green dress with diagonally cut pockets. From one of them she produced a lighter and briefly held it above her head as if it was a trophy. Even then, I was convinced she would walk away. I'm sure the press thought so, too. In those later years, Rachel of Chalkham's protests always attracted television crews, but nobody could have anticipated that they were about to witness the scoop of their careers.

I am surprised by the details I remember from that day. I can feel the pressure of Tom's arm around my shoulders as we watched my mother. I remember the smell of his fingers as he stroked my cheek. I remember the sky was cloudless, which was unusual for an October day in Hampshire. I remember my mother didn't look at me. Not once. Not as she crouched down, wobbling slightly. Not as she ran her thumb along the top of the lighter, cupping her left hand around it. Not even as she lowered the flame towards the petrol-soaked branches.

What I remember most clearly about that day is that my mother died as she had lived: in complete silence. The pain of melting skin and boiling fat must have been excruciating in the seconds before her nerves stopped carrying signals to her brain, yet my mother did not cry out. Rachel of Chalkham. Silent to the end.

It has been eleven years since my mother's death, but the questions never stop. Everyone remains just as fascinated by her as they have always been and believes this gives them the right to ask me anything. What was Rachel of Chalkham like when she was plain Rachel Morris? How do I feel having the architect of the Event as my mother? Am I proud of her? Ashamed of her? Do I feel any guilt about what she did? Question after question, year after year, until I have had to accept that the questions aren't going away. On the contrary, my silence seems to fuel their obsession (just like her silence fuelled everything that happened).

Rachel's story has been told multiple times; at least that is what the authors of all the biographies on my desk would have you believe. They are unofficial because I have never let anyone have access to my mother's notebooks, and my father and I have never given interviews, except in those terrible hours immediately after the Event. Every so-called biography of Rachel is cobbled together from the internet and all of them contain information ranging from the downright false to the wildest conspiracy theories.

For years, I did my best to ignore the existence of the note-books. They were in a box which was first stored in an attic, then beneath the stairs, then under a bed. I didn't want to read them, and I didn't want anyone else to read them either. Sometimes, I would even hope that I might be burgled and the box stolen. Wasn't there already enough obsession with my mother without publishing her notebooks? But I've come to realise that the demand will not go away. The Community has made sure of that.

It has been widely reported that my father disagrees with my decision to allow publication of my mother's notebooks and I want to take this opportunity to state that this is not correct. The decision was a difficult one, and we both have mixed feelings about it. My father is apprehensive about the consequences of making my mother's words public; however, on balance, we both believe that publication is essential in light of what the Community has become.

The day Rachel stopped speaking she turned away from our family and towards the publicity that she and her Community courted. The Community may be my mother's legacy, but the twenty-nine notebooks chart her life between 24 May 2003 when she left our home and 31 October 2011 when she lit those branches and changed the world for ever. The notebooks are legally mine, but in every other way I accept that they belong to everyone. They belong to all those people whose lives have been shaped by what Rachel did and all the actions taken in her name since her death.

Countless people who never met her claim to understand who Rachel was. She was a demon. A heroine. The most important person to have lived. A saint. A devil.

Rachel was none of these. She was neither saint nor demon. No matter what she did, Rachel was very human. She was deeply flawed and deeply courageous. She was a bad person and a good one. She was also my mother.

This is my account of the life and legacy of Rachel Morris. It is intended to be a companion piece to her notebooks. An explanation, in so far as I am able to provide one, of what it was like to be the daughter of the woman who changed the world. It is an attempt to explain why Rachel did what she did, how she convinced all those other women to do what they did and how their collective actions changed the course of history. Scientists and political commentators believe my mother's actions averted catastrophes on a global scale, but in doing so, she set in motion countless other tragedies, many of which are still taking place as I write. The Community today is a malignant and rapacious organisation, entirely unrecognisable from my mother's original silence project.

In endeavouring to provide a truthful version of Rachel's story, I have written very little about events that I wasn't personally present at, such as what she did in the years I was at university. For people who wish to cross-refer, I have included page references where I've quoted from the notebooks. To add context, I've used various contemporaneous reports and I am indebted for the permissions I was given to reproduce the many articles to which I refer.

I asked several people to provide accounts of their recollections; some agreed, others didn't. I am extremely grateful to those individuals who were brave enough to revisit often distressing memories.

Most of all, I have to thank my father. Being the man who was married to Rachel of Chalkham is an invidious cross to bear, and although Dad remains deeply uncertain about this whole enterprise, his support and love for me is steadfast.

Finally, it is with the greatest of respect that I ask when you've read what I have to say about my mother, please draw your own conclusions, then grant me the freedom to step away from the suffocating shadow cast by Rachel of Chalkham.

Emilia Morris

Editor's Note

As mentioned in the author's preface, this book contains extracts from Rachel Morris's twenty-nine notebooks (published by Rampage Press). The location of each extract in the notebooks is identified using the referencing style: (# of notebook, page number(s)).

Below are brief descriptions of each of the twenty-nine notebooks. The notebooks themselves have been donated by the author to the British Library.

#1 Mega Jotpad, A4, flexible laminated covers, wirebound, lined, approx. one-third of back cover missing

#2 Moleskine, navy blue, A4, softcover, lined

#3 Oxford Black n' Red, A4, hardcover, casebound, lined

#4 Oxford Black n' Red, A4, hardcover, wirebound, unlined

#5 Pukka Jotta notepad, A4, wirebound, front cover torn

#6 Moleskine, navy, 19cm x 25cm, softcover, lined

#7 Moleskine, pale blue, large, softcover, lined

#8 Unbranded, yellow flowers on grey background, A4, wirebound, softcover, lined

#9 Tivoli, dark brown, recycled leather, A4, softcover, lined

#10 CIAK, dark green, A4, softcover, lined

#11 Paperblanks, floral design, 23cm x 18cm, hardcover, ruled

#12 Ryman, orange, 29.5cm x 21.5cm, softcover, ruled

#13 Moleskine, black, large, hardcover, ruled
#14 LEUCHTTURM1917, red, A4, hardcover, ruled
#15 CIAK, light grey, A4, softcover, lined
#16 Smythson, mustard, A5, leather-bound, lined
#17 Moleskine, lime green, A4, softcover, unlined
#18 Moleskine, black, A4, hardcover, lined
#19 Aspinal of London, neon orange, A4, calf leather, ruled, pp. 45–66 missing
#20 Moleskine, black, large, hardcover, ruled
#21 Moleskine, black, large, hardcover, ruled
#22 LEUCHTTURM1917, red, A4, hardcover, ruled
#23 Rhodia, black, A4, softcover, wirebound, ruled
#24 CIAK, red, A4, softcover, lined
#25 Oxford Black n' Red, A4, hardcover, casebound, lined
#26 Moleskine, red, 19cm x 25cm, softcover, lined
#27 Unbranded, hand-tooled, green leather, *R.M.* picked out on front cover in gold leaf
#28 Montblanc, black, A4, full-grain cowhide covers, lined
#29 Pukka Jotta notepad, green, A4, wirebound, ruled, front cover torn, rear cover missing

Before the Event

24 May 2003–31 October 2011

1.

On Saturday 24 May 2003 – the day of my thirteenth birthday and 3,082 days before the Event – my mother left home.

She didn't go far. After dragging assorted metal poles and canvas paraphernalia past the people enjoying drinks in our beer garden, she managed, with a considerable amount of effort, to pitch a tent beside the stream that marked the boundary between our bottom field and a small wood. At first, I believed the most important thing was to find out where my mother had got the tent, because we had never owned such a thing. However, it wasn't long before I realised that the tent (which had been abandoned in our garage by some campers the previous summer) was the least significant part of the story.

I really wanted to have my thirteenth-birthday party at Hollywood Bowl in Basingstoke, but we couldn't afford it. Instead, my parents had agreed that to mark my entry into touchy-teensville, as Dad insisted on calling it, our pub would stay shut until 2 p.m. My party would begin at 11 a.m., so my friends and I would have the run of the place for three whole hours. For me, the pub wasn't an exciting place to spend my thirteenth birthday. I was as much of a fixture as the 1998 Beer of the Year calendar, which had been hanging above a shelf of glasses for almost five years. It was perpetually turned to November's offering, which I can still remember word for word: *a hoppy delight replete with a sensational fruity palate and an unexpectedly noble head.* Clearly the brewery marketing department had employed an aspiring poet in love with the adjective.

Although I would rather have been somewhere else, my friends had worked themselves up into a frenzy at the idea of a party in a pub.

'JD and Coke, Nick, and hold the ice,' Sarah Philips yelled at Dad as she ran into the pub on the dot of eleven. She was so excited that I wouldn't have been at all surprised to find out she had spent the night sleeping outside. She shouted the same thing several times more, pushing her chest forwards and her bum backwards to such an extent that she looked deformed. At some point in the last twelve months, flirting had become one of our most popular hobbies, but Sarah hadn't even been in the pub for five minutes and she was already crossing a line. Fortunately, Dad was completely oblivious to Sarah's contortions, even though, as Gran was fond of saying, Sarah Philips was thirteen-going-on-thirty.

'What about brandy?' suggested Bea Stevens. 'Mum always lets me have brandy when I'm upset about something. She says letting me drink a little bit now means I won't be an alcoholic when I'm older.'

Bea's mother might have had a point, but nowadays I cannot bear the stuff. Ever since that police officer put some in my tea on 31 October 2011, just the smell of brandy is enough to make me gag. I did wonder afterwards if she had taken one of the bottles from the bar downstairs or whether all police officers carry a hip flask around with them, just in case. She made us sit at the kitchen table while she busied herself with the kettle, murmuring, 'It'll take the edge off,' as she poured a great big slug of brandy into each cup of tea. She meant well, but it didn't help. Nothing could. And it tasted revolting.

My father stood firm on the subject of alcohol at my party –

we were only thirteen, after all – but, being Dad, he did his absolute best to make sure we enjoyed ourselves. He piled fifty-pence pieces on the ledge by the jukebox, and although the machine was full of all the old music that he liked, that didn't stop us queuing up to pick songs, self-consciously shuffling our feet while doing bad lip-synching to bands called Human League, Culture Club, ABC and Howard Jones (who Mum always used to joke was Dad's twin, because they had the same long face and floppy hair). There were no boys present. They were the main topic of conversation, obviously, but there was no way I would have invited an actual boy to my birthday party because I would have literally died of embarrassment.

Dad had given in to my endless pleas to let us use the pool table, although he said the darts were strictly out of bounds. 'It's bad enough in here on match nights with darts flying around all over the place. Sorry, Ems, but no way am I going to let your lot loose on them.'

He always grumbled about darts evenings, but I knew he didn't mean it because of how often he said we relied on the money from match nights. Apparently it was good for our bank balance when the Boar's Blades won, because the better they did, the more they would drink. The team was named after our pub, which was called The Wild Boar, which was itself named after the huge white boar carved into a hill just outside Chalkham, which, as everyone knows, is where we lived.

So, no darts on my birthday, but the pool table was a great hit, despite everyone initially pretending they had no interest in playing. By the time Dad had wiped clean the blackboard and written down our names, our excitement, fuelled by the limitless supply of fizzy drinks and crisps in five different flavours, had reached fever pitch. Dad rode the wave of our enthusiasm, holding a rolled-up magazine against his chin like a microphone and commentating as if we were at the Embassy world snooker championships.

'And as we watch newcomer to the game Olivia Taylor lining up on the stripes,' he half-whispered, rasping his voice as if he had a fifty-a-day habit, 'all her opponent can do is hope she misses... But Olivia strikes it well...'

Olivia – Livy – who by then had already been my best friend for eight years, really did not strike it well – she was far more interested in making sure that her hair fell the right way, so it would look just as good to everyone standing behind her as it did to those standing in front – but that was my dad all over, always the peacemaker, the pacifier. My wonderful father. The consummate pub landlord.

Once the tournament was finished – I have absolutely no memory of who won – we again congregated in front of the jukebox until my mother made an appearance, carrying a large chocolate-caramel cake that Gran had spent all of the previous day making. My face burned with pleasure and embarrassment as everyone sang happy birthday. Afterwards, we ate slabs of cake, then everyone was given a bag of their favourite crisps to take home, the pub door was unlocked, punters started arriving and my party was over.

If I look over the top of the sofa from where I'm sitting at the table I've commandeered as my writing desk, through the window of the flat, and wait for a gap in the passing traffic, I can see the building on the opposite side of the street. Although it's an old pub in the middle of London and completely different to The Wild Boar, the sight of the sign hanging outside takes me back to my childhood: the beer wheezing out of the pumps and into the glasses with a splurt, the ever-present cigarette smoke (my nickname at school was Ashtray), Dad's terrible music, Mum ringing the bell for last orders and calling time.

It is tempting to write about my life before I turned thirteen, but this is a book about my mother, the choices she made and the consequences of those choices, so I have decided to begin with the day of my thirteenth birthday because, as far as I am concerned, that's when everything changed. Before then, my mother had just been Mum; it had simply never crossed my mind that one day Mum would become somebody else.

At first, I thought my mother had planned the whole tent-by-the-stream thing as a sort of birthday treat, that we would camp out together under the stars, which would have been entirely in character for her. When people ask me what she was like before she left, before her silence, before the Community, they almost always begin by asking what she was like as a mother. 'Tell me about her *parenting style*,' they say and I know they are expecting me to reply, 'Well, it was all there to see in my first thirteen years, if only I'd known what I was looking for,' or, 'Looking back now, it's obvious what she was planning.' But that's bullshit. I mean, she was my mother and it's not like I had another one to compare her to. Honestly, the only thing I can really say about Mum's parenting style was that occasionally it was a bit wearing trying to anticipate which mother would make an appearance on any given day.

For example, sometimes on weekends she would come into my room, snuggle under my duvet and gossip about my friends. Other times, she'd be all bossy and nitpicking, demanding to see my homework, going through it line by line, questioning and criticising, although the rest of the time she displayed little interest in my education. Occasionally, confessional mother would appear, and she would tell me things I *really* didn't want to know, like the time, when I was about ten, when she decided to confide in me in detail, and I mean *graphic* detail, about how, when and where she lost her virginity.

The incarnation I most disliked was counsellor-mother. Mum would sit herself down opposite me and demand that I tell her my worries. Back then, my anxieties usually revolved around my appearance, or which boys hadn't talked to me, or which boys *had* talked to me, and what they'd said. I didn't want to tell Mum those things, though, because when she did finally force me to confess them, she would laugh at me and say, 'Lucky you, Emilia, if that's all you've got to worry about.' What, I always wondered, was the point of asking if she was only going to dismiss whatever I said? Come to think of it, since she subsequently dismissed everything I had to say about what she chose to do, maybe the signs were there after all.

One thing I definitely remember from the afternoon of my thirteenth birthday is staring out of the bathroom window in the direction of the stream, watching Mum jabbing poles in the vicinity of various flaps as she struggled to put up the tent. I assumed that this flurry of activity was a result of yet another maternal incarnation. Perhaps she was planning to try being an earth-mother. 'Look at the stream, Emilia, imagine your negative feelings drifting with the current.' That sort of thing.

Midge was with her, nosing around, and one side of the tent had just collapsed on top of him, leaving only his front paws sticking out, when Dad yelled up the stairs. 'Rachel, I could do with some help down here.'

After a few seconds he shouted again. 'Ems, where's Mum?'

'Putting up a tent,' I shouted back.

'What?' he yelled, although I don't know why he bothered. Once the pub filled up, it was impossible for anyone downstairs to hear what anyone upstairs was saying. But that didn't stop Dad bellowing up the stairs several times a day, then waiting in vain to hear a response.

It is no exaggeration to say that the noise of the pub was the soundtrack of my childhood. Three rooms, all in a line: the bar, the snug and what we called the games room, because that was where the pool table and darts board were. There were doorways, but no doors, so you could stand by the fireplace in the snug at one end and see all the way through to the dartboard in the games room at the opposite end. My bedroom was above the games room, which was usually the quietest part of the pub because Dad never put any heating on in there, except on match nights. I lost count of the number of times the Blades asked him to turn it on for their Monday-evening training sessions, but somehow or other he always managed to forget. That's what he said anyway. In winter, the darts players would bring extra layers of clothing with them to put on once they got to the pub.

I liked Mondays best. Generally, no one got too drunk and I would go to sleep to the *thwunk* of darts hitting the board without any of the shouting that jolted me out of my sleep on other nights. As the week went on, the volume of the punters increased. So too the volume of the jukebox. It was an unwinnable competition: the louder people spoke, the more Dad turned up the music; the louder the music, the louder people shouted.

'Silence is bad,' Dad would say. 'Silence means no punters. And you know what that means…?' I knew all right. No punters, no money.

Sometimes, I try and convince myself that this is why I hate silence. That maybe this is why silence makes my heart thump a bit faster, my mouth go dry and my palms sweat. Perhaps this is why the sound of silence makes my brain fill with thoughts of burnings, drownings, plane crashes, cancer and shootings. The lack of noise lets in thoughts about whether today is the day that I'm going to have a head-on collision in my car or choke on my dinner and asphyxiate or fall, hit my head on the side of a table and die from a subdural haematoma. Silence makes me wonder if this is my last day or hour or minute on earth. I have lived through the worst thing and I'm still here, but that doesn't stop the sound of silence terrifying me. It makes me want to scream, but I don't because what if I open my mouth and nothing comes out?

There was no silence on my thirteenth birthday. The pub filled up quickly after my party – it was hot, the windows were wide open all day long, and sunshine always made people want to come and drink – so by the time Dad called up the stairs to ask where Mum was, it was already really busy. I went back to the bathroom window to check how she was getting on with the tent. She was turning one of the metal poles end over end, as if she was hoping it might spring from her hands and plant itself wherever it was supposed to be. Midge had extracted himself from the canvas, and each time the end of a pole swung past him, he would lunge towards it, snapping his jaws. I looked at myself in the mirror over the sink, examining my face. Back then, I checked for spots at least once an hour. Mum had helped me straighten my hair for the party, and if she wanted me to sleep in the tent with her I would have to find something to tie it up with or else it would be frizzy by the morning.

I went down the stairs, walked five steps along the hallway and then, with the sixth step, I left our home and was in the pub. I stood at the end of the bar, listening to the buzz of voices fuelled by the first drinks of the day. Eventually, Dad caught sight of me and beamed. 'Collect the empties for me, love,' he said, pouring a beer.

'But before that, give Mum a call, will you? It's manic in here.'

'She's down by the stream,' I said.

'What's that?' He frowned at me, puzzled.

'Mum. She's down by the stream.'

'What the f—?' He stopped himself. 'What on earth is she doing? Go and get her would you, Ems?'

'Mum first, or the empties?'

He looked at the shelf of glasses. There were still a few clean ones. 'Mum first. Thanks, Ems…'

The beer garden was warm as I picked my way through the glasses abandoned on the grass; I'd collect them on my way back. Mum was still concentrating on trying to put up the tent and she didn't notice me approaching, so when I said her name she swung around and almost brained me with a metal pole.

'Dad says he needs you behind the bar.'

She put the pole on the ground. Then she put her hands on her hips and looked at me. Midge nudged my leg with his head and I tugged his ear.

'Come on, Mum. Dad needs you – it's really busy inside.'

She shook her head really, really slowly, like she was worried it might fall off.

'What are you doing, Mum?'

She pulled a pen out of her pocket and a notebook, which I was annoyed to see she had pinched from my room. I had an extensive collection of notebooks, although I rarely used more than a page or two of each one, scrawling down a few angst-riven musings about the tribulations of my life, which I'd invariably forget about the next day. *Staying here*, she wrote in my notebook. *Need peace and quiet.*

It is worth noting that this notebook – which, as far as I can recall, was a purple Paperblanks notebook that Mum herself had bought me – should technically be notebook #1, but it was not among her belongings when the police eventually returned them to us several weeks after the Event. I have no idea what happened to it. Perhaps my mother decided there was nothing of any relevance in it and chucked it out, maybe one of the Members took it – who knows? In those very early days, my mother made no attempt to separate what she wrote down for herself from the notes she wrote for Dad and me, and in what is the official notebook #1, you can clearly see messages she wrote for us, mainly mundane requests for things she wanted brought from the house. For example: '*E. pls bring 2 T-shirts and navy jumper that Gran bought me*' scrawled in a margin (#1, p. 13). You can also see my mother's point-blank refusals to even consider leaving the tent and moving back into our home. '*No!!! Stop asking!! I need to stay here. I need to be silent!!!*' (#1, p. 17).

Mum always used a lot of exclamation marks when she wrote about her silence. She would jab the dot in a way that felt like an actual exclamation, as if she really was shouting. Sometimes she did it so hard that she stabbed a hole in the paper, and in the reproduction of notebook #1 you can see several places where these appear as slightly larger, darker circles (see #1, pp. 23, 34, 45, 56, 59 and 72).

But on the afternoon of my birthday that was all ahead of me and, as far as I can remember, in response to the declaration that she needed some peace and quiet I just shrugged and went to pick up the glasses. I was used to Mum's eccentric behaviour. I remember thinking that Dad wouldn't be happy. But that's all I remember thinking. It never crossed my mind – and why would it? – that that afternoon marked a frontier in our lives. Because earlier that day, perhaps when she was singing 'Happy Birthday', or maybe when she was calling goodbye to my friends as they left my party, but certainly at some point during the day I turned thirteen, I had heard my mother's voice for the final time.

2.

I don't remember the sound of Mum's voice, but I do remember when I began to forget it.

It was only a few days after she moved into the tent, and I was still convinced it was just a temporary thing, when I woke up in the middle of the night and knew straight away that something was wrong. At first I couldn't work out what it was. I'd been feeling poorly all day and when I'd said I didn't want any dinner Dad had packed me off to bed early. When I woke up everything was silent, so I knew it was after kicking-out time downstairs. I lay very still, listening to my breathing, trying to understand what had happened. I rolled onto my side, and it was then that I felt my pyjama bottoms sticking to my thighs. I got out of bed, plucking the material away from my skin. I went into the bathroom and pulled the door shut really quietly, so as not to wake Dad. Only then did I put the light on.

I couldn't believe the amount of blood. If I hadn't known better I might have thought I'd been stabbed in my bed while I slept. No one had warned me that I might bleed so profusely. I pulled off my pyjama bottoms and examined the streaks of reddish-brown on the inside of my thighs. Mum had prepared me well, thankfully, so I wasn't scared by the sight of the blood that night.

I was officially a woman now. That's what Mum had always said while making sure I knew exactly what to expect when puberty hit. She was full of aphorisms on the subject: 'Embrace the hormones, Emilia, you'll miss them when they're gone' and, about period pain, 'Proof women are the stronger sex, Emilia' and 'Tampons, best invention ever'.

'Ready for when you need them, Emilia,' she had said some months previously, waving a selection of sanitary products under my nose before heading off with them towards the bathroom.

I ran some water onto the corner of a towel and scrubbed my legs, belatedly realising that perhaps it wasn't the best idea to use Mum's cream towel. She was going to freak out when she saw it. After I had cleaned myself up, I pulled open the bathroom cabinet and shoved various pots and packets around, but there was no sign of anything that looked like a sanitary towel. Bundling my pyjama bottoms up in the towel, I put the whole lot in the laundry basket. I would put another pair of pyjamas on, then go and find my mother. Whatever this living-in-a-tent, no-talking thing was about, when I told her what had happened, Mum would come home.

I crept down the stairs. By the time I reached the bottom, Midge was waiting for me, tail thumping. There was enough moonlight for me to pick my way through the beer garden, but even though I knew that stretch of grass as well as I knew my own bedroom, the dark trees reaching overhead and the garden furniture looming towards me out of the blackness still made my breath catch. Midge bounded around, sniffing everything he could find and snorting happily. The garden smelled different at night, damp and earthy – less brewery and more overgrown woodland. Outside the pub a car crawled down the street, a brief flash of headlights lighting up the rusty swing in the corner of the garden before sliding off the hydrangeas. As the sound of the engine faded, I realised I was holding my breath. I let it out and carried on towards Mum's tent.

A light flickered inside the canvas. The day before, she'd written me a note – *candles and matches, please*. I could only find scented candles she'd been given as presents and I'd delivered them along with the frozen pizza that I'd heated up for dinner. Mum and Dad had always taken it in turns to do the cooking, and as soon as I was old enough, it became my job to deliver a plate of food to whichever one of them was serving in the pub. If they were lucky, and things were quiet, they would be able to pull a stool round to the side of the bar and sit down while they ate. On busy nights, they would just grab a mouthful between pulling pints. But with Mum in the tent and Dad behind the bar, we'd been reduced to eating whatever I could find in the freezer.

The candlelight inside the tent meant Mum must be awake and I was about to poke my head inside to find out when I heard Dad's voice. I stopped so suddenly that Midge bumped his nose into the back of my leg and we both sat on the grass to listen.

'… what do you want me to do?' Dad was saying. He sounded angry. There was silence, and when Dad said, 'That's rubbish,' I realised that Mum must be writing things in my notebook then showing them to him.

'What about Ems?' Dad asked. More silence. 'Of course she needs you, Rachel. You're her mother.'

One of the many lovely things about my dad is that he hardly ever gets angry. Back then he would always say that, with running a pub, you have to learn to swill your anger away with the slops because when people get drunk, they speak so much rubbish that you have to let it wash right over you. But that night, whatever Mum was writing clearly wasn't washing over him.

'This is ridiculous. Why won't you speak? What am I supposed to say when people ask what's going on? I know things haven't been great between us, Rach, but seriously, how can you think this is going to solve anything?'

I'd known they'd been going through a bit of a 'rough patch' as Mum had called it, but to be honest, loads of my friends had parents who genuinely appeared to hate each other, and compared to them Mum and Dad's bickering didn't seem so bad. Gran always said that my parents were 'meant to be together', that they had 'found their way back to each other against all the odds' and that they 'went together like peaches and cream'. Looking back now, it's obvious she only said those things because that's what she wanted to believe, and of course Gran had played a major part in Mum finding her way back to Dad. Gran was Dad's mum, but she and Mum were so close that people who didn't know often thought she was Mum's mum.

Of course, people who didn't know better also assumed Dad was my biological father.

I can't remember a time before Nick was my dad. It was never a secret, but it was also never a big deal. He is the only father I have cried in front of, been embarrassed by and given Father's Day cards to. He's the only father who swung me up on his shoulders, so high that I cried with disappointment when my outstretched fingertips didn't brush the clouds. He's the only father who taught me to ride a bike and told me funny stories to distract me while the doctor set my arm after I fell off the swing. He is the only father I have ever loved. We've never talked much about the fact that Nick isn't actually my biological father, but I do remember him telling me when I was really little that if he could pick any child from anywhere in the whole world to be his child, he would pick me every single time. I like to believe that's still the case, even now, and although I'll never know whether things would have turned out differently for my mother if she had chosen someone else to be my father, I honestly believe that the best decision Mum ever made was choosing Nick to be my dad.

Here's something no one knows about Mum. When I was a kid, she used to tell me stories about my biological father, my *bio-dad* as she called him. I suppose she thought it was funny to make things up, but I was never comfortable with it, not least because I felt like we were being disloyal to Dad. The first time she made up a story about my bio-dad, Dad was downstairs and Mum had put the news on the television in the kitchen while I ate my tea – I must have only been seven or eight years old – and there was an interview, probably with a politician. I vividly remember shovelling baked beans into my mouth when my mother flicked her hand casually towards the television and said, 'Oh, look, there's your bio-dad.'

I can still hear the sound of my fork hitting the plate and feel the baked beans dribbling off my chin and plopping onto my T-shirt. I looked from Mum to the television and back again. It could only have been a matter of seconds before the programme moved on and the man disappeared from the screen.

'That's him? That's my bio-dad?' I asked.

'Yep,' said Mum, flicking the kettle on.

'Is he famous?'

'Of course, darling, why else would he be on TV?'

'Does he know I'm watching him?'

'Don't be silly, darling. How could he possibly know that?'

While she busied herself making a cup of tea, I thought about what I would say at school the next day. Olivia and I were already best-friends-forever by then and she would be *so* jealous because the previous week we'd had to write about what we wanted to do when we grew up. I wanted to be a vet so I could spend every day cuddling puppies like Midge. Livy – always a bit of a rebel – hadn't written anything; instead, she had drawn herself inside a television set because she wanted to be a presenter and wear a different outfit every day. Livy never did make it in front of the camera but she is a high-powered City lawyer so she hasn't done too badly. You probably already know I'm not a vet.

Back then, for eight-year-old me, it was exciting to see my bio-dad on the television at first; however, by bedtime it suddenly didn't seem exciting any more. It was scary. Would bio-Dad want to take me away from Dad? Would Dad still want to be my father when he found out that bio-dad was famous? In the end, I was in such a state that I got out of bed, trailed down the stairs and stood at the end of the bar crying, waiting for one of my parents to see me. I was only allowed to do this if there was an emergency, but I'd worked myself up into such a state that I was convinced that bio-dad was about to arrive any second to steal me away.

Mum was the one who led me back upstairs, sitting on my bed and waiting for me to calm down enough to tell her what was wrong.

'Oh, darling,' she said, and actually laughed. 'He's not your bio-dad. You're a big girl now – you really should be old enough to understand when someone's teasing you.'

I didn't understand. 'So who was the man on the TV?'

'Who knows? I wasn't even watching it.'

'But why—?' I stopped. Back then I didn't even know what question I wanted to ask.

Now when I think about that day, I have no problem coming up with questions I'd ask my mother if she was still alive. There were so many little 'jokes' about who my bio-dad was: astronaut, actor, author, criminal, musician – anyone, it seemed, who caught her imagination when she was in the right mood. I could start my questions with 'Why would you joke about something like that?' Or 'Why on earth joke about it to your own child?' And, let's face it, she might have pretended they were jokes, but essentially, each time she made up stories about my bio-dad it was a lie, so, 'Why would you lie to me about something so important?'

That night, what I remember most vividly was the relief I felt when I understood that the man from the television wasn't going to come and take me away. I was left with an abiding hatred of baked beans, though. To this day they taste of lies.

In the tent, candles flickered, and the silhouettes of my parents against the canvas flickered too. I shivered and felt around for Midge, wanting to cuddle up to him, but patience was never one of Midge's virtues. Out of the dark his shadow loomed against the tent and he pushed his way inside.

'Midge? How did you get here? I left you in the house...' Dad stuck his head out of the tent, flashing a torch across my face. 'Ems? How long have you been there?'

I shrugged and said, 'Not long.'

'Why aren't you in bed?'

'Something's happened. I need Mum. Don't worry, Dad, she'll come home now.'

I stood up and walked over to the tent, and it was only when I heard Dad gasp that I looked down and realised that a second pair of pyjama bottoms were now bloodstained. Midge sniffed my crotch but I pushed him away, half-crouching in the entrance to the tent, and looked at Mum. She didn't seem particularly pleased to see me.

'Mum, I've got my period. I need the things you bought, but I can't find them. Please come and help me?'

At that point, there was absolutely no doubt in my mind that she would get to her feet, reach for my hand, smile at Dad and say something like, 'Well, this has been fun, but it's time to go back to the house.' We would walk through the beer garden together while she told me how proud she was that I was now a woman. We'd go in the back door, up the stairs, she'd show me where the sanitary towels were, then she'd see the mess I'd made of her cream towel and get annoyed, but when I told her that my tummy was hurting really badly, she'd make me a hot-water bottle and a warm drink and sit on the end of my bed until I felt better.

I was completely certain that's what Mum would do and not one bit of me expected her to do what she actually did.

First, she looked at me. I mean *properly* looked at me, from the top of my head, down over my too-small Hello Kitty pyjama top, pausing for a moment on the bloodstained pyjama bottoms before carrying on down to my feet. Watching her looking at me was the weirdest experience: it was like being examined by a stranger who had never seen me before, as if she was trying to decide what she thought of me.

Then Mum reached for the notebook. Dad's breathing was really loud and I thought he was going to shout at her, but he just squeezed his lips tightly together. Mum only wrote for a few seconds, then held up what she'd written for me to see. I had to squint to read it.

My bedside table. Second drawer down.

That was it. That was the extent of my mother's help.

Sometimes I wonder if I was so hurt by what my mother did that night – or, more to the point, didn't do – that I deliberately made myself forget what she sounded like because, by the start of the school holidays a few weeks later, I was beginning to recognise the ache deep inside me when my period was due, I was using tampons and I could no longer remember the sound of my mother's voice.

3.

From: Nick Wright
To: Emilia Morris
Date: 20 February 2022

Subject: Mum

Hi darling,

Lovely to see you yesterday. I hope you didn't get caught in that downpour on your way home.

Look, I'm sorry the conversation got so heated. I know I probably had too much wine, but I am genuinely concerned what the Community might do when it finds out you're writing a book about Rachel. Having said that, I do understand why it's something you want to do, so I'll try and fill in some background for you, although it's surprisingly difficult to remember what our lives were like before.

I guess I always knew I was living on borrowed time with Rachel. I was never going to be enough for her. I mean, your mother was gorgeous and funny and clever, and what was I? A lonely divorced bloke with a pub that I was barely managing to keep above water. Of course she wanted more than I could give her.

I think you know that Rachel and my mother, your gran, wrote to each other. Gran loved writing to people, sitting at that old desk of hers with a cup of tea and a teacake (always lightly-toasted, heavily-buttered, do you remember?) writing letters with her Basildon Bond paper and matching envelopes. She wrote to so many people: school friends she hadn't seen for decades, people she'd met on a beach in Dorset thirty years earlier, and strangers she'd sat next to on the train and wound up talking to, swapping addresses on scraps of paper. Do you remember that time she joined a pen-pal scheme that matched her with Japanese women who wanted to practise their English? She didn't like those airmail letters one bit. Always complained how thin and slippery they were, like council toilet paper, she said.

The point is that I wasn't particularly surprised when I found out that my mother and Rachel had been writing to each other. I imagine Gran trotted out her usual comments on my failed marriage (she used to call it my starter-marriage!) and no doubt she told your mum that I'd put it behind me. I had, as it happens, and of course I didn't mind at all when I found out they had been in touch with each other – it just would have been nice to know what they were planning.

Your mother arrived late one evening, just as I was locking up. The last time I'd seen Rachel she'd been eighteen, brunette and experimenting with a perm. A decade later, standing in the doorway of the pub, her hair was short, blonde and spiky, but other than that, she looked just the same. 'Am I too late for a drink?' she said, or something like that, but I just stared at her. Rachel Morris. There. In my pub.

You know she was my first girlfriend, but I don't think I've ever told you how your mum broke my heart a few weeks before she went off to university. She sat me down and told me that she needed to unburden herself. At first, I honestly thought she was worried that her bags would be too heavy when she left for university (it's no wonder she split up with me!). It was only after a while that I realised she was talking about me. I was the burden. Your mum wanted to unburden herself of me.

I spent the rest of the time before she left alternately telling anyone who would listen how much I hated her and begging her to change her mind. Eventually the day came that a taxi pulled up outside her house, and when it drove away, I was certain any chance of getting back together with Rachel Morris was gone forever. Indeed, until the night she turned up ten years later, she never did come back. She didn't come home for the first Christmas, and then her parents moved away so she had no reason to return to Chalkham. But somewhere down the line, she'd acquired Gran's address, or Gran had acquired hers, and together they'd hatched the plan that led her to the doorway of The Wild Boar.

Eventually I stopped staring and gave her a hug, and when she hugged me back, I remember thinking that we fitted together like we were still eighteen. This is where it gets tricky, Ems. I want to be honest, but this isn't the sort of stuff a father should talk about with his daughter. I'm not even sure it's relevant, but then again, perhaps everything your mum did was somehow relevant so I'm going to try and tell you as much as I can without causing either of us to feel too embarrassed to ever see each other again!

There was a bit of chit-chat. She was evasive, wouldn't tell me where she'd been living or what she'd been doing or why she'd come back to Chalkham. Thinking about it now, I can see how carefully she'd planned it. God, this is so difficult – I've just had to pour a large glass of wine to fortify myself! What I'm trying to say is that after my first marriage broke down it was difficult meeting women. You know what it was like in the village – everyone knew everyone, I was working every evening, and of course Gran knew that better than anyone. That's why she encouraged your mum. She knew I was lonely. And she had always loved Rachel.

It would be wrong to say that Rachel took advantage of me. After all, I was a grown man and entirely willing, but (and it's an important but) there's no way I would have tried it on with her that night. No way at all. But your mum knew what she wanted, and she did what she needed to do to make sure she got it. Afterwards, I remember we sat on the floor, leaning against the bar, and drank vodka straight out of a bottle. That's when she told me about how she and my mother had kept in touch and how, when Gran heard how difficult things were for Rachel, she took it upon herself to suggest that Rachel come and live with me.

I can practically see Gran's letters. You and Nick were always so close, she would have written. Something like that. There's a spare room at the pub since I moved to the cottage. He'd love to see you. There was no doubt that your gran was right – it was fantastic to see Rachel – but I just wish, looking back, that I'd had at least some sort of say in the decision. It doesn't do much for your self-esteem to realise how easily you've been manipulated. Although, given everything that's happened, it's probably the least of my issues!

That first night, before we finished the vodka, your mum said something about the spare room being fine, but if there was room in my bed…? Goodness knows what rubbish I babbled, but by the time we got up off the floor it was all sorted and your mum was there to stay. She went to get her stuff from the car, and the rest of the story you already know because I've often told you about how Rachel only had two things with her the night she moved in. She had a heavy bag over her shoulder, and in my rush to take it from her I barely noticed the second thing, wrapped in a blanket and held close to her chest. It wasn't until Rachel folded down a corner of the blanket that I saw you. Emilia. Beautiful, perfect baby Emilia. My Ems.

And of course, that was that, and despite every single thing that has happened since, I can honestly say that the best day of my life was and forever will be the day your mum brought you to live at The Wild Boar.

I think that's about as much as I can manage at the moment, Ems. I'm going to send this before my nerve fails me and then I'm going to have another large glass of wine.

Don't forget dinner here next Friday. Looking forward to seeing you – 7 p.m. Don't be late!

Love,
Dad

4.

By the time school finished in July 2003, Dad and I already knew things weren't going to go back to how they were, even if we weren't admitting it out loud. Gran kept saying things to me like, 'Your mum just needs some time out' and 'It's difficult being a woman in today's world'. Gran was nothing if not practical, though, and as soon as she found out what was going on, she vetoed our frozen-pizza diet and hauled bags of groceries into the kitchen, muttering darkly about rickets and scurvy and malnutrition. The tension I had been carrying around with me for weeks eased slightly. At least with Gran taking care of the cooking we were eating proper food and Dad could concentrate on the pub.

I missed Mum. I missed snuggling with her under my duvet, gossiping about the latest intrigues in my thirteen-year-old life. I even missed her nagging me to get on with my summer reading project. Of course, I could go and see her whenever I liked – I only had to walk down to her camp (which is what Dad and I called it, still desperately pretending it was some temporary, fun activity) – but it wasn't the same. It would never be the same.

Looking back, I can see how I began pulling away from my mother right from the start. It was hardly surprising. For one thing, there was her refusal to speak; although, at first, her silence was treated almost like a joke. I've found a mention of it in the archives of the *Mid-Hants Examiner*[1], and as far as I'm aware, this

---

[1] Circulation 7,896; now defunct.

is the first time Rachel was mentioned in the media. If the paper had had any clue what she would become they would have had the scoop to beat all scoops, but instead, in three short paragraphs under the headline *'Silence in Chalkham – Pub Landlady Calls Time on Talking'*, her silence was variously referred to as *'a teasing puzzle'*, *'a disquieting quiet'* and *'an aspiration for henpecked hubbies everywhere'*[2].

Little wonder the *Mid-Hants Examiner* is no longer in print.

Several of Rachel's biographers have suggested that her silence was merely a public-facing protest, speculating that she must have spoken in private, at least occasionally.

> *There can be little doubt that Rachel communicated verbally during the eight years prior to the Event. The idea that she could mastermind the explosive expansion of her Community, undertake the organisation of the many protests that took place during 2007–2010 and coordinate the complex logistics required for the multiple Event sites without speaking a single word stretches one's credulity almost to breaking point.*
>
> (*Speak No Evil*, Dr Jasmine Peterson,
> Leaping Press, 2018)

All I can say is that from the moment my mother left home, I never heard her utter so much as a syllable. Not to me, not to anyone.

For Mum's birthday that year I gave her words. Gran bought some stiff cardboard that I cut into rectangles, and on each one I wrote a word in marker pen: *yes, no, thank you, please, hungry, thirsty, happy, sad, well*. I tried to think of handy answers to questions so when I went to see her I could say, 'Hi, Mum, how are you feeling

---

[2] https://mid-hants-examiner/archive/Chalkham/landlady-falls-silent

today?' and she could hold up the card saying *well*, followed by the one saying *thank you*.

The thing was, I couldn't write the words I really wanted her to hold up. I wanted her to answer questions like 'Why are you living in a tent?' and 'When are you coming home?' and 'Why won't you speak to me, Mum?' but when I asked her those questions (which I did frequently) she'd just look at me, silently.

Once the first notebook – the one she had stolen from my room – was full, Gran and I had gone to WHSmith to buy Mum a replacement, and that is the official notebook #1. Later, Rachel generally used more expensive notebooks (all twenty-nine of them are on the table in front of me and #27 is a particularly lovely example: green leather, hand-tooled and bound by one of the Members, Rachel's initials beautifully picked out in gold leaf) but I've got to hand it to WHSmith, their Mega Jotpad has stood the test of time. There are two brown, interlinked circles (presumably from the base of a mug) on the front cover, which has become detached from four of the wire rings, and there is what looks like a grass stain on what remains of the rear cover, but that's it for damage.

Flicking through it now, I'm reminded just how fast Mum would write, often scrawling at angles across the page before spinning it round for me to read. '*I am listening*' is written so many times (eighteen times in the first ten pages of #1) but I never did know if she meant she was listening to me or she was listening to something else. The cryptic messages quickly became annoying and I began to hate her silence, which was like a malevolent presence hanging between us. From time to time it would occur to me that if she did ever decide to speak to me again, I might not be able to hear what she was saying because of how tightly she had swaddled herself in her silence. I needn't have worried, though, because she never spoke, despite me trying my best to goad her into it. I shouted and yelled and bellowed my frustrations. *Talk to me. Mum. Please. Mum. Just say something.* I even tried swearing at her, using words I'd never said in front of her before, hoping, if nothing else, to shock her into telling me off. *Fucking hell, Mum, this is fucking insane.*

Her response was always the same. Silence.

Looking back, I am ashamed that it never occurred to me how difficult those early weeks must have been for Dad. He did his best, but running the pub single-handedly meant he was busy every minute of every day. Gran did what she could, but by then she was on a waiting list for a hip replacement, so she couldn't stand for long. There were a couple of people who worked occasional shifts, but there wasn't enough money for them to do more than a few hours a week.

I did a bit to help – I would collect the empties and I had become adept at changing the barrels down in the cellar – but I was too young to serve behind the bar, so for most of the time, if Dad didn't work, then the pub would be shut and, of course, a shut pub meant no punters, and no punters meant no money. In the space of just a few weeks, my father went from being tired but cheerful to exhausted and miserable.

The ironic thing is that, in many ways, I had a great time in the summer of 2003. With Dad running the pub and Gran spending her time sitting on a canvas chair down by Mum's tent (when she wasn't cooking meals for us or doing our laundry), no one really took any notice of where I was or what I was doing. Livy's parents were going through their divorce so they weren't keeping tabs on her either, and for eight weeks it felt like my best friend and I ran wild.

Everyone has seen pictures of Chalkham nowadays so it's almost impossible to imagine that back then the village was just a place people passed through on their way somewhere else.

Not that it wasn't lovely, it was, but after the Event there was something like a ten-thousand-fold increase in visitor numbers. I haven't been back since the day Dad and I had to leave, but Livy still visits her mother regularly so I've a good idea of how the place has changed.

The current owners of The Wild Boar are sitting on an absolute goldmine, of course, and I've seen a photo of the plaque on the door which says:

Rachel Morris
1965–2011
Founder of the Community
Lived, Worked and Was Silent Here

There are cafés, a gift shop, an ice-cream parlour and, of course, the Rachel of Chalkham Interactive Visitor Centre. The latest addition is a Community-owned boutique hotel on the edge of the village that offers, so Livy tells me, silent retreats of between twelve hours and twelve days.

After the Event, a new access road was built between the village and the bottom of the Chalkham Boar hill, and although nowadays no one is allowed to walk on the hill itself, that doesn't seem to matter to the hundreds of thousands of visitors who travel from all over the world to stand behind barriers and ogle the site where the Event occurred. I suppose there are always people who want to visit places where awful things have happened – just look at all the visitors to Auschwitz, say, or Chernobyl. Sometimes I wonder what my mother would say about the hordes of people drawn to visit sites of atrocity and I honestly have no idea if she'd be happy or not at the thought of the Chalkham Boar being one of them.

But I'm getting ahead of myself. Back in 2003, there wasn't really a reason for anyone to stop when they drove through

Chalkham, and for the most part, that suited the residents just fine. The village was sleepy and safe, which meant that us kids were often left to our own devices. That was certainly the case during the summer of 2003. It was also hot that year. God was it hot. Head-fryingly hot, which meant that Livy and I could get away with wearing barely there wisps of material and prancing around as if we were much older and far more worldly-wise than the thirteen-year-olds we actually were. If it wasn't for everything with Mum, it would have been the perfect summer, one of those times you look back on and think: *Then. Then was the time that I was happiest. Then was the time I would go back to in a heartbeat.*

That was the summer we perfected the moves to Beyoncé's 'Crazy in Love' video, practising and practising until I swear we were millisecond perfect. We were convinced that if only Beyoncé could see us, if only she was driving through Chalkham and happened to glance through the tinted windows of her limo and see Livy and me thrusting away on the village green while our tinny little speaker blasted out 'Crazy in Love', then she would literally beg us to be in her next video.

It was also the summer that we started cycling over to the Chalkham Boar. We'd been there on school trips, of course, our teachers trying and failing to interest us in what was basically just the shape of an enormous pig carved out of a chalk hill. What had finally piqued our interest was what some of the older kids at school had been saying. Later, I realised that the same story did the rounds every year, but 2003 was the first time Livy and I had heard rumours about the annual mega-orgy. Every second Saturday in August, so the story went, people came to have sex on the chalky pig. It wasn't a fertility thing (the Cerne Abbas Giant had that angle covered); instead, as two breathless Year 10s had told us outside the science block, couples who had sex on the Boar would stay together for ever. Something like that, anyway.

Livy and I weren't interested in the finer details, we just thought it would be hilarious to see a load of people actually doing it, all at the same time, on the Chalkham Boar.

Much to Livy's annoyance, I refused to go there when it was dark, which was when all the exciting stuff was supposed to happen. For one thing, I had no lights on my bicycle. And for another, I didn't want to worry Dad. Obviously Mum wouldn't have a clue whether I was in bed or not, but once Dad had got rid of the last of the stragglers and locked the door, he often came to check on me. Sometimes, he'd pull my covers up a little or brush my hair away from my face, and I always pretended that I was asleep because if he realised how often he woke me up he might stop doing it. I was too old to need checking up on, but it made me feel safe and I loved that he still did it.

So we didn't cycle over to the Boar until the day after the night of the supposed mega-orgy. Initially, all we saw was a handful of hung-over people, piles of blankets, a load of empty bottles and several patches of burned grass just below the pig's belly. Livy spotted a packet of cigarettes on the ground and picked it up, flipping the top open, but it was empty. She squinted inside the packet hopefully, as if a cigarette might suddenly materialise. Something that looked very much like a used condom was draped over one of the empty bottles of wine and I showed it to Livy, who shrugged.

'Told you. If we'd have come last night, we'd have seen them all at it.' She dropped the cigarette packet on top of the condom and squished them together with her foot. 'Listen, Ems,' she said, 'There's something I need to tell you...'

Before she could finish, a skinny arm poked through a pile of blankets, throwing them to one side, revealing a naked couple underneath. The man's penis was nested in a messy thicket of pubic hair and barely visible, but that didn't stop us staring.

Next to him, the woman yawned and stretched, completely un-concerned by the audience. She squinted up at us and said, 'Either of you girls got a fag on you?'

Livy and I shook our heads, looked at each other, giggled and ran away, back down the hill. By the time we reached our bikes, we were laughing so much I thought I was going to wet myself.

'Did you see his thing?' I said, when I could finally breathe again.

'Even my brother's is bigger,' said Livy. Harry was seven.

'Re. Vol. Ting,' I said.

'Do you think they did it?'

'Bet they did.'

'Yuck. You couldn't pay me enough money to go near *that*.'

We got on our bikes, but before we set off I said, 'What were you going to say?'

'What do you mean?' she said.

'You know… up there… you were going to tell me something.'

'I'm not sure if I should say…'

I'm surprised that we ever managed to make ourselves understood. All those elliptical half-sentences.

'C'mon, Livy. Tell me.'

'It's about—'

At that point, two post-orgy revellers – fully clothed, thankfully – approached us, holding out black binbags. 'Come to help tidy up, girls?'

'Nah, you're all right,' said Livy. She pushed off from the kerb and rode away, leaving me to follow in her wake. I caught her up by the first corner and called across, 'Tell me, Livy.'

'It's about your mum.'

I hadn't been expecting that and braked hard. As soon as Livy realised I had stopped, she did a U-turn and cycled back towards me.

'What about her?'

Livy dropped her head slightly, so her hair fell forward over her face, which she still does today when she's embarrassed.

Up until then, I hadn't really said much to Livy about my mother. I mean, obviously she knew Mum had moved into the tent, but I hadn't really said anything about how she wasn't talking. Livy had her own issues because of her parents' divorce and we had an unspoken pact not to mention what was going on at our respective homes.

'What about my mum?' I said.

Livy pulled her bike lock off the handlebars and started fiddling with it. 'You know how your gran said your mum's just having a bit of a break and it's no one's business but your mum's?'

I shrugged. 'Yeah.'

'Well, that's what I say to people when they ask if I know anything. They think I might, 'cos of you and me being so close...'

I sensed a *but*.

'But...' she said, then fiddled with the lock again.

She was annoying me now. 'But what? C'mon, Livy. Tell me.'

'But I heard some stuff yesterday when I was outside my house, waiting for Dad to pick me up.'

I felt a bit sick, even though I had no idea what she was going to say.

'I was sitting on the pavement because Dad was late and Lyra's mum came out into their garden. I guess she couldn't see me.' Lyra was six and lived next door to Livy. 'Anyway, Lyra's mum was on her phone and she was telling someone about your mum. She was all, like, "So, you'll never guess the latest gossip..."'

Livy had Lyra's mum's fake-posh accent down to a tee, but I didn't laugh.

'Then she's, like, "So, there's this woman, owns the local pub, who's totally gone off the rails."'

There was a pain, as if I was sunburned inside my stomach. I couldn't bear the idea of anyone talking about my mum like that.

Livy reached over and put her hand on my arm. 'Sure you want to hear the rest, Ems?'

I nodded. It was better to know.

'She kept going "so" in that stupid way she does, you know? She was all, like, "So she's moved into a tent, and you've got to feel sorry for her hubby because it turns out she's providing a floorshow."'

'I don't get it,' I said.

'Apparently neither did whoever Lyra's mum was talking to, because she had to explain. I don't remember the exact words she used, but it was about how your mum's been encouraging the local boys to watch her when she goes swimming in the stream without any clothes on. Oh god, Ems, I've made you cry. Don't cry. Please don't cry.' She let her bike fall onto the road and put her arms around me. 'Don't cry, Ems. It's not that bad and the stupid old cow is probably making it up anyway. That stream's freezing.'

The minute I got home, I stormed down to see Mum. The pub was packed and there were loads of people in the beer garden, but a couple of weeks before, Gran had arranged for someone to put up some old fencing panels and a wooden gate between the garden and Mum's tent to give her some privacy. It was cooler down by the stream and Mum was lying beside it on an old towel. I banged the gate shut and she sat up.

I don't remember exactly what I said (or more likely yelled), but it was along the lines of how could she do this to me, everyone was laughing at her, everyone was laughing at me, I was so embarrassed, she was so embarrassing, was she a sex-addict, what even was a sex-addict, why wouldn't she just come home, why wouldn't she talk to me, how could she do this to me, I would never be able to go out ever again, why was she doing this anyway, and thanks very much for basically ruining my entire life.

Although I may not know exactly what I said, I can tell you my mother's reply word for word because I have it in front me now:

> *Yes, I swim in the stream. No, of course boys don't*
> *watch me. There's an important lesson here for you,*
> *darling. When people are threatened, they lash out.*
> *Silence threatens people because it's only when you're*
> *silent that you can hear the truth behind their words.*
> *Courtney tells lies and hopes no one will hear what she's*
> *really saying. She wants people to listen to her lies, but*
> *she does not want to be heard, not really. Just ignore her.*
> (#1, p. 58)

Almost certainly Courtney (Lyra's mother) was lying. In the early days, there was a lot of suspicion among Chalkham residents about Rachel's motivations, and I can't say I really blamed them. Nothing about what my mother was doing was normal in any accepted sense of the word and some people, including Courtney, used her as an endless source of gossip. Just a few weeks after this an awful rumour briefly circulated that Mum had moved into the tent because Dad had hit her. I absolutely knew this one was a lie, but when I confronted her she again told me to *'just ignore it and it will blow over'* (#2, p. 4). It did, eventually, like all the other lies, but my mother's failure to defend Dad against that particular piece of gossip is one of the many things I have never forgiven her for.

I'm certain the idea that she was luring teenage boys to watch her swim was untrue, but at the time I was completely mortified. Not only that, there was something else I wanted to say to my mother that afternoon. I wanted to tell her about being at the Chalkham Boar and seeing the man's penis, which had upset me in an obscure way that I didn't really understand. More than anything, I needed to hear her laugh and say something typically Mum-like to make me feel better, but in the end I didn't tell her. I already understood that there was no point.

5.

Boxing Day 2003 and an earthquake directly beneath the city of Bam in Iran kills 40,000 people. Post-Christmas television must have been full of images of collapsed buildings and survivors scrambling to rescue buried relatives, but I am ashamed to say that I have no memory of it. So many people dead, and I can't remember a thing.

Multiple newspaper articles about the Bam earthquake are tucked into notebook #3, which my mother was using at the end of 2003. The first article is slipped between pages 3 and 4 and marks the beginning of Rachel's fascination with large-scale human tragedies. From that point on, her notebooks are peppered with cuttings about earthquakes, tsunamis, landslides, wildfires (these articles are included in the reproduction of the notebooks between the pages where they were found).

The earlier notebooks clearly reveal connections between these devastating events and the development of the Community. Many of the articles found in notebooks #3, #4 and #6 are about the two Boxing Day tragedies because a year to the day after the Bam earthquake there was a tsunami in the Indian Ocean in which hundreds of thousands of people died. Even I remember the tsunami. Mum appears to have kept every article she could find about both events, annotating many of them.

At some point she started to use a type of shorthand when she wrote messages to me or Dad or Gran, dropping extraneous consonants and almost all vowels from her notes to us, except for an E for Emilia. It was quicker for her to write messages, but it had the effect of making the E look demanding. At least, that is how it always sounded in my head. I never read it as a loving E; instead I always heard it as fractious and impatient, as if she just wanted me to get on with doing whatever it was she wanted me to do. For example: 'E tll D t gt sm vg sds, pts, bns, crts' (#3, p. 7), which meant Emilia, tell Dad to get some vegetable seeds: potatoes, beans, carrots. With a few minor exceptions, notebook #3 was the final one in which she combined messages to us with her more private thoughts. Thereafter she used scrap paper for day-to-day communication, which is why so few of those notes survive.

Incidentally, I remember this request for seeds. As always, or so it seemed, Dad did as she wanted, and I remember him coming home from the garden centre and handing me several packets to take to Mum. She nurtured those seeds with great care, carrying water from the stream to the little patch of ground she had cleared beyond her tent. It's not like she had anything else to do, and with so much care and attention, it wasn't a great surprise when they yielded a decent supply of food. Those seeds turned out to be the start of a large vegetable garden that would help feed all those Members who would later come to live with her. It also marked the point at which my mother became a vegetarian (which, many years later, led to the Community's Leaf not Beef campaign).

Notably, Rachel never used shorthand when she wrote about her thoughts and feelings, or her notes on articles, or the ideas that eventually underpinned the Community. She wrote every word of those things in full. Did she realise from the beginning, I wonder, that she was writing herself into history?

Her annotations on the two Boxing Day tragedies are typically brief. For example, 'What can we do?' crops up over and over.

'*Waste of death*' is another. One picture, originally from the *Times of India* and taken in the aftermath of the tsunami, is particularly gruesome. I can't imagine the scene was ever shown on the television here in the UK – it would have really put people off their turkey sandwiches. There is a blue and red inflatable boat at the top of the picture, two people crouching at the nose, one person standing. The boat is pushing through brown and white debris. At first glance, the debris could be wreckage. But when you keep looking, you realise you are looking at dead people. All of them face down, bloated buttocks bobbing above the water, skin on their backs burned to a black crisp, arms and legs pale, star-fished out. In the margin of the article, my mother has written, in capitals, '*MAKE DEATH COUNT*' and underlined it several times (the article with her annotations is reproduced in #6, between pages 114 and 115).

By the time of the December 2004 tsunami, my mother had been living in her tent for just over eighteen months. She continued to bathe in the stream and, to the annoyance of many Chalkham residents, it turned out that swimming naked was not a crime. A curious fact about my mother is, despite everything, despite the Community, the Event, all the terrible things she's responsible for, not only while she was alive but in the years since her death, and all those Members who justify their brutal policies by claiming moral authority from Rachel of Chalkham, my mother never broke the law except for three instances of non-violent criminal trespass in the 2007/8 protests. Despite everything she did, everything she persuaded other people to do, everything that people are still doing in her name, some of which *is* criminal, of course, Rachel of Chalkham is still whiter than white. At least as far as the law is concerned.

My mother spent every night of that first winter in the tent huddled inside a four-seasons sleeping bag that Dad bought her, sandwiched between a piece of tarpaulin and heavy woollen blankets that Gran had found in various charity shops. Sometime in early spring 2004, after several days of almost continual rain, the tent began to leak and my mother started work on a more permanent structure.

Word got around that Rachel would make use of any spare junk, and for several weeks various people trailed through our beer garden with rusty sheets of corrugated iron, bits of timber, fence panels and the like. Someone even took an old bath down there, although Mum continued to wash in the stream and eventually used the bath to rig up a sort of greenhouse for the plants. Dad, ever solicitous and compliant, brought her a tool set and kept her supplied with nails, screws and whatever else she needed to enable her to construct a surprisingly robust shelter.

There cannot be anyone in the world who hasn't seen pictures of the camp at the time of the Event: all those interconnected huts, that bucket-shower with those intricate carvings and the long-drop toilet, painted pink. But before the Community, when Rachel still lived alone, there was just a small shelter with fence panels for walls, a corrugated iron roof and tarpaulin on the floor. After a first failed attempt, my mother successfully managed to cut two windows, which she glazed with opaque plastic. You couldn't really see out of them, but that also meant that nobody could see in, which suited Mum fine. You could only get into the shelter by crawling through a hole in the back of the tent, which she kept as a sort of leaky vestibule until it finally fell apart sometime during the winter of 2006/7.

Inside the shelter there was an old wood-burning stove that Gran had spotted in a skip and persuaded Dad to pull out and transport to the stream in a wheelbarrow. Although the stove vented through the roof, it was virtually impossible to control the heat well enough to maintain a comfortable temperature, and since Mum used the stove for cooking, the little shelter was sweleringly hot all year round. Often she burned unseasoned wood and the acrid smoke made my eyes water. Once a week, Gran would scoop up Rachel's clothes for washing, returning them clean and ironed only for them to get muddy and stinking of smoke all over again.

I don't know if it ever occurred to my mother just how lucky she was that she had Dad, Gran and me and, before the first Members joined her, how difficult her life would have been without us. I lost count of the times that I made up my mind to ignore Mum's demands for me to fetch and carry things for her, but then she'd write something like *E nw tthpst pls*, and more often than not it just seemed easier to go along with it and bring her a new tube of toothpaste. I suppose she was still my mum after all, even though she had stopped behaving in any recognisably maternal way. And when it came down to it, she wasn't actually that demanding. Besides, if I wasn't in the mood to help, I just stayed away for a day or two.

I may be giving the impression that my life back then was dominated by my mother, but that's not true. It was surprisingly easy for me to give her no thought from one day to the next. It was odd and embarrassing to have a mother living first in a tent, then in a shed built of other people's scrap, but at least I knew where she was, I could see her whenever I wanted and Dad and Gran looked after me well, suffering through my teenage preoccupations. I came in for quite a bit of stick from kids at school and around the village, but the attention span of teenagers isn't great at the best of times and other things soon caught their interest. I'm not saying it was easy – there was always the risk that my mother's behaviour would crop up in conversation – but when I think of everything that Dad and I have been through since, those first eighteen months seem positively tranquil.

And of course I had Livy. As friendships go we were a very self-contained twosome. We still are, really. Obviously we had our disagreements – we didn't see eye to eye about absolutely everything. For example, although we were united about the vital importance of doing whatever necessary to acquire a yellow Livestrong wristband (despite having no idea at all who Lance Armstrong was, and the fact that Gran said they made us look as though we'd been identified as carriers of an infectious disease), we almost came to blows because Livy refused to acknowledge that 'Dry Your Eyes' was plainly *the* song of 2004. She genuinely considered herself to be in love with Harry Judd and thought I was insane to rate The Streets above McFly. Livy still has no taste in music.

Most of the time when we weren't at school we roamed around unsupervised. In our summer holiday that year, whenever the weather was good enough and there wasn't anything pressing to watch on the television and no one else to hang out with, we didn't even need a discussion to know we were going to cycle over to the Chalkham Boar. I'm really not sure where our compulsion to spend time at the Boar came from. Everyone has seen the footage from 2011, of course, when helicopters beamed pictures around the world of first the fires, then the smoke and later the charred remains, but that all came later, and it's impossible for anyone who didn't visit the Boar before the Event to really understand how insignificant the place was back then.

Thinking about it now, perhaps Livy and I went there to put some distance, albeit only a mile or so, between ourselves and what was happening at home (Livy's younger brother had been diagnosed as autistic a few months before her father moved out, which translated into her mum doing a lot of shouting about how Livy wasn't doing enough to contribute to the household). Or maybe we were drawn to the Boar by unresolved memories of seeing the naked couple there the previous summer. Most likely, however, we just got into the habit of going there for no particular reason, like almost everything we did back then.

Then, one day, we saw my mother.

Rachel had begun to do a lot of walking. At first, her new habit of rambling around the local area was something else for the residents of Chalkham to gossip about, and for a while anyone who saw my mother wandering along lanes and across fields took it upon themselves to tell Dad or me exactly where they'd seen her, as if they expected us to run off and bring her back. After a while, though, Mum's walks became part of what *that woman from the pub does* and no one talked about it any longer.

But until that day in August 2004 neither Livy nor I had ever seen my mother at the Boar. We had been there for a while, lying on the grass and listening to music, when we saw someone walking through the field on the other side of the road. From a distance this person did not look like my mum. She was thinner and older. For my whole childhood, Mum had had short hair, which she coloured blonde, kneeling beside the bath every few weeks to massage bleach into her head. But in the fifteen months since she had moved out, her natural darker colour had come through, along with plenty of silver. She cut her hair herself and it was lopsided. I guess my mother looked like what she was: a woman nearing forty who was living outdoors and not taking particularly good care of herself.

It wasn't until the woman crossed the road and started making her way up the Boar's back leg that Livy tugged one earphone out of her right ear, the other one out of my left and said, 'Ems. Is that your mum?'

I stuck the earphone back in – we were listening to 'Dry Your Eyes' for the hundredth time that day – and squinted at whoever it was. Then I sat up abruptly. It *was* my mother.

I yanked the earphone out again and stalked over to her. 'Mum. What are you doing here?'

She didn't have a pen and paper with her that day, or if she did, she didn't use them. She just gave me a sort of half-smile, touched my cheek, waved at Livy, then turned and made her way back down the hill. I don't know if she'd been there before or if that was the first time. But here's the thing: when I think back to that day, my memories of everything else are clear, but my mother herself is fuzzy and unfocused. I don't think it's too much of a stretch to say that that's because Rachel still wasn't sure where she was heading. Her walks, like her thoughts, were aimless, untethered from any particular destination.

But then in December 2004, the tsunami struck and 230,000 people died. I am convinced that the twin Boxing Day tragedies were highly influential in shaping the early views of Rachel of Chalkham, moulding her vague convictions into something more focused. The first eighteen months were primarily about establishing foundations, but eventually my mother began to look beyond her little patch of land, beyond Chalkham, beyond her own silence.

To the best of my knowledge, on or around 1 January 2005, after 588 days of silence and 2,494 days before the Event, Rachel founded the Community.

6.

From: Olivia Taylor
To: Emilia Morris
Date: 3 April 2022

Subject: Your Mum

Hi Ems,

Well, writing an email that might end up in your book is a bit weird. I'm really not sure about this. You're my best mate so I'll do it, just don't come crying to me when it all backfires. Actually, you can come crying to me, but you'll have to put up with me saying *I told you so* for the rest of your life. And you'll have to buy the wine for the rest of your life, too.

You and me, we've been friends forever. I can't remember a time before I knew you, which means I can't remember a time when I didn't know your mum, and when I was little, I used to love coming over to yours. You lived in a pub, your dad was adorable and your mum was great.

Do you remember that phase we went through when we were about nine and we really got into putting on plays? Our scripts were always some variation on a love story involving a prince and a princess, and by the time we'd finished arguing about who got to play the princess, we'd forgotten our lines. But your mum was completely happy to let us dress up in her clothes, use her make-up and shove the living-room furniture around to make castles. As far as I can remember, she sat through every single one of those stupid plays and laughed and clapped and pretended to cry in all the right places. She was brilliant. I don't think I've ever told you this because it's kind of embarrassing, but for a while I used to secretly hope that there had been some terrible mistake and your mum was actually my mum. I mean, now I'm obviously bloody relieved she wasn't, but when we were little, your mum was totally amazing.

But she could also be really fucking weird. Like, sometimes she'd look at me and I'd think what the bloody hell is she going to say now? It was like she had a sort of obsessive-compulsive disorder for tragic events. You should look that up – maybe it's an actual thing. Even before the Community, she would become totally obsessed with something in the news and go on and on about it, reading everything she could find, looking stuff up on the internet, boring people to death talking about whatever it was.

And why were they always really fucking horrible things? People dying, disasters, wars, famines. I mean, bloody hell, why couldn't she have developed an obsession for shoes, or *Friends*, or Leonardo DiCaprio? Anything other than horrendous human tragedies. To this day, if I ever hear anyone mention Omagh it takes me right back to being five years old and standing in your kitchen while your mum goes on and on about the bombing and some poor woman who died while she was pregnant with twins. For ages after that, I honestly thought if someone said they were having twins, it meant they were going to be blown up. And don't get me started on 9/11. Jesus, it was like bloody catnip to your mother. I mean, I get it, it was awful beyond words, of course everyone was talking about it, but your mum was obsessed way past when everyone else had started to try and move on.

Here's the thing, though, Ems. All parents are weird, and up to a point your mother was no weirder than lots of parents. Under normal circumstances, I'm sure I'd probably remember far more of the fun stuff about her than her weird obsessions. But these aren't normal circumstances, are they? Your mum wasn't a normal mum. She was Rachel of Chalkham. And I fucking hate Rachel of Chalkham.

Don't get me wrong, though. I don't hate her for the Event – although, god knows enough people do. That's not why I hate Rachel of Chalkham. Your mother ruined your life and that's why I fucking hate her. And that's why I'm concerned about you raking up the past for this book of yours and why nothing you say is going to stop me worrying about you.

Livy xx

7.

In front of me are several biographies of Rachel written by literary heavyweights. No doubt you know the writers I mean. They've each published books about at least one senior politician (ideally a disgraced cabinet minister), a billionaire-business-person-turned-philanthropist (gritty stories of achievement against all odds) and an obscure Victorian (or, at a push, Edwardian) architect, garden designer or engineer. Then at some point in the last decade, they all felt the inexorable pull of Rachel of Chalkham and turned their attentions to my mother.

When I spread out these weighty tomes, they take up most of the table. They have titles such as: *The Quiet Enigma* (Dr Elisia Portman, Vertigo, 2012), *Fuelled by Fire* (C.R. Loneton, Sporadic Publications, 2015) and *Speak No Evil* (as previously mentioned, Dr Jasmine Peterson, Leaping Press, 2018). I also have a copy of *Shhhh...* (H.T. Truelove and S.K. Morrison, Porcupine Press, 2013) that I found in a second-hand bookshop (the book has been out of print since the Community sued the – now defunct – publishers for using its slogan as the book's title).

I've read them all and I suppose I shouldn't be surprised that I learned nothing about my mother that I didn't already know. All the biographies are light on detail about Rachel's life before she became *of Chalkham*, and there is hardly anything about Mum as a child. As far as I'm aware, no one has ever managed to trace her parents. I've never met them and they've never shown the slightest interest in me. Gran said that when they lived in Chalkham they were very private, polite but distant, never had people round, never came to the pub or went to any of the events in the village hall. Then Rachel left for university and my grandparents left for goodness knows where, never to be heard of again. In this day and age it seems almost impossible that anybody can vanish so completely, but Gran always said there was no mystery about it: they just hated all the fuss surrounding Rachel and wanted no part of it.

In *The Quiet Enigma*, Dr Portman speculates that Rachel may have been adopted, although she presents no real evidence to substantiate her claim. My mother's birth certificate says she was born in Dundee on 7 August 1965 to Margaret Ellen Morris and Tobias James Morris, which are the names of the people Rachel lived with in Chalkham when she was a child. Perhaps if you are writing an unauthorised biography there's more latitude to spice it up a little if you feel it's getting boring (take it from me, *The Quiet Enigma* is not exactly a page turner). In any case, despite what Dr Portman alleges, I have no reason to believe that my mother was adopted.

Everyone knows that Rachel studied English Literature at Exeter University. She graduated in 1986 with a 2:1 and the university has spent the last decade or so milking every last drop from its association with Rachel. Her contemporaries variously recall Rachel as being 'great fun', 'the life and soul of every party' and 'full of energy'. Her personal tutor, Dr Louisa Triona, said she was 'naturally clever', 'engaged and engaging' and someone who 'could have gone far in academia, had she decided to do so'. Less positive recollections include accusations of Rachel being 'prone to exaggeration', 'a downright liar' and 'pathologically unreliable' (although the supporting anecdotes are rather tepid, including such things as 'we were friends but then she slept with my boyfriend' and 'she agreed we'd house share in our second year, but backed out at the last minute').

An anonymous source quoted in *Fuelled by Fire* claimed that Rachel was an 'inveterate bully' and another that she was 'a thief', although, again, there is no evidence that either of these accusations are true. And, as you no doubt already know from the publicity surrounding that particular book's publication, the author of *Fuelled by Fire*, C.R. Loneton, was hell-bent on depicting Rachel as a sort of satanic psychopath.

After graduating, my mother stayed in Exeter and began an MA in twentieth-century literature but abandoned her studies within a matter of months. She lived in Bristol for a while, sleeping on sofas here and there and picking up temping jobs and bar work, before moving to London in May 1987. At the beginning of 1988, she landed herself what Gran would have called a 'proper' job, working as a researcher at the British Library. It sounds like a great job, but my mother's enjoyment, or not, of it became moot at the end of August/early September the following year when she became pregnant.

The biographies are relatively consistent about the details of my mother's final months in London and are in line with what Mum told Gran. Things went downhill pretty fast after she fell pregnant. She left her job (my mother once told me that the British Library sacked her, but the HR department sent me copies of records that instead suggest she just failed to turn up for work one day and never returned), she ran out of money, squatted in a horribly damp flat, had me and then conspired with Gran to return to Chalkham and throw us on Dad's mercy. Thank god for Dad.

An online search for 'Rachel of Chalkham' currently returns approximately 2,567,341,000 results. Universities around the world now offer degrees in 'Silence' and 'Silent Listening' and, of course, there are the well-publicised Community-sponsored research fellowships. In addition to the unofficial biographies and dozens of television documentaries, hundreds of books have been published about my mother's silence specifically and silent listening generally.

Over a bottle of wine the other evening, I made the mistake of asking Livy if it was stupid of me to think I had anything interesting to add to all the material that's already out there. Livy immediately launched into a diatribe about how she'd told me that writing about Rachel was a bad idea and how she and my dad were both really worried and couldn't understand why I didn't just put all this 'Community stuff' behind me and get on with my life. We drank a second bottle of wine while we had a bit of a bicker, then I dug out some sloe gin and I have no recollection of what we talked about after that.

The next day, Livy felt so guilty about having a go at me that she spent ages trawling through Facebook and eventually unearthed an early photograph of Mum's camp. The picture was posted by someone called Briony Evans who, according to the Community's roll of honour, burned at an Event site in New Zealand. I have no recollection of Briony, although we were obviously in Chalkham at the same time at least once because my Converse high-tops are just visible in the bottom of her picture (my lifelong love of high-tops was cemented later that year when the best Doctor Who of all time regenerated wearing the exact same Converse as mine).

In Briony's picture, which she posted on 27 April 2005, several women are lounging around on blankets. Rachel is leaning against the side of her shelter and what I find most striking is her fierce concentration. My mother's silence wasn't just vocal: she trained herself to be completely quiet in every way, to be silent with her whole body. She stilled her breathing, ignored every itch, every throat tickle, every muscle twinge, every curious insect that might land on her skin. She never fiddled with zips or buttons, her hands would remain by her sides or folded in her lap, she never fidgeted, or bit her nails, or played with her hair, or scratched her arm, or tapped her foot.

In the photo, Mum is squinting against the bright sunlight, her cheeks puckering with lines. A leaf is caught in her hair, and behind her concentration she looks tired. There's something else in her expression. Melancholy? Curiosity? I can't read it and I can honestly say that any sadness I feel looking at Briony's picture is for the mother who had already left me, not the mother who had yet to leave.

Assuming the date of the photo is accurate, Mum will have already been holding regular Guided Silence Sessions for several months. I should make it clear that, although I was present, I never actually participated in them. I was only there because one of my favourite subjects at school was art and I had decided to make the women in the camp the subject of my GCSE portfolio (I got an A*, in case you were wondering).

In Briony's photograph, the first set of camp rules are painted on the side of the shelter in bright orange, standing out vividly against the dull greens and muddy browns which dominated the rest of the camp back then. She's captioned her post *Shhhh... Learn to listen...* which almost certainly makes Briony the first person to use the *Shhhh...* slogan online.

These days, of course, the slogan has rather fallen out of favour with the Community but, as everyone knows, for several years it was literally everywhere: on T-shirts, baseball caps, posters, billboards, and on the sides of trains and buses and taxis and aeroplanes, and beamed onto the Houses of Parliament, the White House, the Kremlin (although, of course, that particular protest did not end well). And there was even that (failed) attempt to use a laser to reflect *Shhhh...* on to the face of the moon. If only that was the extent of the Community's ambition today!

Holding those Silence Sessions was Rachel's first step in growing her fledgling Community, and something I've never told anyone before is that it was me who designed the original poster for them. There was no subtlety about my design: I drew a gigantic pair of lips with an oversized forefinger pressed against them. It wouldn't have looked out of place on an advert for a porn site. The poster, which was printed on ordinary A4 paper, invited anyone who felt they might benefit from a couple of hours of 'guided silence' to come along to the field behind The Wild Boar pub, Chalkham. Livy and I cycled around the local villages taping posters to lamp-posts and asking people to put them in shop windows. Initially the sessions were only once a week – on Saturday mornings at 10 a.m. – but it wasn't long before there was sufficient demand for my mother to hold more frequent sessions.

In those early days, the women who came along fell into two distinct categories. Some – mainly locals from Chalkham and the surrounding villages – had already spent a considerable amount of their adult lives floating around various yoga and Pilates studios, and spending hours in spin classes, and it was pretty obvious that, for those women, the attraction of the whole silent-listening thing was simply that it was something new. They were ahead of the wave and they loved that.

But then there were the others. The ones who were far more likely to actually end up living in the camp, at least for a while. The ones who would come along for a Silence Session and then stay afterwards, hoping to spend time with Rachel in the Hearing Place. If you've ever seen the documentary *Inside the Camp* (given how frequently it's still broadcast, surely there can't be anyone who hasn't seen it) you'll be familiar with the original Hearing Place, the wooden structure that resembled a birdwatching hide, with its single long, thin window overlooking the stream. Mum and one other person would sit inside and Rachel would hand over a piece of card on which she had written '*If you want to talk, I will listen and I will hear you*'. They would talk and she would listen. That was it, as simple as that.

The irony of all ironies, of course, is that Mum had become so obsessed with everyone listening to everyone that somewhere along the line she had forgotten to listen to her own daughter. Almost every time I tried to talk to her she would put her finger to her lips and mouth *Shhhh*... Our relationship had essentially been reduced to my mother's instructions and requests, which she continued to scrawl on bits of paper and which I generally received with a sullen silence (I may not like silence, but never let it be said that I didn't learn how to wield it).

Everyone assumes that the Hearing Place was Rachel's idea, but that isn't correct. The idea came from someone who is first mentioned by my mother in notebook #8. This particular individual was so important to the pre-Event Community that I've reproduced below some of what Rachel wrote about her decision to come to Chalkham. The relevant extracts appear between a clipping from the *Guardian* about a suicide car bomb that killed at least 120 people in Iraq in February 2005 (#8, pp. 6–7) and three pages from the *New Statesman* about the collapse of a garment factory in Dhaka, Bangladesh two months later in which 1,134 people died (#8, pp. 78–79). That dates these entries to March and April 2005.

> *A woman came today. She watched me plant seeds which E had bought for me. Usually I know immediately if visitors want to talk, but with her, I couldn't tell. I finished the planting before she started speaking. She talked for a long time and then she cried. Before she left she hugged me and*

thanked me for hearing her. That's what she said, 'Thank you for hearing me.' When did we forget to hear? Everyone talks, but no one hears. (#8, p. 29)

The crying woman came back. This time she spoke only a little but she cried again. We sat in silence for a long time, listening to the stream, which is running fast today, and a tractor in the far field. (#8, p. 43)

Since the crying woman came I've been thinking a lot about the relationship between silence and listening. I now see that in the past, before my silence, when people spoke to me I didn't hear what they were saying, not really. Instead I would be thinking about my reply. I listened to their words only as much as I needed to in order to work out what I was going to say next. Although I listened, I did not hear. Only if we hear what people are saying can we understand them. And if we understand everyone better – friends, strangers, enemies – surely then we will feel more compassion for them. Everyone deserves to be heard. Otherwise our lives are just one long cry into a void. (#8, p. 51)

The crying woman is here again. She didn't cry this time but she talked a lot. She believes that what I'm doing is vital. It is more important than anything else, she said. I am showing people how to hear voices other than their own. She wants to join me. She wants to help me spread my message of silent listening. She wants to help me show people that we must learn to hear each other. She is beside me now, putting up her tent. (#8, p. 65)

Many people will already have realised that Mum's crying woman was Tabitha Kenny. In her notebooks, Rachel never recorded any details of what people spoke to her about, and in that respect, my mother's silent listening was akin to a confessional (although as an atheist she would not have welcomed the comparison). This anonymity throughout the notebooks has made their publication much simpler than it might otherwise have been. However, the reason I know the woman she is referring to is Tabitha is not only because the dates fit, but because on many occasions I heard Tabitha call herself 'Rachel's crying woman'.

As someone who burned in the Event, Tabitha's life story has been told and retold, and so, although it's impossible to know what she spoke to Rachel about during those early visits, even a cursory internet search reveals that in the spring of 2005 Tabitha had had a series of failed IVF attempts, her mother had died after a long battle with cancer, and she had found out that her husband had cheated on her (I should make it clear that Robert Kenny has always denied this). In any case, Tabitha appears to have had reasons enough to fuel several crying sessions.

Aside from the trauma in her life, Tabitha was a highly successful, highly ambitious 'internet marketing senior account executive'. I don't need the internet to know this about her, because later on, when she started appearing on radio and then television, she took every opportunity to remind people about where she had worked and what she had achieved before *choosing the Community*, as she would always say, as if there had been any number of other options available to her at the time. Tabitha also had the gift of being flawlessly turned out, and whereas almost everyone else (including my mother) generally looked ever so slightly grubby and damp, Tabitha swanned around with her blonde hair piled high, perfectly made-up and immaculately clothed as if she'd just stepped out of Jigsaw. How she managed this was one of the biggest mysteries of my teenage years, although I suspect she single-handedly kept the local dry cleaners in business.

Tabitha was also, evidently, either extremely decisive or impulsive because less than two months after attending her first Guided Silence Session, she had quit her job, left her husband, moved from Teddington to Chalkham and appointed herself the Community's marketing guru and my mother's second-in-command.

All of which is to say that the Hearing Place was Tabitha's idea. She believed it was vital to have a private space for women to speak to Rachel and be heard by her, and it took her only a matter of days to marshal a group to construct the first one. There seemed to be nothing Tabitha couldn't accomplish when she put her mind to it. I'm aware of disagreement among commentators over whether the Community would have become as successful if it wasn't for Tabitha Kenny and, personally, I have no doubt that it would. However, what is undeniable is that, without the benefit of Tabitha's expertise and her absolute dedication to Rachel's cause, the pace of the expansion would have undoubtedly been much slower.

Another crucial thing about Tabitha was that, although she followed the rule of silence in the camp, she was perfectly prepared to talk when she was away from there, provided it was in the interests of the Community for her to do so. Regardless of my personal feelings towards Tabitha, Rachel benefited hugely from having her to speak on her behalf, and Tabitha's strident voice only served to highlight the potency of Rachel's silence.

Before Tabitha had time to really get stuck into her new self-appointed role, there was the matter of her aggrieved husband to deal with. The first time Robert Kenny came to Chalkham he was alone, pulling up outside the pub one Saturday morning in a very flash car and storming inside, bellowing, 'Where the fuck is my fucking wife?' or something along those lines. At first, Dad hadn't a clue who he was, and when he tried to ask him, the man started yelling, 'She sends me an email telling me she's found her true purpose or some shit like that. I'll give her true purpose. Where is she?' Some of our regulars started saying unhelpful things like 'Just have a drink, mate' and 'We're trying to enjoy a quiet lunchtime bevy, pal,' and the whole situation was threating to get really out of hand, so in the end a whole procession of us trailed through the beer garden to find Tabitha.

As soon as he saw Tabitha, Robert Kenny started yelling awful things, but Mum and the other women were in the middle of their Saturday Silence Session and of course they didn't speak. Midge didn't know he was supposed to be quiet, so he was barking madly and I had to hang on tight to his collar. In the end, Robert Kenny became so frustrated that he ripped Tabitha's tent out of the ground and punched the side of Mum's shelter until one of the panels split in half. At that point, Dad rang the police and several punters pushed Robert onto the ground and kept him there until the officers arrived.

When his arrest was reported by the local press, Tabitha pounced on it. She had a real talent for turning seemingly innocuous opportunities to the Community's advantage, milking any passing interest, no matter how insignificant. Thanks to her, the story of her husband's 'attack' was picked up by several online news sites and, to the best of my knowledge, it was in these reports that the word 'Community' was used for the first time in connection with the camp.

A quick search online returned these two articles from back then: *Women in Silent Community Attacked by Crazed Husband* and *Fledgling Women's Community Takes Flight – Despite Man Trying to Ground It*[3]. Both articles were illustrated with the same picture of

[3] https://thisisnewz.com/UK/178439.89/080605; https://whatsnews.co.uk/nationalnews/hants/chalkhamanddistrict/9June05

the camp rules on the side of Rachel's shelter and that was that: the Community was officially out there.

Camp Rules

- *Shhhh...*
- *No talking except in the Hearing Place.*
- *Practise silent listening.*
- *Don't just listen, hear.*

8.

From: Nick Wright
To: Emilia Morris
Date: 7 May 2022

Subject: Mum

Hi darling,

You asked me to think about whether there were any signs of what Rachel would end up doing and I don't have to tell you that it's something I've asked myself over and over again. I was obsessed with trying to work out what I'd missed. Why didn't I see what she was planning? Why didn't I do more? There must have been a point when I could have stopped her. The clues must have been there about the Event, and there must have been signs of what the Community would become. For far too long I blamed myself for not anticipating what happened. All I can say is, thank god for my therapist!

Before she left to go to university, I don't remember Rachel being particularly interested in anything outside of school and friends, but after she came back to Chalkham and you both moved in with me, it wasn't quite so straightforward. Almost from the beginning it was like she put on a different Rachel each day, choosing which person to be as casually as she'd choose which clothes to wear. I know how confusing you found it, especially when you were younger. Was she going to be fun mummy or strict mummy? Did she want a minute-by-minute account of your day at school, or would her attention drift as soon as you started talking? Was it OK for you to have friends round, or was it one of the days when she wanted you to herself? She didn't neglect you and I don't really believe any of her behaviour with you was inherently bad, but she constantly filtered what she gave of herself, even to us.

All these Community people claim to understand the real Rachel of Chalkham, but I'm honestly not sure that anyone ever truly knew who the *real* Rachel was. Since her death, it's as if she's become a bottomless vessel for the passions and actions of others, and I've always believed that because no one could ever pin down Rachel when she was alive, it makes it all the easier for the Community to claim she was whoever it wants her to be.

There is something from back then that you don't know. I wasn't going to mention it, but you've said so many times that you want me to be completely honest, so I have decided to tell you, though you might find it upsetting.

Your mum got pregnant in the autumn of 1995. I never wanted you to be an only child like your mum and me, and I was thrilled when she told me, but Rachel refused to even discuss the possibility of keeping the baby. It was the reason she gave that might be relevant to the bigger picture, because every time I tried to talk to her about it she would just say that there were already far too many people and she couldn't live with the guilt of bringing yet another person into the world.

We're talking twenty-seven years ago, and I'm sure it was unusual back then to feel guilty for having a baby. It wasn't like

I was suggesting we have a football team's worth of children. But the reason it struck me as particularly strange was because, until that point, your mother had appeared to travel through life remarkably unencumbered by guilt for anything at all. I honestly think it was the first time she'd ever mentioned guilt in any context. Of course I respected her right to do whatever she wanted, but I never agreed with her that we should feel guilty about having a child. I didn't see it that way and I still don't, despite everything.

At the end of the day, who knows if Rachel's guilt is significant? Maybe she was using it as an excuse because she didn't want my child. Maybe she didn't want the whole palaver of having another baby around the place – I mean, you were already five, just starting school and already much less dependent on her. She might even have been concerned that we couldn't afford it, although we'd have made it work. All I know is that she didn't say any of those things because all she would ever say was that she couldn't deal with the guilt of bringing another person into an already over-crowded world.

And here's the thing. When it's put like that, it isn't a great leap from what she said back then to the more radical Community policies today, is it?

Anyway, darling, I'll leave it at that and hope that some of my ramblings prove useful. I really hope none of this has upset you. Call me any time.

Love, Dad.

9.

It is accepted by all commentators – regardless of which side they stand on – that without the Community's presence on social media, far fewer women would have burned at the Event. The first major opportunity for Rachel to leverage external circumstances for the advantage of the Community and for Tabitha Kenny to display her expertise in harnessing the power of the internet was in the days following the London bombings on 7 July 2005.

I was in London that day, on a school trip to the Science Museum, and my class were on a tube when the bombs exploded. We were stuck in a tunnel with the lights flickering on and off. Eventually, the train crawled into a station. Our teachers told us to walk, but everyone around us was running, shoving each other and shouting, so we ran too. Above ground, our teachers tried to find out what was going on, but their phones weren't working. Some of the boys were joking about alien invasions, someone else was shouting about zombies, and two of the girls started crying, but then one of the teachers went into a nearby office which had a big TV screen on the wall and found out about the bombs.

In the aftermath, people in leafy mid-Hampshire were appalled (*How could this be allowed to happen to* us?), and grieving (everyone knew someone who knew someone), and angry (*How* dare *something so awful disrupt our lives?*). For many people, there was no consolation to be found in talking, and large numbers of women gathered at Mum's camp, finding solace in being silent together.

Seizing the opportunity, Tabitha accelerated her plans for a Community website and had the first version up and running within days. She also printed flyers, which looked considerably more professional than the poster I had designed. On one side of the flyer were the camp rules, together with the days and times of the Guided Silence Sessions and JustGiving details for donations. On the other side was something Rachel had written in the immediate aftermath of the bombs. These words can be found on the final page of notebook #8:

> *We don't hear each other.*
> *To hear you must listen. To listen you must be silent.*
> *Everyone is shouting. No one is listening.*
> *People are angry, but no one is listening.*
> *People are scared, but no one is hearing.*
> *We believe our voice must be heard above all others, but*
> *all voices deserve to be heard.*
> *When no one hears, no one cares.*
> *When no one cares, no one matters.*
> *Stop shouting.*
> *Listen.*
> *Hear.*
> (#8, p. 163)

No one who came to the camp was allowed to leave without taking a handful of flyers and strict instructions to distribute them as widely as possible. Sitting here now, reading my mother's words, I vividly remember those women clutching their piles of flyers, eager to share Rachel's message.

Looking back, it's obvious how much of an opportunity the

London bombings presented. Before then, the Community was already up and running – a handful of women were living in the camp with Rachel, and plenty more came to the Guided Silence Sessions – but you couldn't really say the Community stood for anything specific. It was only about being quiet and listening and hearing and so, although it was still about those things afterwards, the bombings illustrated in the most terrible way *why* listening and hearing were so important. The Community was a response and, Rachel proposed, an antidote to what was happening around us. An antidote to the horrific atrocities we inflicted on each other. All the natural catastrophes that we humans were responsible for accelerating. All the violence and harm we were doing to ourselves and to the world itself. Humanity had to change and the Community would show us how.

Not only did the London bombings allow my mother to formulate a purpose for her silence project, but they also had the effect of focusing the intentions of the women who sat by the campfire threading coloured wooden letters onto pieces of wire and leather cord, making the *Shhhh...* jewellery. (If you didn't have one of the *Shhhh...* bracelets yourself, you probably remember them because for a while they were almost as ubiquitous as the yellow Livestrong wristbands I had so coveted the year before).

It would be easy to dismiss those early Members as foolish and naïve but, despite everything, I believe that the original intentions of my mother's silence project were untainted, idealistic, pure even. I honestly don't think that Mum or anyone else back then could possibly foresee what the Community would become. Of course, it's tempting to claim that I saw signs of the controlling malevolence which runs through the organisation today, but the truth is that there was absolutely no indication in those early days that the Community would come to wield the immense power it now has, that it would manipulate the lives of so many or wreak such devastation around the world.

Having said that, because I actively avoided reading anything online or in the press about Mum back then – positive or negative – it was not until I was doing research for this book that I became aware that even in the earliest days a few voices did speak out against the Community. For example, the Guided Silence Sessions, which I thought were pointless but hardly *dangerous*, were considered exactly that by some people. Although Dad remembers reading negative reports and hearing discussions on local radio, I can't find anything on the internet. All I have is a single article which appeared in *The View from the Far Shore* in October 2005, written by Georgia Sweeney who, back then, was a twenty-six-year-old unknown journalist, and not the television personality that she is now.

I found the article in notebook #9 between pages 20 and 21 and, given the spiky, acerbic accusations, I can't help wondering what made Rachel fold it in half and half again and tuck it away for safekeeping. Why keep *this* article in particular? Perhaps she kept similarly negative articles, but they've been lost? Perhaps she intended to issue a rebuttal? As always, no explanation is forthcoming.

Reproduced below is an extract from Sweeney's article detailing her experience of attending Guided Silence Sessions. For anyone familiar with her current affairs programme *Talking Shop* and its inflammatory reports on the Community, the tone of this article will be instantly recognisable.

> *Remember when you were a child and someone handed*
> *you a tube of soapy water and a plastic wand?*
> *Remember how, when you dipped the wand into the tube*
> *and blew gently, beautiful bubbles would appear?*

Remember how enticing they were? Remember the urge to reach out and touch their fragile, insubstantial evanescence? But then, as soon as you did... POP! The bubble was gone.

Rachel Morris is like one of those bubbles – captivating and enchanting (there's certainly no denying that both Morris and her nascent organisation exude a powerful allure), however, as soon as you reach out to try and understand it, the magic vanishes, revealing how superficial an endeavour the whole thing is.

In the two consecutive weekends I spent with Morris and her followers in the pretty village of Chalkham, nestled in a spur of the South Downs, I saw nothing to justify the positive attention she is receiving or to substantiate the claims that her so-called 'Community' is teaching people to be sympathetic, empathetic and kind. Instead, I witnessed an atmosphere more akin to a cult, with Morris the enigmatic charismatic leader, feeding on the gullibility and neediness of others.

For example, there are the so-called 'Guided Silence Sessions' that last ninety minutes and take place three times a week. The first time I experienced a Guided Silence Session I was expecting, not unreasonably, to receive some guidance. But in this (as with all matters connected with Morris and her 'Community') my expectations were thwarted. The 'guidance' merely consists of Morris sitting crossed-legged, guru-style, while her followers face her adoringly. Some sit, others prop themselves up on their elbows, a few lie down. Participants are furnished with laminated cards exhorting them to 'Shhhh... Be Silent. Be Silent and Hear Yourself. Be Silent and Hear Others. Shhhh...'

In Morris's camp, speaking is forbidden at all times, apart from in designated 'Hearing Places'. Followers are permitted to speak when not in the camp, provided they remember to devote equal time to listening, but to be in the camp is to be silent. So, what, you might ask, is the difference between their run-of-the-mill day-to-day silence and a guided silence?

According to one of their press releases, the everyday silence of the camp is both a literal and symbolic opportunity for 'Members' to acknowledge their affinity with Morris's ideology. Apparently, by maintaining a strict silence in the camp, Morris and her followers are undergoing a more profound lived experience. In other words, by being silent in the camp Morris's followers are practising what they preach.

By contrast, so the press release explains, 'Our Guided Silence Sessions promote the importance of collective silence and enable Members to explore the transformational effects of collective listening as we learn how to hear not only ourselves but those around us.' Everyday silence in the camp is an individual act, whereas Guided Silence Sessions are about harnessing the benefits of collective silence. Having experienced them in person, all I can say is that as I was waiting for the transformational effects of the Guided Silence Session to hit me, I couldn't help wondering if I'd stumbled into a post-modern, feminist production of 'The Emperor's New Clothes'.

There is no charge for attending the Guided Silence Sessions, although donations are welcome (and the committed individuals who choose to stay at Morris's camp are expected to help out as much as they can, particularly with the provision of food), so it would be

*easy to dismiss Morris as a harmless charlatan. However,
this would be foolhardy in the extreme.*

*There is an intensity and focus to Morris and her
inner circle that belies the wordy press releases and
amateurish instruction cards. Sitting on the ground,
watching Morris 'guide' the silence sessions, I couldn't
help thinking about the doomed followers of Jim Jones,
David Koresh and their ilk, who all began their own fatal
journeys with similarly benign activities*[4].

Few people shared Georgia Sweeney's view, and in the wake
of the bombings a steady stream of women arrived in Chalkham.
Rachel had trained a handful of Silent Listeners who could
deputise for her and a second Hearing Place was built. The camp
now sprawled across the whole meadow beyond our beer garden,
and more permanent shelters continued to be constructed from
donated materials, which gave the settlement an appealingly
quirky look. Wood stoves and the open-air firepits were lit and
aromatic plants were burned to mask the smell of the long-drop
toilet, which could be overpowering when the wind was blowing
in the wrong direction. The whole thing was a terrible fire hazard,
but more of that later.

Georgia Sweeney and a handful of others may have doubted
the intentions of the women who gathered around Rachel in the
early days, but I honestly believe that they simply wanted to be
heard. Then, in the wake of the London bombings, they began to
ask themselves whether this new movement – the Community
– with its focus on listening and hearing was too important to only
have a life at the bottom of our garden. They questioned whether
they were content to keep for themselves what my mother was

[4] Georgia Sweeney, 'Bursting Bubbles', *The View from the Far Shore*,
14 October 2005, pp. 13–21.

offering, or whether they wanted to try and push the Community out into the world as far it could go.

Many commentators question how the Community managed to transform itself so rapidly from a single camp in the Hampshire countryside in 2003 into the cohesive, well-organised, multinational organisation that it had become only a few years later. The present-day leadership claims this astonishing growth was the result of a well-executed plan, akin to an unbroken chain of events, one step leading to another and another and so on, but in my opinion, that ignores the enormously significant roles played by chance and luck.

Instead of a single thread of actions, I believe the development of Mum's silence project was more akin to a web of interconnected circumstances and opportunities, punctuated with frequent doses of good fortune (or misfortune, depending on your point of view), and there were a small number of extremely fortuitous occurrences without which the Community may well have never left our garden.

The most significant of these is undoubtedly the connection with Tabitha Kennedy's niece, Jodie Parker. Millions of people around the world are familiar with Jodie, one of four young women brought together on a UK reality-TV programme to form a band called Kiss the Apex. Although they finished as runners-up, less than a year later Kiss the Apex's first album, *A Deep Cut with a Sharp Knife*, was a double-platinum number one album in both the UK and America, and their Community-inspired breakout single, 'Silent Chic', had been nominated for a Grammy. Everyone knows the words.

> *Don't bore us with your shouting*
> *Don't tell us what to do*
> *Don't keep on with your talking*

You ain't our silent crew
Be quiet; hear our voices
Listen when we speak
Just like the women in the camp
The ones with silent chic
Silent chic
Silent chic
(Silent chic)
(Silent chic)
(Silent chic)

(Jodie Parker and Winston Langsworthy, 2004)

As lead singer and principal songwriter, Jodie had the highest profile of the four members of Kiss the Apex and inevitably fronted the interviews. Every time she was asked about the inspiration for 'Silent Chic', Jodie would explain how her aunt Tabitha was part of the Community, which was an organisation led by an 'amazing woman called Rachel' who was urging people to talk less and listen more. Time after time, Jodie credited my mother and the Community with inspiring not only the song but also her personally, and thanks to Jodie's superstar status, the Community was discussed on shows with audiences of millions, including *Saturday Night Live* in America and, in the UK, *Jools Holland's Hootenanny*. Kiss the Apex headlined music festivals around the world, appearing in 2005 at venues such as Lollapalooza and the Fuji Rock Festival. And, of course, Jodie and the rest of the band made their now infamous appearance on Band Aid 20's 'Do They Know It's Christmas?'

Few things can rival the reach of a globally famous band and their most iconic song, which (at the time of writing) has been streamed more than 510 million times on Spotify. However, there were other lucky interventions that helped spread awareness of

Rachel and her Community. One thing that really caught the collective imagination was when, in late 2005, two investigative reporters (perhaps influenced by Georgia Sweeney) 'infiltrated' the Community, intending to 'expose' it. The story of Caroline Cooper and Emily Savage is well known: how they spent several weeks in the camp, throwing themselves into complying with the rule of silence, joining in the Guided Silence Sessions and generally making themselves as useful as possible before they both decided it had been such a life-changing experience that there was nothing to expose and instead signed up to become fully fledged Members. Caroline and Emily wrote extensively about their decision to join the Community and, working alongside Tabitha, they both continued to produce pro-Community journalism right up until they died in the Event.

And, of course, there was that well-loved, slightly goofy BBC documentary maker who made one of his *Curious Collections* programmes in the camp. I don't remember exactly when it was filmed but I would have been fifteen or sixteen and Livy and I spent hours hanging around the production crew, making nuisances of ourselves. Embarrassingly, I make a brief appearance halfway through the programme, drinking tea with Gran. Not only is the *Curious Collections* series repeated regularly on UK television, but the episode about the Community won the Grierson Award for Best Documentary on a Contemporary Theme, thus ensuring it was sold to dozens of additional overseas territories, introducing Mum's silence project to yet more audiences.

All these things and more, plus Tabitha's ability to capitalise on any hint of publicity, helped drive the Community out from Chalkham and around the world. The website rapidly went through its second and third iterations, and bank accounts were set up to receive donations from women desperate to support

Rachel's silence project. Before long, a whole infrastructure was in place to assist with the establishment of overseas branches of the Community.

Where supporters of other organisations might have marched, in the Community they established silence camps. In those early years, many of the overseas camps were more symbolic than anything else – places where women gathered once or twice a week to be silent together. But increasingly, permanent camps were being set up, and as far as possible these mirrored the one at the end of our garden.

According to official estimates, by the middle of 2006, the Community already had a presence in more than thirty countries, across every continent. I haven't been able to find any record of the number of permanent camps compared with symbolic ones, but there is no doubt that the Community had gone global. Rachel and her team were delivering the right message at the right time to the right audience, and with the help of enormous doses of luck, almost overnight it had become cool to be quiet.

No matter what successes Tabitha had with regards to publicity, although she had the PR nous, and although she knew who to speak to and how to maximise every opportunity that came her way, she made sure that Rachel was always the face of the Community. There is no better example than when Rachel was the subject of the 2006 Portrait Photograph of the Year. I can only assume that when Della Markham asked for permission to come and photograph Rachel for what turned out to be the winning entry, she could not have imagined in her wildest dreams how iconic her picture of my mother would become.

Of course, everyone has seen the photograph; I have a copy in front of me now. In 2006, when the picture was taken, Rachel was forty-one. With remarkable prescience, or perhaps just plain good luck, Della made the decision to photograph my mother at the Chalkham Boar, and although the background is deliberately blurred you can make out a little of the chalk outline. Staring down the lens, the future site of the Event behind her, Rachel confronts the world head-on.

Her hair is tucked behind her ears, grey at the roots and light brown where it falls to her shoulders. It needs brushing. She's wearing a jumper knitted by my grandmother. Although Gran never officially became a Member, after Mum moved out my grandmother divided her time between her home, the pub and the camp, where she established her own little corner, sitting on one of those folding chairs that people take to festivals, a blanket over her lap, a huge green golf umbrella for when it rained or was too hot, and she would knit. She knitted everything and anything and there was a long waiting list filled with things people asked her to make for them: scarves, socks, gloves, hats and jumpers.

Mum is wearing one of Gran's jumpers in Della's portrait. It is navy blue, boat-necked with a pattern of diamonds picked out in white that runs from collarbone to collarbone. The pattern continues around the back – I know this because I have the jumper. After the Event, the police took it from the camp along with Mum's other possessions, but eventually it was returned to Dad and me with the rest of her belongings.

My mother isn't smiling. She looks tired; the bags under her eyes have settled in for the duration and they give her ferocious gaze just a hint of vulnerability. She is, as always, communicating without speaking, challenging you to look away. The thing that dominates the photo, the thing that draws your eyes to it, that keeps them fixed on the picture, is her right forefinger. Rachel's fingernail is clean but bitten and on the second knuckle there's a tiny scratch and a smudge of blood. Her loosely curled fist sits below her chin, but that forefinger is pressed tight against her lips. *Shhhh...*

Della Markham's portrait of my mother was recently voted the most iconic picture of the first two decades of the twenty-first century, and there is absolutely no doubt that it helped propel Rachel onto all those Person of the Year lists in late 2006.

10.

When the backlash arrived, it was both brutal and, I suppose, inevitable. Put your head above the parapet, try to be different, to make a change, and inevitably there will be plenty of people who want to shoot you down.

I don't propose to dwell on the antagonism that Mum generated close to home, but for anyone interested in finding out more about the relentless pressure brought to bear on Rachel to leave Chalkham, I would recommend both *Pivot – From There to Here* by Caroline Hartnell (Spoken Press, 2017) and *My Chalkham Community* by Roger McKinley (Saltmine, 2016). Both Caroline Hartnell and Roger McKinley lived in Chalkham. Caroline, in particular, was highly vocal in her opposition to Mum, the Community, the camp and, more generally, anything that, as she put it, 'tainted the enviable reputation of Chalkham as a haven for peaceful, law-abiding citizens'.

As the book title suggests, Caroline Hartnell later underwent a complete reversal of opinion, was one of the thousands who joined the Community in the immediate aftermath of the Event and today is on the UK executive board. However, that doesn't excuse the role she played back then in trying to evict Rachel from what was, after all, our own land. Among my mother's belongings when they were returned to us after the Event were nearly three dozen letters, including several from Caroline herself.

These letters accuse my mother and her 'commune of ladies' of, among other things, polluting the stream with 'feminine products', encouraging a 'blatant disregard for the sanctity of marriage', inciting an 'anarchistic revolt against traditional English ways' and effecting a 'catastrophic reduction' in Chalkham's house prices. Underneath their high-handed, condescending tone, this stack of letters is a bullying, grubby testament to the strenuous efforts made by certain people – people my mother had previously considered friends – to put an end to her Community almost before it had begun.

Several of the letters are anonymous and these are particularly nasty. Printed on plain A4 paper, they are all addressed to 'Dear Bitches', purport to come from 'Concerned residents of Chalkham' and contain such choice phrases as 'No one wants you here so why don't you fuck off out of Chalkham', 'What you lezzas need is a right good seeing to', and 'You should sleep with one eye open'.

I can't help but wonder what the authors of these letters feel about my mother and the Community now. Do they still live in lovely leafy Chalkham? If so, they will have benefited from the astronomical rise in house prices resulting from the never-ending demand from people who want to live as close as possible to where Rachel spent so much of her life.

As with Mum's other belongings, the letters have been stuffed in a box for the last decade, and reading them for the first time in preparation for writing this book made me rethink what I understood about how things were for Mum back then. I had no idea that by calling for us all to talk less and listen more my mother had put herself in the firing line of every woman-hating, small-minded, progress-loathing little-Englander strutting self-importantly around Chalkham.

As personally upsetting as this must have been for Rachel, it pales into insignificance compared to the outrage her Community was causing in a more public arena.

The principle trigger for this anger wasn't Rachel's plea for silence per se: it was what she was saying we should *do* in the silence. The Community's opponents back then fixated on her assertion that we should *listen to the angry people*. They twisted her words, claiming that Rachel was justifying what the terrorists did by saying it was our fault for not listening to them. Therefore, her detractors bellowed, Rachel was blaming the victims, bystanders and innocent people for all the atrocities around the world, including the London bombings. Rachel, they said, believed those terrible events were our own fault.

From there it was only a small step for the anti-Community voices – most notably The52 – to claim that Rachel was an apologist for terrorism and that she and her Community were advocating for terrorists, murderers and extremists.

To believe that this is what the Community was about is to entirely miss the point. Lord knows I have my own issues with my mother and good – possibly the best – reasons to feel profoundly bitter towards her, but I do not believe that Rachel or anyone associated with the Community ever promoted or celebrated terrorism. Additionally, nothing in the notebooks or any of the surviving pre-Event Community material or any of my mother's personal effects condones acts of terrorism. Quite the opposite, in fact. Back then the Community wasn't about vilifying or blaming any specific group of people or belief system. It was about Rachel's absolute conviction that because we were living inside our own thoughts, we were unable to hear anyone else. My mother's words express it better than I ever could:

While ever we don't hear others, we ourselves will never
be heard and so we just shout louder. After a time, we

*realise all our words are pointless, and we feel angry and
some of us are moved to take action. Action born of
anger can never be positive. Our world needs positive
action. And that can only happen if we stop shouting.
First, we must fall silent. Then we must listen to others.
Only when we hear others, will we ourselves be heard.*
(#9, pp. 43–4)

Before I continue, I should make it clear that not a single family member of the fifty-two people who tragically died in the London bombings ever actually joined The52, and nothing has ever come to light which implicates any of them in what transpired. Although The52 ceased to exist as an organisation around the end of 2010, its vitriolic hate-filled agenda lived on in other guises, coalescing around the so-called BFB (Britain for the Brits) policy. In touting their anti-immigration agenda, members of The52 conveniently disregarded the fact that three of the four bombers were born in the UK, instead insisting that what they called 'criminally lax immigration rules' were to blame for what happened in London on 7 July 2005.

The absence of a single shred of evidence of terrorist sympathies on the part of my mother or any Member did not stop The52 spearheading a campaign to try and discredit Rachel. As far as they were concerned, anyone that didn't agree with them was automatically an enemy. In the end, of course, they were *so* vocal, *so* determined to find what wasn't there to be found, that the Community received far more publicity than it would otherwise have done. Moreover, The52 completely underestimated how formidable an opponent Tabitha would prove to be. There are links online to several radio and television programmes where she appears alongside someone called Stuart. You might remember Stuart – for several months he was the The52's go-to spokesperson.

He had greasy hair, which he always tied back with a rubber band, weirdly long fingernails, and in every television clip I've seen he's wearing a Guns N' Roses T-shirt allegedly stained with blood from when he went to the assistance of a young woman injured on the Tavistock Square bus. That's what he claimed, anyway.

Earlier today, I listened to an archived interview from 15 September 2006 with Tabitha and Stuart on Radio 4's *Today* programme[5]. Tabitha comes across as considered and calm but also warm and caring – in other words, the complete antithesis of a terrorism-glorifying zealot. On the other hand, after failing to get a rise out of Tabitha, Stuart becomes increasingly wound up until his voice is shrill to the point of ear-splitting. Eventually he resorts to name-calling, claiming the Community is anti-British and pro-terrorist. He follows that up by calling it a cult and alleging that Rachel had brainwashed Tabitha and the other women to join her. Finally, he ends up literally shrieking that the Community is a 'hotbed of toxic lesbianism'. There was no going back for The52 at that point, and the BBC was forced to broadcast an apology to Tabitha, Rachel and the Community for how catastrophically it had lost control of the interview.

Not long after that interview, Robert Kenny – Tabitha's husband – made a return visit to Chalkham, and this time, he brought members of The52 with him.

Dad and I were having breakfast. It was a school day and it wasn't yet properly light outside. I remember the smell of toast and coffee and listening to Terry Wogan's breakfast show on the radio. When we heard the sound of air brakes hissing in the road, Dad went to the window.

---

[5] https://www.bbc.co.uk/radio4/today/listenagain/listenagain_673249.shtml

'Strange,' he said.

'What is?' I asked, and when he didn't reply, I got up to look for myself.

A coach had pulled up and people were piling off it. The side-gates were locked, so everyone was milling around on the pavement.

I looked at Dad. Worry lines cut deep into his forehead.

'Stay here,' he said.

'It might be dangerous.'

'Which is why I want you to stay here, Ems.'

He gave me his phone. 'Ring the police – 999. Say it's urgent.'

I'd never rung the emergency services before. Just dialling the numbers felt scary, and when the woman asked me, 'Which service do you require? Fire, Police or Ambulance,' the answer got stuck in my throat. She asked me again, and this time I managed to say, 'Police.'

I looked out of the window and by then at least two dozen men were outside the pub and the ones at the back were pushing the ones at the front and the ones at the front were banging on the door. Everyone was shouting. Someone wrapped a scarf around his arm, raised it and jabbed his elbow through one of our windows. I heard the glass shatter at the same time as Dad must have wrenched the door open because everyone started pouring into the pub.

'The Wild Boar pub. Chalkham,' I gabbled. 'Please come quickly. There's a lot of people. They've broken in. I think they've come for my mum.'

The woman at the end of phone was unnaturally calm. That's one of the things I vividly remember. I could hear the mob surging through the pub. I heard them shouting at Dad for the key to open the back door, which he always kept on top of the door frame. I heard him pleading with them to calm down, and then I couldn't hear his voice, only their yelling. And the whole time, the woman on the phone was speaking in that calm voice, confirming our address, telling me she would stay on the phone until the police arrived.

I left the phone on the table while she was still talking and ran downstairs. The mob was already at the end of the garden. I ran to catch up with them, praying for the police to come. In the camp, the women were clustered together in a group, my mother in the centre. Either side of them were the firepits – once autumn arrived and the temperatures dropped, the fires were kept burning almost constantly. The women had grabbed whatever they could lay their hands on: pieces of wood, saucepans, even a couple of knives. I went over to Dad.

'Did you ring the police?' he said and then, 'You should have stayed in the kitchen,' but he knew I wasn't going anywhere because he put an arm around my shoulders.

Robert Kenny took a step towards the women and said, 'We've come to take you home.'

No one moved. No one said a word. Tabitha put her arm round my mother's shoulders and pulled her close, protecting her, just like Dad was protecting me.

'You don't understand what's going on here,' Robert said, 'but we've come to rescue you.'

The expressions on the faces of the women changed. At first I thought they were grimacing, in pain. But then I realised they were laughing. An eerie, soundless laugh that went on and on.

One of The52 shouted, 'They're all mad.'

Someone else yelled, 'She's brainwashed them, it's how she operates.'

Several of them pulled ropes out of their backpacks. I remember wondering if they were actually planning to truss the women up and lead them away like animals.

'It's for your own good.'

'This is an intervention.'

'You need to come with us.'

'We'll save you.'

'Don't be scared.'

Nothing on any of the faces of the Community's women suggested they were scared or had any requirement to be saved. They pressed closer together, brandishing their sticks and knives and saucepans.

A police siren wailed along the main road.

'Thank god,' said Dad.

The mob surged forward and Dad pulled me further away.

From that point on, my memories are strangely detailed, cinematic almost, as if I were there, watching it happen all over again.

The mob presses forward but the women hold their ground, makeshift weapons raised. The two groups meet and the aggressors try to take hold of individuals but the tight group of women starts rotating en masse, which makes it almost impossible for them to be separated. Someone grabs a woman's arm, for example, and one of the other women jabs him in the ribs with a stick so they let go, and the circle of silent women keeps turning.

Finally, I see police running towards the camp. Dad sees them as well.

'Oh shit,' I hear him say.

There are only two of them: a man and a woman. Is that it? What use are they going to be? They obviously come to the same realisation because even before they reach us the female officer is on the radio, presumably calling for back-up. They stand at the edge of the mass of people, shouting, but no one pays them the slightest bit of attention because everyone is pushing and shoving. The mob is yelling and the women are silent, but they are all brawling and it almost looks like choreographed wrestling as they move this way and that, backwards and forwards, round and round. Then someone, I don't know who, shoves Robert Kenny and he stumbles, trips over his own feet and falls backwards into a firepit.

The screaming. Oh my god, the screaming. People thrust their arms into the flames and drag him out. Blankets are thrown over him. Buckets of water are brought from the stream. Wet blankets are wrapped round the arms of the people that rescued him. At some point, Dad tries to make me turn away, but I don't move. The police are on their radios. The women don't make a sound. The mob is pressing forward, reaching for my mother, calling her name, baying for her to be handed over. The women press close to her, protecting her. My mother is kept safe.

Finally, we hear sirens. A lot of sirens. Police pour down the bank and into the camp. At the sight of them, the fight goes out of the mob. Ambulance crews arrive and bend over burned flesh.

Everyone except my father and me was arrested, but in the end no one from the Community was charged. Robert Kenny survived, although he will carry the scars for the rest of his life. No one ever admitted to pushing him. An injunction was taken out against every member of The52 to stop any of them coming near Chalkham. Later, the Community would manage to successfully apply for a more sweeping injunction which prevented any member of The52 ever discussing Rachel or the Community in public. While Robert Kenny was still in hospital, an injunction was taken out against him too, which prevented him from returning to Chalkham, although given what had happened, I can't imagine he'd have been in a rush to come back.

When I contacted Robert Kenny to ask him if he would be

prepared to talk to me about his involvement with The52 for this book, I received a letter from his solicitor enclosing a short statement from Robert with permission to reproduce it, provided I did so in full, unedited and without an accompanying commentary. What follows, then, is Robert Kenny's unexpurgated statement.

Regardless of your supposed good intentions in writing a book about your mother, I do not wish to enter into any dialogue with you about my ex-wife or my involvement with The52.

You were just a child when I came to see Tabitha, but you were the spitting image of your mother. I wonder, do you resemble her in other ways? It seems to me that you must, given how you are trying to manipulate me into discussing what happened back then. Well, it won't work.

I've got no desire whatsoever to rake up the past and frankly I'm staggered that you have the gall to ask me. You're an adult now, so you must have an idea of how difficult it was for me to move on emotionally. You must also realise that my physical scars mean that, in some part at least, I have to relive what happened to me every single day of my life. I honestly cannot believe you would choose to ignore that and expect me to talk to you about my life with my ex-wife before she was brainwashed into joining the Community.

I hope both Tabitha and your mother are rotting in hell. Burning to death was too good for the pair of them. I could say that I don't know which one of them was more evil, but that's not true. It was obviously your mother, since the whole thing was her idea. Isn't it bad enough that the Community dominates so much of our lives nowadays, without you publishing a book that'll just serve to glorify Rachel of Chalkham even more? Because you know that that's what will happen. While I accept that The52 was not correct in its assertion that the Community was concerned with terrorist activities, as far as I am concerned, its motivations were and still are just as sinister. Rachel's legacy is pure evil.

I'll give you one piece of advice. The best thing you can do is to try and pretend that your mother never existed. If you pretend hard enough that someone didn't exist, you'll find that eventually you can forget about them for days at a time.

11.

During 2007 Rachel began to ramp up the Community's public protests, and one of the most successful early events (in terms of the publicity it generated) was the burning of the origami cranes. It was also the Community's first international protest.

I don't need to speculate about Mum's reasons for choosing cranes, because she wrote about it extensively in notebook #14. My mother really admired the women of Greenham Common (there are over a dozen references to them in #14 alone) and among the belongings returned to my father and me was a well-thumbed copy of *Greenham Common: Women at the Wire* (The Women's Press, 1984) which contains first-hand accounts edited by Barbara Harford and Sarah Hopkins, who were themselves Greenham Women.

In August 1982, the women of Greenham Common made one thousand origami cranes which they presented to the military officer in charge of the base on the thirty-seventh anniversary of the Nagasaki bomb. The Greenham Women were inspired by a Japanese folktale, which says if someone folds one thousand paper cranes they will have a wish granted, and a Japanese schoolgirl called Sadako who, as she was dying of leukaemia caused by radiation from the atomic bomb, was desperate to make one thousand cranes so she could wish for an end to all wars. Sadako died in 1955 before she completed them all.

For weeks during the spring of 2007, everyone in the camp

spent every spare second folding paper. Even Gran put down her knitting needles for a while and started folding. Livy and I were roped in to help whenever we weren't at sixth-form college or working in the pub (we were both doings shifts to help Dad out, albeit neither of us was eighteen yet). Tabitha got her hands on huge amounts of scrap paper and for weeks all of us folded and folded and folded. Members in other countries were doing the same and the piles of cranes grew larger.

It takes twenty-five folds to make an origami crane and it only takes one wrong fold for the thing to resemble a ball of scrunched up paper. I made one this morning and I was delighted to find that I could still do it. Granted, I used to be faster because it took me around five minutes today and back then, at our peak, most of us averaged a crane every two minutes or so. That meant, for a few weeks, we were each churning out around thirty cranes for every hour of folding. And each and every crane, no matter how small, how poorly made, no matter what bit of scrap paper they had been folded from, each and every one of those cranes had *Shhhh...* written on them. That was Rachel's wish for us all.

Many people will remember what she did with those cranes because it was the Community's first overtly political protest.

In May that year, UK Prime Minister Tony Blair had announced that he would be stepping down and endorsed the chancellor, Gordon Brown, as his replacement. Along with many other organisations, the Community asked, in countless press releases, opinion pieces and the occasional late-night panel show that Tabitha managed to wangle her way onto, was it fair for the prime minister to be someone who hadn't stood in a general election as leader of his party? For the prime minister, therefore, to be someone who hadn't listened to his electorate? Was it fair for a party that had so catastrophically failed to listen to anyone but George Bush about non-existent weapons of mass destruction to continue to run the country?

Rachel chose the day that Gordon Brown became prime minister – 27 June 2007 – as the moment to use those origami cranes to make a highly visual plea for there to be a lot less talking and a lot more listening.

During the morning, the paper cranes were taken up to the Chalkham Boar (notably, this was the only time other than the Event itself that Rachel used the Boar to stage a protest). I'm not sure what Mum and the others would have done if it had been raining that day, or if it had been windy. Luck was on their side, though. The weather was fine and the cranes were piled on the ground beneath the Boar's belly. I imagine the fact that they were liberally doused in petrol helped stick them to the grass.

In the early afternoon, when Gordon Brown was being driven along the Mall to meet the Queen, every Member of the Chalkham Community was at the Boar, unfurling a huge banner which read *Shhhh…* flanked at either end by a painted origami crane. The women must have used leftover paint from the camp because one crane was green, the other was red, and all the letters and full stops were different colours. In other parts of the world other Members were doing something similar (they had no particular connection with UK politics, of course, but elsewhere it had become a more general 'our politicians don't listen to us' protest). Back in Chalkham, thanks to Tabitha calling in yet another favour, a press helicopter hovered above the Boar.

At the precise moment that Gordon Brown stepped out of the car and walked half a dozen steps towards the palace, my mother also stepped forward, holding a flame. Tabitha had distributed a press release, a copy of which I found tucked in the back cover of notebook #15. The press release begins: 'Give Silence a Chance. The Time for Talking Is Over: Now Is the Time for Listening' and continues for three paragraphs explaining that a politician's first responsibility is to listen to their electorate, something which, the press release claimed, 'the current generation of politicians has failed to do because they are so in love with the sound of their own voices, they can no longer hear ours'.

As Gordon Brown disappeared inside Buckingham Palace, Rachel set fire to the *Shhhh...* peace cranes.

If you search online for 'burning cranes', there are videos from every site that took part that day. The fire at the Boar was by far the largest and because of the helicopter it was the only one filmed by a news channel, but the most impressive crane burning was undoubtedly the one on top of a mountain in British Columbia – as much for the logistics of getting all the cranes up there as for the flames. In some places where it was night-time, Members had come up with ingenious ways of making their message visible. The Australian site was particularly good. They had taken all their cranes and banners into the outback, somewhere near Uluru. In the middle of the night, in the middle of winter, their display was spectacular. They had painted their banners in special paint and hooked up ultraviolet lamps which made the huge letters of *Shhhh...* glow with a fierce intensity.

No one knows exactly how many cranes were burned that day. I've seen estimates as low as 80,000 and as high as 800,000. The actual number is probably somewhere between the two. Another thing that no one knew was that when all those paper cranes were set alight back in June 2007 the flames were a tiny foretaste of the burnings that would happen 1,587 days later.

The cranes burned, Rachel's profile grew, the Community gained traction, but nothing really changed. Not then. Not yet. Gordon Brown failed to stop the British economy going into freefall after the collapse of the financial markets. Three years after that, he failed to win the next general election and failed further when he couldn't form a coalition. Poor old Gordon failed to burn as brightly as Mum's cranes, and his departure from Downing Street in 2010 was as inevitable as it was ignoble. As fast as his star descended, my mother's rose.

Between June 2007 and May 2008, Rachel participated in many protests and almost all of them are mentioned in her notebooks. The protests had a strict policy of silence (of course) and at each one the women were accompanied by a seven-foot-high rubber ear they called Shelly. (For readers unfamiliar with the term, the name Shelly is derived from the colloquial English phrase 'shell-like', meaning ear). Although I've focused on UK-based protests, it's worth remembering that wherever in the world there was a branch of the Community, women were protesting and their message was always the same: *Stop Talking, Start Listening*.

At the beginning of September 2007, Rachel took part in the Community's first sit-down – at the Hampshire County Council offices in Basingstoke. The protest lasted for little over an hour, police were called, and the women left (#15, pp. 87–89).

That was followed less than a month later by a sit-down at Waterloo station during the morning rush hour. On page 6 of notebook #16 Rachel notes that police were present, but all they did was observe the protesters, presumably to make sure no one tried to get onto the train tracks.

Three weeks later, there was a sit-down on a train line immediately outside London Bridge station. Rachel writes about tying Shelly to the tracks like she was the heroine of an old black and white film rather than a large rubber ear (#16, p. 49). When the police arrived, the women refused to leave and in the end they were physically carried off the tracks. Rachel claims several women were injured while they were being removed. She said they were '*hit hard*' and '*dragged away*' (#16, p. 50), that some of

them (although not her) were *'clubbed on the arms and legs'* (ibid.).
She also wrote that the police *'spat on us and called us crazy fucking
bitches'* (ibid.). She writes about two women who suffered broken
arms and one who broke her leg as they were *'dragged off the
tracks'* and how *'they were left untreated for hours'* after they were all
bundled off to a police station and charged with aggravated trespass
(#16, p. 51).

They were convicted, but since it was the first offence for
everyone, no one went to jail. Instead, they were all fined, and
the Community paid the fines on their behalf. Mum writes
about how, funded by the Community, several of the women
subsequently brought claims against the police for the unnecessarily
brutal way the police had removed them (#16, p. 72), although
if you search online for the 'London Bridge Sit-Down October
2007', you'll see that the Independent Police Complaints
Commission completely exonerated the police of all accusations
of brutality.

In November 2007, there was a sit-down in the Great Hall of
Westminster. Given the proximity to Parliament, armed police
arrived within minutes and several protesters were arrested,
although my mother wasn't among them. Everyone was released
without charge and the protest resulted in the question 'Is it time
our politicians started hearing the demands to start listening?'
being asked on the BBC's *Question Time* programme.

The episode isn't available online but an online review lists
panellists' answers ranging from a cabinet minister who claimed
that Labour was already the 'Listening Party', which the audience
greeted with 'booing and shouting', a Green Party representative
who said she was already a Member, a notorious right-wing
journalist who called the Community 'a sign of our times'
demonstrating 'just how far removed from normal people the
government of the day are', and a well-known musician who

rounded everything off by saying 'yes, of course politicians should start listening more', and while they were at it, 'perhaps they might also listen to my latest album'[6].

There's no doubt that this heralded a step change – the Community's message was now being discussed in a serious forum on mainstream media.

After the parliamentary sit-down, there was a lull in the protests for a few weeks, but early on the morning of Christmas Eve a chain of Members wearing oversized prosthetic ears (dubbed Little Shellys) barricaded the entrance to the BBC Broadcasting House. A considerable amount of footage of this particular protest is available online because numerous people (both men and women, Members and non-Members) decided that since it was the last day before Christmas a protest was the perfect excuse for an impromptu party; social media worked its magic and people headed over to the BBC in droves.

In one video there is a close-up of my mother. She is holding hands with a man wearing a Rudolph jumper with a flashing red nose and a woman in a long green coat and a red scarf. The man and woman are both laughing, belting out 'The Holly and the Ivy'. What strikes me about this video is that not only is Mum not laughing, but she isn't even smiling. For Rachel, the protests weren't supposed to be fun. For her, they were deadly serious. She couldn't, or wouldn't, lose focus, not even for a second, and so she is staring straight ahead, her serious, cold face framed by those ridiculous prosthetic ears.

You might wonder what she had to say about so many people joining them that day, and the answer is: nothing. I have no idea if she was pleased by the hordes that swelled the Community's numbers. I have no idea if she believed her message was diluted

---

[6] https://tvtoday.co.uk/BBCQT/HowDidTheyDo?/

by the raucous singing. I have no idea if she hoped the publicity might persuade more people to join them, or at least to talk less and listen more. Rachel's typically inconsistent (and often frustrating) approach to recording events meant that she simply wrote:

> *Christmas Eve. Cold day. Protest outside BBC.*
> (#17, p. 14)

Still, it was seven words more than she said about Christmas Day with her family that year.

Gran, Dad and I had planned Christmas Day 2007 so as to include my mother in our celebrations. In our house, Christmas had always been less a celebratory day and more a celebratory half-day. It always amazed me quite how many people couldn't pass even a single twenty-four-hour period without feeling the need to pop out to the pub for a drink and, of course, Dad couldn't afford to ignore them. The only concession was that he didn't open the doors until 1 p.m., so right from when I was a toddler, we always opened our presents first thing, before settling down to an early Christmas lunch at around 11.30.

The plan for that year wasn't any different, except at some point Gran had suggested to Dad and me that we take our meal down to the camp to share, not only with Rachel, but also with the other women who hadn't gone home to their families for the festive period. Gran and I spent days and days preparing enough food to feed an army. There were bite-sized sausage rolls, miniature Scotch eggs, the obligatory pigs in blankets, cheese and pineapple on little sticks (Mum's favourite) and tiny turkey burgers which Gran spent ages making. Dad had been to the cash and carry and bought bottles of fizzy wine (I'd extracted a promise from him that I would be allowed to have some) and a stack of plastic glasses.

Gran was up before dawn, cooking everything that needed heating through, filling containers and piling them carefully into boxes. The three of us loaded ourselves up with as much as we could carry and made our way down to the bottom of the garden. There was too much for just one trip so Dad and Gran went back to fetch the rest. It was freezing cold, but there was always a ready supply of spare coats, hats, gloves and scarves, not to mention piles of blankets. The firepits were lit and at the far end of the camp I could see my mother and the others.

'Happy Christmas,' I shouted, letting excitement win out over my desire to appear cool at all costs. I may have been seventeen years old, I may have had an unusual home life, but it was Christmas Day and we'd spent so long planning this surprise for them all. Obviously I didn't expect anybody to reply – camp rules were camp rules and Members could only speak in the Hearing Places, no matter which day it was. I set the food down on their main table (which was made from scaffolding boards resting on tree trunks) and called out again but no one even looked at me. I remember hoping they weren't doing what I thought they were doing. Not today. Not when we'd gone to so much effort to give them this wonderful treat in the precious couple of hours before the pub opened.

But they were. They really were. The women were in the middle of a Guided Silence Session. Christmas morning and they were actually holding a Silence Session. By then the sessions took place on Tuesdays, Fridays and Sundays between 11 a.m. and 1 p.m. Christmas Day 2007 happened to be a Tuesday, but it had never crossed my mind – nor, judging by their faces when they reappeared with yet more food and drink, the minds of Dad or Gran – that Rachel would hold a Guided Silence Session on Christmas morning.

When I think about it now, I'm surprised we were surprised. It had been apparent for a long time that Mum's commitment to the Community's cause was utterly uncompromising. Somewhere along the line, Mum had taught herself to be incapable of distraction. Her focus was formidable and absolute.

There's no point lying about how upset I was. This story doesn't paint me in a good light. I ran among the women, shouting, trying to get someone, anyone, to pay attention to me. Why, I yelled, if they were supposed to be listening, were they not listening to *me*? I may not have been able to get Mum to listen but surely I could provoke someone into reacting? But only the most hardcore Members had remained in the camp over Christmas, and my efforts were futile. Their eyelids didn't even flicker. Their silence was deafening.

I'm not proud of my behaviour that day, which was more akin to that of a seven-year-old than a seventeen-year-old, but I was desperate to smother their stupid silence with as much noise as I could. I shouted. A lot. I swore. I shouted some more, then I turned on my mother. I don't remember exactly what I yelled at her, but my outburst went something like this.

'You pretend you're so important, that all this stuff you're doing is going to change the world. Well, it won't, Mum, it won't. And if you carry on like this, I won't be here for you. Dad and Gran won't be here for you. You'll be alone and forgotten and no one will care about you and your stupid silence.'

You may laugh. I can almost laugh about it too now. I mean, how completely wrong could I have been?

Gran, Dad and I left most of the food and drink for Mum and the others, and the three of us went back to the house and tried to pretend we were having fun while we forced down a few minia-ture turkey burgers and pigs in blankets. At 1 p.m., Dad unlocked the door of the pub, and Christmas was over for another year.

12.

The first half of 2008 saw an acceleration of the protests, and in February the Community beamed gigantic images of *Shhhh…* simultaneously onto the Houses of Parliament, the Senedd in Wales, the Scottish Parliament in Holyrood and the Northern Irish Parliament in Stormont. I have no idea how they managed to achieve this, although presumably by then membership had reached a critical mass so the skillset of Members would have covered almost every conceivable discipline, including open-air cinematography.

Women wearing Little Shellys sat down as close as possible to each parliament building. Mum was in London, where a Sky News reporter tried to interview her. He asked her whether she agreed that the Community was gaining momentum and if she hoped that political leaders might soon start talking less and listening more, and then he shoved a microphone in her face. I don't know if he'd somehow managed to miss the fundamental premise of what she was doing, but there was a long silence as he waited for a reply, while over Rachel's shoulder a massive *Shhhh…* logo blinked through different colours on the Palace of Westminster. Eventually the reporter realised that she wasn't going to speak and he handed back to the studio.

In the weeks that followed, the headquarters of each of Channel 4, Sky, ITV and the BBC (again) were barricaded by women wearing Little Shellys, and the frequency and visibility of the protests both galvanised and polarised the public. There was not only a sharp upturn in membership, but also a corresponding rise in the number of counter-protesters, who were generally male, although not exclusively, and carried signs saying things like 'Viva the Voice' and 'Free Our Speech'. They seemed to revel in deliberately misunderstanding the Community's message. Rachel never wanted to remove anyone's right to speak or say what they wanted to say: she was simply urging people to devote an equal amount of time to listening. I suspect many of the counter-protesters didn't particularly disagree with the Community; I think they were angry people (many of them men with unspecific grudges against women) who took the opportunity to shout in public by jumping on the bandwagon of the Community's popularity.

On 17 May 2008, one week before my eighteenth birthday, the Community orchestrated an international protest that eclipsed anything that had been done before, generating a huge amount of publicity, not all of it positive. I am genuinely surprised that at no time during the planning stage did anyone point out what a stupid idea it was.

Rachel's notebooks shed no light on whether it was her idea – by the time she first mentions it in the notebooks, arrangements were obviously well underway.

> *Branches in nine countries have so far confirmed their participation in the airport protest, with many others still considering it. Target date is mid-May. This will carry our message further than anything we've done previously.* (#19, p. 6)

What became known as the Airport Protests were the first internationally coordinated multi-location protests since the crane burnings, and at the time they were carried out there were associate branches of the Community in forty-five countries. There was even a Member in Antarctica, because on New Year's Day 2008 there had been pictures on the news of a huge message saying *Shhhh… Happy New Year* right outside the Amundsen–Scott South Pole Station.

Although protests in other countries had been sporadic at first and not particularly well attended, by the middle of 2008 they had been gaining momentum. Many of them were along the same lines as those carried out in the UK: sit-downs, human barriers, projections of the *Shhhh…* logo, the targeting of political buildings and media organisations. In several places where transport links and logistics were more challenging, Members held monthly re-enactments of the crane burnings, which were relatively easy to organise, but no matter what they were doing, almost every branch of the Community was publicly protesting, doing their best to get the *Talk Less, Listen More* message across.

The logistics (not to mention the cost) of organisation made it prohibitive for Members in many countries to participate in the Airport Protests. However, on pages 36–41 of #19 Rachel records details of simultaneous action in at least fifteen countries, including Nigeria, Kenya, Brazil and Japan.

As is widely known, the protests involved the release of huge numbers of helium-filled Shelly-shaped balloons next to as many airports as possible. Although normal balloons don't generally damage aeroplanes, with the help of an aeronautical engineer the ear-shaped balloons were designed to be large enough that they could, theoretically, cause problems if they were sucked into an engine.

Nothing suggests that the Community was protesting against air travel per se; rather it was a collection of stunts which, if successful, would bring its message to a great deal of people around the world. For anyone interested in seeing the footage, there are numerous videos online of teams of women inflating, sealing and releasing balloons to rise into the air space around some of the world's busiest airports, as others wave huge banners the size of swimming pools saying *Shhhh... Talk Less, Listen More.*

Not all of the airports were forced to ground aircraft. Wind conditions in certain places meant that air traffic controllers could direct planes to land and take off in a particular direction to avoid the balloons that were filling the skies. In Mexico City, the helium containers were faulty and the footage shows protesters surrounded by hundreds of ear-shaped balloons bobbing around on the ground. But in so many countries, at so many airports, the protests succeeded and planes were grounded.

As far as Mum and her Community was concerned, the protest was a triumph. It generated publicity on an international scale that far exceeded anything that had come before. But, as I mentioned previously, not all the publicity was good. There was no way to positively spin the damaging environmental impact of releasing so much rubber into the skies. All the balloons had a card attached, with a message that read (in whichever language was appropriate):

Shhhh...
Talk Less, Listen More.
I was given the gift of flight by the Community.
The Community wishes to give you the gift of being heard.
Become a member of our Community.
Join us.
We will listen to you.

That was followed by the Community's main website address

and contact details for the local branches[7]. Underneath all of that was the message *I am recyclable. Please take me to your local recycling centre.* The Community put out statements asking people who found the balloons to make sure they were recycled. That's all well and good, but how many recycling centres are there in, say, the Bolivian salt flats? And, more to the point, what about all the wildlife that got to the balloons first and choked to death on them?

It was a curious misstep, made even more notable in light of the eagerness with which so many environmental groups flocked to affiliate themselves with the Community only a few years later, organisations which are now at the heart of its Climate Health Sector. I assume the Community's post-Event ultra-green credentials are the reason why the Airport Protests are often either ignored or reduced to a mere footnote in many biographies of Rachel of Chalkham. I can imagine the pressure the Community must bring to bear on authors to ignore the catastrophic effects of the release of all those balloons. Clearly an organisation which has been responsible for single-handedly reducing global meat consumption by 30 per cent in the wake of the Leaf not Beef initiatives would rather avoid any reminder of the many online forums dedicated to graphic photos of the wildlife killed by wrinkled, deflated Shellys.

There was another unforeseen postscript to the Airport Protests when, shortly afterwards, a worldwide shortage of helium was announced and anti-Community protesters blamed Rachel. Of course they did. The Community is blamed for many things, and while plenty of the accusations are fair, I don't think the shortage of helium can entirely be blamed on ear-shaped balloons.

[7] The Community website address was the same back then as it is now: www.community.sh

At the time, I was completely unaware of how much technological and logistical expertise the Community was amassing, but having watched all the available footage of the Airport Protests, what I find most striking is the Community's ability to marshal the resources necessary to coordinate a large multinational protest, even back then. Not only did they have to arrange for the manufacture of the ear-shaped balloons, printed with messages in multiple languages, but they had to ship them around the world, source helium suppliers in every country, and arrange transport to the airports for the women, the balloons and all those bulky helium canisters.

It may well be the case that most of the planning and coordination was undertaken by Members who were not living fulltime in one of the Community camps and so had unfettered access to the internet and the ability to make whatever phone calls were necessary. Nevertheless, the Airport Protests demonstrate just how astonishingly quickly the Community had transformed from a group of women sitting in silence at the bottom of our garden into a seriously powerful, not to mention seriously wealthy, pan-global organisation.

I also can't help thinking of the irony of the fact that just when her Community was flying as high as those balloons, the most significant attempt was made to bring Rachel back to earth, because one week later, five years to the day after she stopped talking, on 24 May 2008, the day of my eighteenth birthday, my mother was taken away.

13.

I had a meeting with the police this morning. Dad insisted that I speak to them because he's worried about the death threats I've been receiving on social media.

Despite the non-disclosure agreements that my publishers made everyone connected with this book sign, we always knew it was just a question of *when* not *if* word got out that I was writing about my mother. Probably the leak came from someone who was approached as a potential contributor and refused to participate. In any case, the news is out and the outrage has begun. How dare I have the audacity to write about my own mother.

At least I've had a lot of practice over the years trying to ignore the lunatic fringe Members who believe Rachel of Chalkham genuinely belongs to them, the people for whom silence is justification for all sorts of wacko theories. They're always doing those crazy stunts, like those Final Eventists who hold a festival every October in the Chihuahuan Desert in Mexico where they 're-enact' the Event and make all new initiates hold their fingers over open flames to burn off their fingerprints, while maintaining complete silence (of course). Not only are they honouring Rachel's sacrifice (as they see it), but they also believe they are symbolically ridding themselves of their own identities in order to be more receptive to other people's voices.

However, the Eventists seem relatively normal compared to the Daughters of the Redundant Voicebox, the group from South

Korea which makes adherents undergo a traumatic procedure to induce vocal cord haemorrhages to permanently silence themselves. Unlike the Eventists, the Daughters of the Redundant Voicebox believe that it is only when you remove your ability to speak entirely that you will truly be ready to hear the voices of others. Even though it is widely reported that between 15 and 19 per cent of people undergoing the procedure die of asphyxiation, membership of the Daughters has risen sharply over the last two years.

It may be that the death threats are coming from one of these groups – it's impossible to tell. One of the messages was from someone calling themselves EXCISETHELARYNX. It said: '*u bitch ur no daughter of Rach. Stay silent or u will b silenced 4 EVA.*' Less than an hour after that, SHHHH1983 posted: '*publish ur book n u die.*' And right before I left to meet the police I saw a post from LISTENANDHEAR97 which said: '*shut yr fucking mouth u ugly cunt, Rachel was a saint. If u say 1 bad thing abt Rachel, I will find u and I will cut ur throat.*'

We went through all of this after the Event so I already knew there wasn't really anything the police could do. They just gave me their usual advice: don't go out alone at night, don't open the door to people I don't know, don't engage and refrain from posting on social media. The police did say they would speak to the Community's membership team, although it will be a complete waste of time because they are excellent at distancing themselves from these sorts of things and scrupulous at appearing to be above board in their reprisals against anyone who questions the Community's claim to be the exclusive authority on Rachel's legacy. I'm sure it's no coincidence that I received a lawyer's letter earlier this week. I won't reproduce it in full – it's far too long and dull – but here are just a few choice phrases.

Whilst the Community welcomes the long overdue publication of Rachel of Chalkham's notebooks, we are extremely concerned by information we have received suggesting that you are in the process of writing an unauthorised account of the life of Rachel of Chalkham.

We take this opportunity to remind you that the Community exclusively owns all image rights, logos and trademarks connected or in any way associated with Rachel of Chalkham and/or the Community.

We hereby put you on notice that in the event of any actual or anticipatory breach we will enforce our rights to the fullest extent of the law, both in the United Kingdom and overseas... [and we] reserve the right to issue proceedings without further notice and recover costs and expenses in full.

So it went on. Pages and pages of legally acceptable threats.

Before my proposal for this book was accepted, my publisher and I discussed the likelihood of me receiving threats – both legal and otherwise – which is why my husband and I moved into this flat a few weeks ago. My publisher rented it for us and neither of us has our names on any of the bills, so no one can find out where we are. Other than Dad and Livy, anyone who needs to contact us has to go via my publisher. We even met the police at their offices.

I do understand why Dad is worried, and obviously I'd be lying if I said that I wasn't worried too, but I always knew this would get nasty. I was ready for it. I've been through it before. I refuse to be intimidated.

In any case, this story I'm telling, it's not just Mum's story, it's mine, too, and no one has the right to stop me telling my story. The Community's letter doesn't fool me for one second: they aren't worried about a breach of 'image rights'. What they're worried about is that I might reveal a truth about Rachel of Chalkham that doesn't fit with their own 'truth' about her. I know things that don't fit with their narrative of what the Community 'stands for'. I know things that they have worked extremely hard to suppress. I know where the skeletons are.

14.

From: Nick Wright
To: Emilia Morris
Date: 15 June 2022

Subject: (no subject)

Hi darling,

I'm taking a break from marking a stack of finals papers on metaphysics and epistemology, so I thought I'd have a cup of tea and write this email, which I know you've been waiting for.

I'm pleased that you don't remember very much about when they took your mum away. God knows there's a lot I've done over the years that I'm not proud of, but at least shielding you from what was happening back then was one thing I could do. It's difficult to imagine you would have done so well in your A levels if you'd known what was really going on.

Mum disappeared on the day of your eighteenth birthday, of course. You had a day off from revision for your exams, and you, me and Gran had Buck's Fizz with Gran's special birthday eggs Benedict before you went to meet some of your friends. I remember dropping you and Livy off at the train station on my way to the cash and carry.

I found out later that Rachel had got up early – around 5 a.m.

– and left the camp for one of her walks. She was due to lead a Guided Silence Session at 10 a.m. and she'd never missed one before, so when she didn't come back the Members were worried something had happened to her. A couple of them came to see if I had any idea where Rachel was, but I was still out so they spoke to your gran. Call it sixth sense, or what you will, but Gran was convinced from the beginning that something terrible had happened, and as soon as I got back she insisted we go down to the camp.

It's funny the things you remember, isn't it? So often when I think back, my clearest memories seem unconnected to the thing I'm trying to remember. For example, when I think about going to the camp that particular morning, what I remember most vividly is a kingfisher skimming between the trees at the edge of the stream. In all the years of living there, I had never seen a kingfisher before. It was tiny, with a bright blue flash of feathers, and once it caught my eye, I couldn't stop watching it. Despite all the Members milling around waiting for a Silence Session that wasn't going to happen, and Gran going on and on about how worried she was, what I remember most clearly is watching that kingfisher.

I suppose I must have started paying attention eventually because I realised that some of the Members had come to the conclusion that Rachel had been kidnapped (although it wasn't clear who they thought had kidnapped her). Your gran was more inclined to believe she had been in an accident and was injured (or worse) and insisted that I report your mum missing, but when the police realised that I was talking about a grown woman who had left of her own accord, they told me that she would almost certainly turn up safe and sound and to ring them again if she hadn't reappeared by the next day.

For the next couple of hours I was too busy with the lunchtime rush to give your mum much thought, and she was the last thing on my mind when the phone rang around 4 p.m. The man on the other end said someone was coming to talk to me about Rachel and that I was to remain in the pub until they arrived. My first reaction was *What the hell gives some stranger the right to tell me what I can and can't do?* But then I began to worry, not only for Rachel, but for us, too. After all, it hadn't been that long since those thugs from The52 had forced their way into the pub, and the Airport Protests had happened the week before and I'd already seen reports about the harm done by those bloody balloons. I wondered which vigilante group Rachel had pissed off this time!

When the guy arrived he couldn't have looked less like a vigilante. Apart from anything else, he was wearing a suit, which is most definitely not what you expect to see on a Saturday afternoon in a pub. I left Gran behind the bar (which, as you can imagine, she was *not* happy about) and took the man upstairs so we could talk in private. He flashed some ID, said he was from the security services and then without any preamble told me the Community had been put on a watchlist containing groups displaying patterns of activity indicative of radicalisation. I think I must have been in shock because it was quite a while before I actually thought to ask him where Rachel was. All he'd say was that she was 'safe and well' and that they just wanted to talk to her. I remember thinking, *Good luck with that because she hasn't said a word for five years.* He told me they had 'temporarily removed' her while she'd been out walking that morning and that it was imperative for national security that as few people as possible knew where she was. Then he threatened me with being 'temporarily removed' myself if I told anyone what he'd told me.

The only saving grace of the whole thing was that you had no idea about any of it because you were still out with your friends, and when you came home, I told you that Rachel had made the last-minute decision to go to a protest in Edinburgh. You were annoyed that she'd gone on your birthday, but her absence didn't affect your plans, and you accepted it considerably more easily than if I'd announced that your mother had been detained by the security services on suspicion of being a terrorist! Someone must have spoken to Tabitha, too, because after that first day there was very little fuss down in the camp.

As far as what actually happened to Rachel during her detention, there's not a lot I can tell you. You already know they kept her for seventeen days. She had nothing with her except the clothes she was wearing. She wasn't allowed to communicate with me or, as far as I know, with anyone. She was kept in a room that looked more like a B&B than a prison cell. She was interviewed by three men and a woman, who spoke to her sometimes in pairs and sometimes alone. She said they didn't physically hurt her. She was given plenty of food and water.

The day they brought your mother home, no one knew she was coming. You were sitting your final exam (thank god!). The stress of everything had hit Gran really hard (I'm convinced this was when her health started going downhill) and she was spending most of her time in her cottage. I was restocking shelves when I heard the car; I opened the door and there she was. I tried to persuade her to stay at home, at least for a night, so she could have a bath and sleep in a proper bed, but she wasn't having any of it and so I went with her down to the camp.

Everyone immediately crowded around us and I remember
getting really angry (I'm pretty sure I told them all to fuck off!). I
was still her husband, after all. It was *my* job to make sure she
was OK. I sat with her in her hut while she wrote a few words
– just answers to my questions, really. Had she been hurt? *No.*
Did she need a doctor? *No.* Was there anything I could do for
her? *No.*

You asked me whether I think the detention changed Rachel
and the answer is yes, I do. There's no doubt that it did.
Whatever happened to her in those seventeen days filled her
with anger that never left her. She was consumed by the need
to get her message out there and she'd do anything to make
people listen. I know you felt it yourself, how there was no room
in her thoughts for anything but the Community, certainly no
room for me and, increasingly, not even you.

The question I can't answer is whether there was any reason to
be concerned about the Community back in 2008. At the time, I
assumed everything that the man had said was complete
rubbish. He was talking about my wife, your mother, and, sure,
the Community's protests were increasingly disruptive and
headline-grabbing, but all your mum wanted (so I thought,
anyway) was for people to talk less and listen more. Where was
the harm in that? The idea that Rachel was spawning an
extremist organisation in her camp was, frankly, completely
ridiculous.

Now, I'm not so sure. I mean, there's no doubt that Rachel
would have loved all the progress the Community has made
with its environmental initiatives and conciliation programmes.
Even I can admit that some of the achievements are positive,
but we both know that behind those stories are the ones it pays

huge sums to keep out of the headlines. And the question is: where did these ideas come from?

God knows you don't need me to tell you this, Ems, you have witnessed so much of it first-hand, but you know I think Rachel would be appalled by what her Community stands for today. I have never, ever believed that this was her plan. However, I do accept that if someone knew what to look for, maybe they could have seen the awful potential of the Community even as far back as 2008.

The thing is, even if I am wrong, even if Rachel was deliberately laying the foundations for everything that goes on today, then we still have to ask, *what if?*

What if they hadn't taken her away? What if she had never been subjected to detention? What would have become of the Community if that had never happened? Removing your mother from her camp, holding her against her will, subjecting her to such an awful experience, *must* have had a huge effect on your mum. How can it not have changed how she thought about everything?

I have always believed that Rachel's decision to take her own life can be traced back to what happened to her in the summer of 2008. I loved your mother and I hate the Community, and as far as I am concerned the government is at least partly to blame not only for what your mum did to herself, but also for the toxic, dangerous, hateful organisation that the Community has become.

Love, Dad

15.

It is time to address the missing pages. Nine consecutive pages torn out of notebook #19 leaving only their slivered edges. Many of the notebooks have the odd page missing, either partially or in full, but only #19 has consecutive pages removed in their entirety.

My father has one theory about the missing pages and I have another. No doubt, when the notebooks are published other theories will emerge.

What Dad and I do agree on (as does the Community) is that, as Dad's email has already explained, between 24 May and 10 June 2008, Mum was bundled into a car while she was out walking and detained against her will. The government has always refused to officially acknowledge that these illegal detentions – Johnson-Hill detentions as they are now known – took place, but it's always handy having a lawyer as a best friend: the other day Livy talked me through a copy of a judgment by the European Court of Human Rights in 2009 which proves otherwise. The applicants in that case were four British citizens detained by security forces in December 2007 on the order of then Home Secretary Timothy Johnson-Hill[8]. When you set aside all the legalese, what it comes down to is that all four people were detained against their will as a result of a violation by the British government of its citizens' rights.

[8] J and Others v. the United Kingdom

According to Livy, this case (and others like it) is definitive proof that the Johnson-Hill detentions happened. She said it is accepted in legal and political circles that both the Home Secretary and the security services were acting outside the scope of their authority, but after Johnson-Hill was forced to resign from the cabinet 'for personal reasons', the whole thing was just hushed up and swept under the carpet. Apparently no one knows for sure how many people were detained illegally because the government papers are protected by the Official Secrets Act, but no matter how many detainees there were in total, one of them was definitely my mother.

When the notebooks are published, the absence of any mention by Rachel of her detention will no doubt be used by the government to claim she was never subject to a Johnson-Hill detention, which is why understanding what was written on the missing pages of #19 is so important. (To clarify: each missing page represents two page numbers – facing and rear – so the missing nine pages contained entries spanning pp. 49–66).

I have mentioned previously how Rachel rarely dated her notebook entries, but it is possible to work out the time period covered by the missing pages by looking at specific events that she wrote about on the pages immediately before and after.

On page 48, the final page before the missing ones, Mum refers to an online article in the *Asahi Shimbun* (a Japanese English-language newspaper) about a Macaque monkey found choked to death on an Airport Protest balloon[9]. The article was dated 23 May 2008, which was the day before Rachel was taken away.

The writing on the first intact page after the missing ones is heavily scored through and very few words can be made out. However, from page 68 onwards, the entries are legible and on

[9] http://www.asahi.com/ajw/articles/27840226

page 69 Rachel mentions a new branch of the Community established in Denpasar, Indonesia. According to the Community's website, the Denpasar branch was set up in June 2008, which means that between page 48's note on the poor dead monkey and the celebratory reference to the opening of the Denpasar branch on page 69 were pages with entries written by Rachel immediately after her return from detention.

Dad believes that in the weeks after the Event, when Rachel's belongings were in the hands first of the police and then the security services, the notebooks were scrutinised for any mention of her detention. Dad thinks details of where she was taken, who she was interviewed by, that sort of thing, was information that they did not want to ever be made public and so they removed the pages.

It's plausible, but I don't believe it.

Apart from anything else, why would the security services rip out the offending pages rather than confiscate the whole notebook? After all, would anyone have even realised if they *had* kept it? I'm not sure I would have done. At the point they were confiscated immediately after the Event, neither Dad nor I had ever really seen the notebooks, so even though each of them is numbered 1 to 29 on the inside front covers, when I did finally read them and realised one was missing, I would be far more likely to assume it had been lost or destroyed by Mum. As far as I am concerned, for the security services to have returned a notebook with deliberately ripped-out pages raises far more questions than if they had just kept it.

Instead – and this is *my* theory – it is possible to see the absence of these pages as perhaps Rachel's most profound silence because I am convinced that the pages were removed by Rachel herself.

It is easy to forget, but before Rachel of Chalkham, before the Community, before the Event, silence was a passive concept, only ever defined by what it was not. In the second edition of the *Oxford Dictionary of English* (2003) the three definitions of silence are: *complete absence of sound; the fact or state of abstaining from speech;* and *the avoidance of mentioning or discussing something.* Nowadays, of course, silence is well understood to be active, defined as much by what it *is* as what it is not. Thus, in the fourth edition of the *Oxford Dictionary of English* (2020), although *complete absence of sound* remains as the first definition, the second definition is now *the state of active listening to a voice or opinion other than one's own.* My mother not only changed the world, she also changed the language used to describe it.

For all that she never spoke a word for the last eight years of her life, Rachel's silence was startlingly ostentatious. It was an unignorable, confrontational, in-your-face, do-as-I-do display of her *Talk Less, Listen More* philosophy. But what most people don't understand, except those of us that knew her best, was just how often my mother also used her silence to distract and deflect. By wrapping herself in a thick miasma of silence she filtered out her flaws, diluted her weaknesses, her vanities and her conceits. You don't have to look very far today to see how successful she was at doing this. Just consider how Rachel of Chalkham is venerated as the unblemished embodiment of all that the Community stands for. Do as Rachel of Chalkham did. Aspire to be like Rachel of Chalkham. Strive to follow Rachel of Chalkham's example. And so on and so on.

What is often forgotten, though, is that underneath her flamboyant silence, Rachel had the same emotions, the same doubts and, frankly, the same (if not considerably more) flaws as anyone else. I believe that in the missing nine pages of notebook #19 she recounted experiences of her detention that laid bare fear, doubts and pain that did not meet my mother's perception of herself. Earlier, I pointed out that from the beginning it seems

Rachel may well have anticipated an audience for what she was writing, and I have no doubt that by the time she reached #19 she had one eye firmly on the day her words might be read by someone else.

I am certain that, at some point, my mother remembered what she had written in those nine pages and, despising the vulnerability on display in her words, she tore them out and destroyed them.

Notwithstanding the missing pages, I believe there is a surviving account written by Rachel about her detention.

In November and December 2008, as part of a campaign to force the government to come clean about the Johnson-Hill detentions, *The Guardian* invited ex-detainees to share their experiences in a series which they ran under the banner 'My Detention and Me'[10]. These pieces were not journalistic in nature, they were not polemics, instead the articles all contain highly personal recountings of the minutiae of the experience of being detained by the security services. At the time of original publication all the writers were anonymous, although the majority of them later came forward to identify themselves.

There are seven articles in total. Six of them are infused with fear, bewilderment, confusion and a deep sense of injustice. These experiences of rendition are uniformly difficult to read. The writers of these pieces were terrified about what might happen to them. Extraordinary rendition was never far from their minds – Guantanamo Bay is mentioned repeatedly. The articles are testimonies to a short-lived, unjust and illegal policy born of fear and suspicion in the aftermath of the London Bombings.

[10] https://www.theguardian.com/mydetentionandme/2008

The articles are all remarkably similar, except the seventh and final one.

This particular account was published by *The Guardian* approximately six months after Rachel's detention, and as far as I am concerned it has her fingerprints all over it. For reasons that are not clear to me the Community does not agree that my mother wrote the article and accordingly it is not included in their publication *Voicing the Silence – Collected Writings of Rachel of Chalkham* (Community Press, 2016), which purported to bring together all of my mother's published articles.

However, there are turns of phrase in this particular 'My Detention and Me' piece that are undoubtedly Rachel's, and the direct, often didactic style is familiar from the notebooks, together with her habit of addressing a reader directly. More compelling still, as far as I am concerned, is the depth of detachment on display. The writer of the article relays their experiences of detention as if describing a visit to a council office, or something similarly underwhelming. Contrast that with the other pieces published in the series, whose writers express genuine terror about what they were experiencing.

There is also, notably, an absolute lack of concern about the writer's family and friends. By then Dad and I were accustomed to Rachel's ability to feel distress and empathy for countless distant 'others' unknown to her personally, while completely ignoring any pain or unhappiness being experienced by her own family. While the other six articles focus heavily on the writers' debilitating concern for what they imagined their families were suffering or, as one writer puts it, their 'agonies of despair', and mention crippling guilt about being responsible for the ordeal their families were going through, the seventh article contains no such concerns.

I asked *The Guardian* if they could confirm that it was indeed Rachel who wrote this article, but they refused – citing duties of anonymity to the writer; however, they permitted me to include the following extracts from the article, for which I am grateful.

As far as I am concerned, there is no doubt that what follows are my mother's words.

> *I was walking alone when I was bundled into the back of a Range Rover with blacked-out windows. I was driven for between one and a half and two hours, and when we stopped, I was walked onto a small boat, where I was forced to stay below the deck while we were at sea. I wasn't on the boat for long before I was taken off and led onto a small landing area on a huge concrete structure. I now believe this to be one of the fortified towers in the Solent[11].*
>
> *The routine was the same for seventeen days. Breakfast (stodgy porridge), followed by between two and three hours of questions, lunch (something stodgy), in the afternoon either nothing happened or there were more questions, dinner (more stodge). There was no fresh fruit and few vegetables. I did not let these things bother me. Those things I could control, I did. I controlled how I felt. Should I have felt scared? Is it strange that I didn't? I rejected fear. Fear is corrosive, but anger can empower, so I chose anger.*
>
> *I directed my anger into my silence. This is how I countered the endless, pointless questions. My silence was deafening. How else could I respond? I refused to speak. For seventeen days I was silent. I told them nothing, but*

---

[11] There are several online forums dedicated to gathering evidence to support theories that one or more of the four nineteenth-century forts in the Solent (also called Palmerston's Follies), previously converted to hotels, were used for a short time in 2007/8 as a base for government detentions. For example, see: https://palmerstonfollies.johnson-hill.depository/.

*then there was nothing to tell. I controlled my response
and my response was silence.*

*The solitude was not a problem. I am comfortable
being alone. I choose solitude often, although I'm far less
able to find it nowadays. In solitude I listen to myself. At
first I merely listened to my own thoughts, without
seeking to direct them, but after the first few days, I chose
to control my thoughts. I used the time to review my
hopes and aspirations, and my disappointments, and I
used the time to make plans, for the first week, first
month, first year after I was released. I made decisions,
important decisions, and writing this now, five months
later, those decisions seem to me to be as valid and as
well-reasoned as when I first made them.*

Rachel never acknowledged this article, which is notable only
because she later claimed ownership of a number of other articles
she had written that had originally been published anonymously.
Having said that, it's easy to assume there was always a well-
thought-through rationale behind each of Rachel's actions (or
inactions), and of course the Community has a whole department
– the Interpretative Sector – to analyse everything my mother did,
no matter how insignificant. It is a trap I have found myself falling
into on many occasions, spending hours analysing the smallest
incident, trying to work out why she did what she did. But of
course, there isn't always an explanation for everything, and it is
my opinion that my mother never publicly acknowledged writing
the article because, having submitted it to *The Guardian*, it held no
more interest for her and she simply forgot about it.

16.

While Mum was protesting, building the Community and, as it transpired, being subject to a Johnson-Hill detention, I was trying my best to live my own life. During 2008, I not only turned eighteen and sat my A levels, but I also fell in love.

Tom was the son of a Member called Libby. They lived in a nearby village, and like so many others, Libby's connection with the Community began when she came to take part in Rachel's Silence Sessions. After a while, Libby volunteered to help with administrative tasks and eventually ended up running the team responsible for setting up new branches overseas. After she was banned from driving for twelve months in 2007 it usually fell to Tom, who was nineteen and on a gap year, to drive his mother to Chalkham.

I'd had a couple of boyfriends before Tom, but the boys from school always seemed really immature. Tom was different. He had been sixteen and his father forty years old when a Lynx helicopter was shot down by a surface-to-air missile in Afghanistan. Tom's dad was one of five service personnel killed. Tom's life fell apart. Libby's life fell apart. I met Tom three years after his father had died and by then, against all the odds, he had managed to sit his A levels and get the grades required to study history at Bristol University. By contrast, Libby self-medicated her grief with enormous quantities of vodka until she ran her car through the plate-glass frontage of a Southampton Burger King. Amazingly, no one was injured and in the circumstances she managed to avoid a custodial sentence. Tom deferred his university place for a year to stay at home with his mother, driving her to the court-mandated AA meetings and grief counselling sessions and, of course, to Chalkham.

Libby spent hours with Rachel inside the Hearing Place, talking and talking until eventually her grief began to loosen its grip enough for her to realise that, although what had happened to her husband was appalling, if things didn't change Tom would be left without either parent, which would be even worse (although, arguably, once his mother became an active Member he all but lost her anyway). In any case, the Community gained one of its most devoted Members in Libby, and in Tom, I gained a boyfriend mature enough for a genuinely equal relationship. I applied to do English at Bristol University because that's where Tom was going. I might well have ended up marrying him, perhaps even having kids with him, until the Event robbed us of any chance of a future together.

But in 2008, there were still three years of my pre-Event life left, and that summer was a particularly wonderful time for me. I was in love for the first time in my life. I was also demob happy, treading water in that liminal period between school and univer-sity. I put in a lot of shifts at the pub, but when I think back to that summer, the weeks seem to have passed in one long round of parties and picnics and planning for the next stage of my life, which only heightened after the A-level results came out. I'd managed to get the grades I needed to join Tom at Bristol while Livy, to the surprise of everybody, had pulled four top grades out of the bag and would be going to Durham to study law.

It's funny, but I have almost no memories of Mum from that summer. At that point, I was still completely unaware of what had happened to her during those seventeen days in May and June.

Thanks to what Dad had told me, I believed she had been at protests in Scotland and the north of England, and after she returned, when she wasn't away at other protests, she was almost always surrounded by her cabal of women. To the best of my ability, I simply ignored the camp, the Community and all those women traipsing back and forth through our beer garden. I felt sad about the idea of leaving Dad and Gran to go to university, but really I was counting down the days until I could go somewhere where I would be someone other than Rachel of Chalkham's daughter.

The evening before I was due to leave for Bristol – Tom and I were going in his car, which we'd crammed full of our belongings – I went to say goodbye to Mum. Although the Shellys were made off-site and the Community had storage units around the country, there was always protest-related paraphernalia lying around the camp and fake rubber ears were stacked all over the place, some of them with weird 'comedy' piercings and a handful with fake hearing aids. A few of them had protuberances that it had taken me a while to realise were supposed to be old-fashioned ear-trumpets. There were banners and piles of flyers and stickers and posters everywhere. Another hut had recently been constructed and was referred to as New Protest HQ (old Protest HQ having been repurposed as a food-preparation area).

Everyone used small scraps of paper to communicate about day-to-day minutiae in the camp, most of them adopting Mum's minimal missing-vowel-type communication, and the scraps were then used to light the fires. There were also several large blackboards (attached to the outside of huts and enclosed in wooden boxes with glass fronts, to keep the rain off) and a seemingly infinite supply of chalk. I have no idea where all the chalk came from, but their use of it always seemed very apt, since the camp was sandwiched between the Chalkham Boar and the

River Chalk. As a general rule, the blackboards were used for lists, timetables, menus, rotas and instructions, as well as the inevitable numerous reminders to *Shhhh…*

By contrast, inside New Protest HQ there was a bank of state-of-the-art computers. As the Community grew, and the donations increased, New Protest HQ began to resemble a futuristic control room in a TV spy drama, and for the three or four years prior to the Event, it was the centre of the Community's entire operation and a key factor in how Rachel was able to plan her protests both locally and further afield, without breaking her silence.

I'm not aware of any book written about my mother which seriously considers what would have happened if Rachel had embarked on her silence project before the existence of the internet. It's difficult to imagine how silence could ever have been a force for change without the ability to make sure everyone knew about it.

Critics of the Community maintain that Rachel's silence was not a real silence precisely because of her use of the internet to make herself heard. I wouldn't go that far, but I do think that the role of technology in the success of the Community has not received the serious academic consideration that it deserves.

Rachel's silence was a weapon, and her Community used technology to wield that weapon.

When I arrived at the camp to say goodbye to my mother, the temperature was still mild after a warm day, and Mum was on the bank of the river, sitting with her back against a tree. I sat down next to her. Just beyond our feet, the River Chalk dawdled past, the water level still low after the summer months. I remember thinking that I wouldn't stay long – I was due back up at the pub for farewell drinks with some friends – and in any case, when your mother refuses to speak, it rather detracts from prolonged farewells.

Rachel put her hands on my shoulders and pulled me close, kissing me on the forehead. I was a sucker for any sort of physical affection from Mum and I snuggled up to her, letting her hug me tightly. We sat like that for a while, until one of my legs started going numb, so I pulled away from her and shuffled along to lean against another tree. She reached into her pocket and pulled out some folded paper which looked like it had been torn from a cheap pad (it didn't come from any of the notebooks).

These three-and-a-half handwritten sides of A4 paper are one of only two surviving letters written to me by my mother. The second one is reproduced later, but here, in its entirety, is the first.

My darling girl,

Can you believe that I've been your mother for eighteen years? As this new chapter of your life begins, I want you to know that I'm very proud of the young woman you have become. I have no doubt that you will love university and embrace every opportunity it gives you. I was going to write a long list of dos and don'ts, but in the end they boil down to just four things.

1. Study hard and play hard — they're not mutually exclusive.
2. Don't spend all your time with Tom. Join societies, make friends, socialise widely.
3. Be proactive in your studying. The next three years is your chance to learn and absorb as much as you possibly can. You will not regret this.
4. Always remember to talk less and listen more.

Don't just hear what someone is saying but try
and hear what they are not saying too.

If you follow my advice, Emilia, the next three years
will be the best you've ever had!
   So many times you've said I should break my
silence and speak to you even if I don't speak to
anyone else. But you know why I can't. If I make
any exceptions, even for you, then there will be
another time and another time when exceptions
will be justified. I made a promise to myself to be
silent. People believe in my silence. I believe in my
silence and if I can't trust myself to keep my own
promise then how can I possibly expect anyone else
to trust me? You assume because I don't speak to
you that I don't care what you think, but I care
deeply, which is why I've decided to have another
go at trying to answer some of the questions that
I know you still have. I may not be able to give
you my voice today, darling, but I will give you
my words.
   Do you remember how, right from when you
started school, when I dropped you off each morning,
you'd give me a smile and a wave and run inside
without even a backward glance? I know it sounds
stupid, but it was such a shock when I realised
that you were already so independent. It felt like I
had lost any sense of purpose in my life. I always
remember standing behind the bar one day pulling a
pint for old Mr Robson and thinking, Is this all there
is? Am I doomed to only ever serve pint after pint
for the Mr Robsons of the world?

Once I'd started thinking like that, I couldn't stop. You became less reliant on me with each year that passed and I began to spend more and more time wondering whether this was all our lives amounted to. We're born, grow old and die. What is the point of anything if that's all it comes down to? I was overwhelmed by the idea that my life was completely pointless because it felt like — it still feels like — we are all just marking time until either we die, or someone, somewhere, does something so awful that the world is destroyed, in which case we'll all die anyway.

By the time you were eleven or twelve, both your dad and gran believed I was depressed — they tried to make me see a doctor — but I knew I wasn't depressed, rather I was terrified that if I didn't do something, my whole life would end up being completely pointless. The problem was that I didn't know what to do. That's why I stopped talking. I needed peace and quiet and time to myself to work out whether there was anything I could do to give myself a purpose, a reason to get up every morning and carry on. If I hadn't moved out when I did, darling, I'd have probably gone mad. Or killed myself. One or the other.

At first I became silent in order to listen to myself, but then I realised that if I couldn't even hear myself without silence, how could I possibly hope to hear anyone else? I stopped talking to listen to myself, and I stayed silent to listen to others. It's ironic, really, when you think about how much my silence spoke to people. But when I saw how appealing the whole Shhhh... thing was to people, then I knew I had found what I had been looking for. I now understand that the only way to live a life with purpose is to leave the world in a better state than when you arrived in it. So that's what I set about trying to do.

And that's what the Community is about, too — persuading people to listen to each other so they leave the world in a better state. Decision-makers have to listen to how people affected by those decisions will feel. People who want to inflict pain must listen to those on whom they would inflict that pain. We have to hear the voices of others when they speak of their needs and desires and upset and hurt. We have to break our addiction to our own voices.

There is nothing as important as this. Nothing. But I'm terrified that it might already be too late. Our protests get lots of publicity, the membership numbers are rising fast, and so are donations, but we're still not getting our message heard by the people who most need to hear it. It's always the same — when did sit-ins and occupations and disruptions ever really change anything? No one listens to anyone. No one ever listens. Our world is hurtling towards complete destruction, but people refuse to believe that we have to start listening to each other. Why can't they understand? Their ignorance makes me so angry that it feels as if an animal is tearing at me from my insides, clawing and biting its way out of my body.

I'm sorry, darling, to end on such a dark note. But I wanted to help you understand why this

Community of mine is so very important, perhaps more important than anything. This time tomorrow you'll be at university and I want you to have the best, most wonderful time. But I also want you to remember that everything I do is for you because I want the world you live in to be a better place than it is right now.

All my love, Mum xx

Back then, on the riverbank, when I'd finished reading the letter, I folded it into a small square. I was as silent as Rachel while I thought about what I wanted to say.

My immediate reaction was embarrassment. Throughout my childhood and teens, I hated it when either of my parents displayed an excess of emotion. It felt inappropriate somehow, like they should have been able to control themselves better. OK, so Mum was scared, Mum was angry. But why was it necessary for Mum to tell me she was so scared and so angry?

But then I began to feel something else. At first I wasn't sure what it was. I glanced at my mother, and she saw me looking and flashed me a smile before returning her gaze to the stream. I've said before how Mum was silent with her whole body and how much it infuriated me because it always felt like a barrier between us. So many times I shouted at her to try and get her to react, but all my shouting was a substitute for what I really wanted to do, which was to hurt her. I wanted to force my way through Rachel's silence and find my mum. Countless times as a teenager I would imagine myself shoving her so she fell, punching her arm so it bruised black and pink, jabbing a sharp stick so hard into some soft part of her that she wouldn't be able to help herself but to shout at me. By the time I was sixteen I was taller and stronger than my mother, and then I began imagining how our hugs could become something less loving, and I'd fantasise about how I would tighten my grip, crushing her to me, squeezing her silence tighter and tighter until Rachel of Chalkham exploded and all that would be left in my embrace would be my mum.

My thoughts were only ever thoughts. I didn't hurt my mother. And that evening before I left for university, there was a significant shift in my feelings towards Mum's silence. I looked at her again and this time I didn't look away. Leaning against a tree in the gathering gloom, she was dwarfed by one of a pair of multicoloured ponchos which, although neither of us knew it at the time, were the last things that Gran would knit for Mum and me. To all intents and purposes Rachel was the picture of relaxation – slow, regular breathing, open hands lightly resting on her lap – but she was betrayed by a twitch at the corner of her right eye. I finally realised what it was that I was feeling. It was pity. I *pitied* Mum for her delusion that she was doing this for me. I pitied her for her fear. I pitied her for being so angry. But most of all I pitied her because she was trying to achieve something that was, I thought, completely unachievable.

That evening marked a turning point for me because I didn't shout at her or tell her she was wrong or selfish or stupid or try to make her feel guilty for laying all her emotions on me. I put my bitterness at what she had written aside, and when I finally spoke, it was without rancour.

'I'm sorry that you're feeling so angry and scared, Mum. I'm sorry more people aren't listening to you. At school my art teacher always told us, "If you want people to notice your work, you have to be bold and brave and you have to leave something of yourself behind, because if you don't care enough about your art to do that, then you can't expect anyone else to care about it either." Perhaps that's what you need to do, Mum – you need to leave something of yourself behind in your protests. Then people will pay attention. You should try and do something that no one has ever done before. Like when you burned the cranes and you got all those new Members. You need do something else like that, but bigger and better. That's the thing to do, Mum: leave yourself behind in a bigger, better burning.'

When I finished speaking, Mum reached over, picked the folded letter out of my hands and scrawled eleven words on it.

Bigger, better burning. Leave myself behind. Great advice. Thank you, darling.

I'm looking at those words now and I feel sick.

17.

I went off to university and, as it turned out, I ended up doing pretty much everything Mum told me to do and had a fantastic time. Although I went home for the holidays, Rachel was often away from Chalkham and my connection with the Community, tenuous at best before I left, was pretty much non-existent once I moved to Bristol. The final three years before the Event are extremely well documented elsewhere, and for anyone wanting to know more about this specific period of Rachel's life, I particularly recommend *Status: Meltdown* (Redoubt, 2014) by Kenzo Hashimoto, Emeritus Professor of Sociology and Social Anthropology at the University of Tokyo.

As well as cataloguing the unstoppable rise in popularity of the Community, Hashimoto explores as his central premise the idea that not only was the Tōhoku earthquake and tsunami on 11 March 2011 which triggered the meltdown of the Fukushima Daiichi Nuclear Power Plant responsible for the remarkable increase in the number of Japanese women (and, after they were permitted, men) joining the Community (by 2014, 26 per cent of the population of Japan were Members, making it the highest membership in the word by proportion of population) but also the resulting humanitarian disaster marked the point at which Rachel decided that she had no choice but to stage the Event.

Hashimoto considers how the tsunami brought together several of Rachel's major preoccupations: natural disasters, humanitarian crises, environmental destruction and nuclear threat. And it is certainly the case that notebook #27 is full of cuttings about Fukushima: several pages contain lists of facts that she gathered from various sources[12]. However, Hashimoto makes it clear that the earthquake, tsunami and resulting nuclear meltdown should not be seen as an isolated trigger, but instead as representing the culmination of a series of mass deaths and appalling atrocities over preceding months and years that served to galvanise not only Rachel, but also the rank-and-file Members.

Hashimoto and his team recorded many interviews with Members who were particularly active in the months prior to the Event, and their accounts portray an increasing willingness to do whatever it took to promote Rachel's message of listening and hearing.

Her sense of urgency was fuelled, Hashimoto suggests, by the acceleration in terrorist incidents between 2008 and 2011; in addition to a grim litany of attacks in Pakistan, Iraq and Afghanistan (among others), he explores in detail the link between the 2008 Christmas massacres in the Democratic Republic of the Congo and the subsequent explosion in popularity of the Community throughout sub-Saharan Africa in 2009 and 2010.

For reasons that will become apparent, I had the opportunity to meet some of the survivors of those massacres, which were carried out by the Lord's Resistance Army, a Ugandan rebel group which murdered 620 civilians, many of them hacked into pieces, decapitated or burned alive. Several Congo Members told me that

---

[12] For example, #27, p. 73 contains the following details: 15,899 people died; 40.5 metre tsunami waves; Earth shifted on its axis by 12 centimetres; 70% higher risk of developing thyroid cancer in girls exposed as infants; 7% higher risk of leukaemia in boys exposed as infants; levels of radioactivity exceeding legal limits detected in milk, spinach, spring onions, celery, parsley, beef and salmon.

when they heard what had happened, they were determined to try and find a new way to resolve the problems that plagued their country. One woman, who saw her husband murdered in front of her before she herself was brutally raped, told me that she joined the Community after coming to the realisation that 'if the faithful of God kill the faithful of God, then faith in God is no longer enough and we must look for a new way to find peace'.

Hashimoto's research revealed that after every atrocity there was a consequential exponential rise in membership numbers; although, as an aside, his investigations conclusively debunked the persistent rumour that the 2010 Moscow Metro bombings were perpetrated by Members. The only reason, it seems, that these suicide bombings (carried out during the morning rush hour of 29 March 2010, killing forty and injuring over a hundred) were attributed to the Community was because the two suicide bombers were women. Hashimoto proves that the allegations of Community involvement were entirely false, born of misogyny and perpetuated by the Russian state-controlled media. According to Hashimoto, the persistence of these false claims is one of the principle reasons why membership of the Community among Russian citizens remains so notably low to this day.

In contrast with Hashimoto's engaging style of writing about my mother's actions and motivations in the final three years before the Event, Rachel's overwhelming schedule of protests and public appearances resulted in increasingly terse and uninformative entries in her later notebooks.

I'm well aware of how much excitement there is about the forthcoming publication of the notebooks. Della Markham's portrait of my mother is already plastered all over the place, framed by the words *THE BIGGEST PUBLISHING EVENT OF ALL*

TIME. No one outside the editorial team is allowed access to the text, although I know people have offered the publisher staggering amounts of money for the opportunity to read a proof copy. The translators of the foreign-language versions (all seventy-two of them) are sequestered on a private island somewhere near Barbados. I suppose all the money and fame will make being trapped on an island for six months worthwhile.

My publisher calls it Project Moonbook because she's anticipating as much hysteria on publication day as there was for the first moon landing. I'm not convinced because, apart from anything else, reading the reproductions of all twenty-nine notebooks is going to be a really expensive endeavour – although they are also publishing a single-volume abridged version (which runs to about nine hundred pages). It is a lot of money to spend to read entries in the later notebooks that consist predominantly of dates and locations, because in those final two or three years Rachel didn't have the luxury of time that she had had in the early years, and the notebooks reflect that.

Obviously, there are some interesting entries. For example, my mother writes about her '*delight*' (#23, p. 47) at the numbers of Members who participated in the Silent March from Poznań in Poland (location of the 2008 United Nations Climate Change Conference) to Copenhagen in Denmark (location of the 2009 conference). The 650-kilometre walk not only generated an enormous amount of publicity for the Community's new Climate Health Sector (countless roads along their route were blocked by the crowds of marching women) but also led to a '*huge swell of new Members around the globe*' (#23, p. 47).

There's also a note about my gran's death, which is unusual because Mum so rarely wrote about anything personal in the notebooks:

I've been really cold since Annie died, and today I
realised that it's because her love and support was like a
warm blanket tucked tightly around me. (#26, p. 18)

Although Gran's knitting slowed considerably towards the
end, she remained a stalwart of the Chalkham camp and one of
my Mum's fiercest supporters. Gran never questioned Mum's
choices. I am envious of her unconditional support for my mother;
how different my life might have been if I hadn't spent years
feeling hurt and angry and frustrated and all the other emotions
that Mum made me feel.

The rest of #26 mainly just contains details about Rachel's
punishing schedule of protests. My publisher won't thank me for
saying this, but in my opinion, other than the entries immediately
before the Event, there's little of interest to be found in the last
eighteen months' worth of notebooks except for my mother's
notes on the Festival of Silence.

In May 2011, less than six months before the Event, the first
annual Festival of Silence was held in Quiet Corner, Connecticut.
Nowadays, of course, Quiet Corner is known for not only the
Festival of Silence, but also being the location of the Community's
North American headquarters. Back in 2011 it had a fine line in
antique shops and not a lot else.

The Community went all out to get as much publicity for the
festival as possible. Everyone who bought a ticket was given a tote
bag full of *Shhhh…* branded memorabilia, including T-shirts,
baseball caps, bandanas and reusable bamboo coffee cups printed
with the new Climate Health Sector's slogan: *Don't Just Hear the
People, Hear the Planet.* Members who couldn't make it to Quiet
Corner in person were encouraged to watch selected festival

events via the Community's new TV channel. However, Mum doesn't really mention these details in her notebook because the US Marketing Sector will have been responsible for almost all of the arrangements.

Instead, in the run-up to the festival, many of Rachel's entries in the notebooks focus on whether men should be allowed to attend. By then the argument about permitting men to join the Community had been rumbling on for quite some time (for anyone wanting to learn more background on this subject, I can recommend both *The Final Divide* by J.P. Northcott [Staunch, 2014] and *Bringing Down the Walls* by Dr Hana Skelton [Turner & Turner, 2017]).

By the beginning of 2011, when festival planning was in full swing, the continued exclusion of men was a divisive topic within the Community.

> *Often, I and my Community are accused of being anti-man, but this is not true. At first my silence spoke more loudly to women and it was women who came to the camp and women who wanted to build a community. But my message is a message for everyone, and for every argument we have among ourselves about whether men should or should not be permitted to join the Community, we are failing to listen to ourselves or to others. (#27, p. 91)*

> *Yet more heated emails today about whether men should be allowed to attend the Festival of Silence. How to reconcile the competing factions? There are those who say that unless we include men the Community will ultimately fail, and there are those who say our sisterhood is our strength. In a way they are both right,*

but at the moment both sides are shouting. I remind
them to listen and hear each other and we will find a
way through this. (#27, p. 97)

The arguments became even more heated once the press got
wind of the in-fighting. Mum saved two articles between pages 8
and 9 of #28.

The first article is short – only four paragraphs – from the
Washington Post. Dated 3 March 2011, the headline is 'Community
Paralysed by Failure to Decide on Universal Membership'. The
second is a longer editorial piece from the *Telegraph* that ran on
7 March 2011 under the headline: 'Hypocrisy of Community's
Message: Listen to All Voices (Unless It's a Man Talking)'.

The debate about membership rights was not resolved until
after the Event, so the decision was taken to exclude men from
the first Festival of Silence (except for boys under twelve years of
age accompanying their mothers). Tragically, there is no doubt
that this decision was instrumental in what subsequently
happened.

As is the case with the festivals today, many different events
were on offer – art classes, silent discos, meditation, listening-to-
nature sessions and so on – but the culmination of the whole
thing was a mass Guided Silence Session run by Rachel. By then
the Community was seeing the huge benefits to both membership
numbers and donations of the transformative work being done by
the Climate Health Sector, and so Mum was not at all sure about
the '*optics of flying to America*' (#28, p. 56). She considered whether
to guide the Silence Session '*via a video link*' (#28, p. 57) but in
the end was persuaded that her presence at the festival would be
such a huge boost to the '*fund-raising elements*' (#28, p. 62) that she
would attend provided that they '*make sure everyone knows*' that she
would be '*planting thirty trees to offset my flight*' (#28, p. 67). So, on

8 May 2011, Rachel found herself in Quiet Corner, Connecticut leading approximately 50,000 women in the world's largest Guided Silence Session.

I was in the middle of my final exams and I hadn't seen my mother since the Easter holidays. I didn't even know she was in Quiet Corner.

It was a Sunday evening and I was lying on our bed in the room that I shared with Tom, reading through my revision notes on twentieth-century feminist literature. Tom (who had finished his exams a few days previously) was downstairs with a couple of our housemates. I remember I was flicking through my notes on Octavia E. Butler and Marge Piercy when Tom bellowed up the stairs. 'Ems. You need to come and see this.'

'I'm revising,' I bellowed back.

'Your mum's on TV,' he called.

I didn't bother to get up. Mum was often on television and I hated watching her, particularly when other people were around. My housemates knew Rachel of Chalkham was my mother, but they also knew not to make a big deal of it so I had no idea why Tom would think I'd be interested.

He came up the stairs and stood in the doorway of our bedroom. 'Seriously, Ems, you've got to come and see this. Something's happened at that festival where your mum is.'

Tom knew Mum was there because he'd had an email from his mother, Libby, which mentioned that Rachel was going to America. I heaved myself off the bed, huffing my disapproval at having to interrupt my revision, and stomped downstairs. In the living room two of our housemates – Serena and Ben – were sitting on the sofa. Ben was drinking a can of cider, which he waved towards the television.

'Tom said your mum's at this thing,' he said. 'There's some bad shit going down.'

On the screen a reporter appeared to be standing in the middle of a post-apocalyptic film set. Everything behind him was shades of black, white and grey and his face was obscured by smoke drifting between him and the camera. Ben turned up the volume and the reporter's voice boomed around our living room.

'... firefighters from Windham County, Tolland County and New London County helped to battle the blaze, which ripped through almost ten acres. Officers from Windham County Sheriff's Department are on the scene now but they have so far refused to confirm reports that the fire was started deliberately.'

The screen cut away to the field behind the reporter and I realised that it must be a camping ground because here and there a few tents had escaped the flames, their colours jaunty against the devastation in which they sat. Thick smoke hung low over the ground – the fires must not long have been extinguished.

The picture cut back to the reporter. 'At this point, it is not known if there are any fatalities. Almost everyone was gathered in front of the main stage for the final event, a Guided Silence Session led by founder of the Community, Rachel of Chalkham. Authorities are hopeful that only a small number of individuals were in the campsite at the time and that those people will have been able to escape to safety.'

The camera panned sideways to a huge crowd of silent women standing on the far side of the field behind police tape. Behind them was the roof of a massive stage. Flags covered in the *Shhhh...* logo fluttered from slender poles. Arrays of multicoloured lights circled round and round, blinking on and off. The camera swung slowly back over the devastation of the campsite, and when it reached the reporter, Rachel was standing next to him. In our living room in Bristol, Tom reached out to take one of my hands while Serena put a large glass of wine into the other.

'At least your mum's OK, babe,' she said. I sat next to her on the sofa, and Tom sat down, too, all of us squeezed together, looking at my mother's face filling the screen.

Rachel was pale and her eyes were red – either she'd been crying or she was tired, I couldn't tell which. She had a smudge of dirt – ash, probably – on her face. Although my first emotion was relief that she was safe, that was very quickly supplanted by irritation, which was basically my predominant emotion towards my mother the whole time I was at university. Why did she always have to be at the centre of things? I'm not proud of myself, but I remember thinking that this fire was yet another example of something which wouldn't have happened if she'd just stayed at home, working in the pub.

The reporter in Connecticut knew better than to expect Rachel to speak. She handed him a piece of paper, which he scanned briefly before speaking to the camera.

'I have here a short statement from Community founder Rachel of Chalkham about this terrible end to what should have been a joyful celebration of silence. Her statement says: "This tragic event is an attack on the Community and everything it stands for. There is no doubt that this fire was deliberate, started by people who close their ears to any voices other than their own. Hearing other voices is the only way to heal our damaged world. We will not be intimidated or bullied. Listen to the Community, listen to each other."'

The reporter handed the piece of paper back to my mother, then he reiterated that, despite Rachel's statement, there was 'no confirmation that the fires were started deliberately', wrapped up his segment and passed back to the studio.

At that point no one was certain if anyone had died in the fire. That only came out the next day, together with confirmation that Mum was right: the fires had indeed been started deliberately. The FBI identified the perpetrators as members of the organisation known as Reclaim Our Voices – a loose affiliation of various misogynistic right-wing groups. Reclaim Our Voices is still active today, objecting vociferously to any suggestion that they should try being silent and listening to others. In the days immediately prior to the festival, online messages posted to various ROV websites spoke of, for example, 'the Community [*sic*] bitches cutting out the tongues of the ordinary man' and (rather histrionically) 'the biggest danger to men since Eve'.

All the publicity about how the festival would be the biggest ever gathering of Members and a global celebration of silence had served to galvanise ROV supporters to 'show the bitches that we've still got a voice', as one of the defendants said during the trial. Of course, Rachel and many others who had been at the festival were no longer alive by the time of the trial, which didn't take place until February 2012, four months after the Event.

The nine defendants – all men – pleaded not guilty to first-degree murder. Their defence attorneys claimed they had deliberately chosen a time when they believed that everyone would be at Rachel's Guided Silence Session and they only intended to burn the tents. However, the jury found that the nine men should have anticipated that it was inevitable that some women would be in their tents and might be unable to escape the fires. Although two hundred and sixty-eight women and children who had been in the campground at the time the tents were set alight did thankfully escape, seven people died.

Twenty-six-year-old Lacey Murgantroth from New York was asleep, having been on duty the previous night at the silent disco; thirty-nine-year-old Sally-Lou Castino from California had hitchhiked to Connecticut from New Mexico with her friend Beth Tozer because she was desperate to see Rachel, but had had to return to their tent at the beginning of the Guided Silence Session because of a severe migraine; four-year-old Spencer

Listera and his one-year-old sister Maria were in a tent with thirteen-year-old Jennifer Seaton, who had been paid $10 by the kids' mum to keep an eye on the youngsters – Jennifer's remains were found alongside her two young charges; and twelve-year-old Liv Harding, who had been sent back to her tent by her mother after an argument between them a few minutes before the Guided Silence Session began, was discovered inside her sleeping bag where she had died of smoke inhalation.

The other person to die was Melissa White who, on leaving the Silence Session to return to the campground for unknown reasons, saw the blaze and immediately rushed to check if anyone was inside the tents nearest to her. Melissa pulled two children out of their tents and led them to safety before tripping on a guy rope and falling into burning canvas. Unlike the other victims, Melissa did not die immediately. She had third-degree burns to 60 per cent of her body. She died four days later.

There are numerous theories about why Mum decided to stage the Event.

Dad is convinced she was radicalised by her detention; Hashimoto links her decision to the escalation of natural and humanitarian disasters. Before I started writing this memoir, I believed that the Quiet Corner festival deaths were the tipping point. For Mum, they were personal. The tragedy was an attack on both Rachel and her Community, and in her notebooks her anger and pain are clear.

> How many more of us have to die for you to listen?
> (#28, p. 100).

It is impossible to know the exact moment when Rachel took

the decision to silence herself forever, but I no longer believe that there was a single trigger. Instead, I have come to believe that everything that she had done and that had been done to her, everything that had been said to her and about her in the previous eight years, was bound up in her decision to stand on an petrol-soaked pyre at 11 a.m. on 31 October 2011 and set herself alight.

18.

You may be surprised to learn that there is not a single mention of the word 'Event' in Rachel's notebooks nor any evidence that she ever actually used that name to refer to what she was planning. I've always thought how ironic the name is, given how 'Event' sounds so, well, *un*eventful. It sounds like 21,078 women were at a series of garden parties, or conferences, charity auctions or prize-givings, not participating in the deadliest mass suicide in history.

I have tried to find out who first called it the Event, but since there are approximately 700,000,000 search results online, I gave it up as an impossible task. Nowadays, most dictionaries include a definition – for example: '**Event** Noun: /i'vent/ deaths of at least 21,000 women on 31 October 2011 in globally coordinated acts of self-immolation'[13] – however, none of the dictionaries I've looked at mention when the word was first used for this purpose.

Not only does Rachel not use the word 'Event', but there are very few direct references to what she was planning. All mentions are confined to notebook #29. This is her final notebook, and out of a total of 200 pages, only 103 pages contain writing.

Unlike several notebooks preceding it, #29 is notably less focused on day-to-day Community activities and the entries once again become interesting. Rachel is more reflective, more

---

[13] *The New World Dictionary*, Illumin Press, 2019.

introspective, and how she writes is reminiscent of her earliest notebooks. For example:

> *Even while the membership numbers grow, our*
> *Community is failing. I'm failing. There's a saying that*
> *goes something like the person who shouts the loudest*
> *gets heard first. All our protests are just a different kind*
> *of shouting and we will never be able to shout the loudest*
> *if we simply carry on like we are. We'll never be heard*
> *in the way that we need to be. We have to find a new*
> *way to protest. We must do something that will force*
> *every single person to fall silent long enough to listen to*
> *us and to no one else. (#29, p. 1)*

There are many other entries in a similar vein, but then on page 49 there is a dramatic shift in my mother's tone.

> *Decision made. Nothing less than our permanent silence*
> *will be enough. Many others feel the same. The more of*
> *us that do this, the louder our message will be. I see no*
> *other way. There is no other way. We must find the*
> *strength to do this. We will find the strength to do this.*
> *(#29, p. 49)*

She sounds so certain. Did she ever have any doubts? Until the moment she set the flame to the pyre, it had never crossed my mind that my mother would have been capable of killing herself. But in the process of writing this book, I believe I am, finally, gaining some understanding. Mum always felt things so deeply. You know how people say 'head or heart'? Well, it was never a choice for my mother: it was heart first, last and always. Once she came to the realisation, as she saw it, that she had no other choice, she would not have questioned where that choice took her. The Community's silence project wasn't working. Not like she wanted it to. No one was listening, not really, not to the Community and not to each other. Rachel understood that it was futile to continue along the same path she had been travelling for eight years. She decided that only by killing herself in such a brutal and public way did she have any chance of making the world fall silent and listen to her message.

And she was right, wasn't she? It worked. The Event changed everything. You only have to look at a sample of news headlines from the day afterwards – 1 November 2011 – to see that, underneath the grief and horror, there was a groundswell of public support for the message that the dead women were trying to convey. There are headlines such as 'The Day The World Fell Silent' (*Washington Post*), 'Shaming the World' (*The Times*), 'Hear Their Message' (*China Daily*), 'Burned – for Us!' (*Sydney Morning Herald*) and 'NOW Will We Listen?' (*Times of India*).

In recent years, less supportive articles that were published back then have disappeared from the internet. I'm thinking of the reports that appeared two or three days after the Event which called the Community a 'death cult' and (just as Georgia Sweeney had done back in the early days) compared Rachel to monsters like Jim Jones and David Koresh. I remember reading some of those articles, and one in particular that described my mother as a combination of 'Ted Bundy's love child', 'the daughter of Satan' and 'an English Pol Pot'. To the best of my knowledge, Rachel was neither a serial killer nor related to the devil nor a genocidal totalitarian dictator. I'm not particularly surprised that you can no longer find these reports because the Community has perfected the art of suppressing anything which runs counter to its narrative.

I'm determined not to give anyone a reason to say that that is what I'm doing; it is important for other voices from that day to be heard, so here is what Tom and Livy have to say about the event.

From: Tom Warren
To: Emilia Morris
Date: 17 August 2022

Subject: Re: Hello Stranger

Dear Emilia,

I hope you're well.

I can't pretend that I was pleased to hear from you, particularly when I realised what you wanted. I was going to ignore your email, but you've got my psychotherapist to thank because she persuaded me that it might be good for me to write to you. Yes, I'm seeing a psychotherapist. There's no reason you would know, but a few years ago I was diagnosed with PTSD. Turns out that watching your own mother set herself alight isn't altogether good for your mental health. Or not mine, anyway.

It sounds like you've got off more lightly than me. You always were the stronger one. You had a way of compartmentalising things and rationalising your issues out of existence. I guess by the time I met you Rachel had already been the way she was for a few years, so you'd had to find ways of dealing with it.

Things haven't gone so well for me. In addition to mental health problems, I also had a serious issue with alcohol, although as of this morning I've been sober for four years, three months and sixteen days. It was when I was in treatment for the drinking that I was diagnosed with PTSD. If I'm honest, I'm amazed no one realised sooner, because I tick just about every symptom box that there is: survivor's guilt (and not only about my mother because lots of other stuff came up about my dad dying out in Afghanistan), flashbacks, suicidal thoughts (two failed attempts) and crippling anxiety. You name it, I've had it, so perhaps it's not surprising that my first instinct was to ignore your email.

But Sam, she's my psychotherapist, helped me see that by ignoring your email I would be perpetuating a cycle of avoidance, so here goes. Oh, and so you know, I'm going to ask Sam to read this before I send it.

Do you know the worst trigger for my flashbacks? It's food. I'm vegan now, have been for years. Funnily enough, a bacon sandwich somehow loses its appeal after you've smelled your own mother's flesh burning. I don't suppose you'll remember that we hadn't had breakfast that morning. It was a Monday, wasn't it? I'd got that shitty job at the estate agent's where I had to work Saturdays but got Mondays off. And you were working in the pub with your dad until 'something better came along'. When I think about it now it all seems so pathetic. How could we have been so completely oblivious to what was going on? There we were, fresh out of university, living in my mother's house, playing at being grown-ups, while my mum and your mum made plans to kill themselves. I mean, how could we not have realised that there was something seriously warped about what they were doing in that stupid camp of theirs?

Anyway, you and I were both really crap at the domestic stuff and, as usual, there was no food in the house. I was really hungry and with all that flesh burning it smelled, just for a bit, like a barbecue and it made my stomach rumble. It made my fucking stomach rumble. How disgusting is that? How fucking disgusting that my fucking stomach rumbled when I smelled my mother burning to death? Sam says that I can't blame myself for unconscious bodily functions (apparently the technical term is 'basic electrical rhythms'). She says it's no more shameful than, say, pissing yourself if you're really scared. But I didn't piss myself, did I? I reacted to all that burning flesh by thinking how appetising it smelled.

When I said I was vegan, I wasn't being entirely honest. It's not just that I'm a vegan but I cannot bear to eat any cooked food at all. It makes me want to throw up. All of which means, thanks to my fucked-up relationship with food, it's really fucking difficult just to stay alive. Most days I'm not sure the effort is worth it (Sam, I know you won't like reading that, but you know it's true).

Anyway, Ems, I'll just tell you what I remember about that morning. That will be straightforward enough. You were at the pub with your dad when you saw all the women leaving the camp. At first, you thought they were just going on one of their usual protests, at some railway station or random council office or whatever. But then you found out they'd actually gone to the Chalkham Boar. You rang me. I came to pick you and your dad up. By the time we arrived some reporters were already hanging about, plus a few random people, probably walking their dogs or something. Every woman had her own pyre, which I guess they must have put together over the weekend because they hadn't been there when I'd driven past the previous week. Each woman climbed onto her pyre. Your mother was the first to set light to herself. The rest did the same. They were all dead before the paramedics arrived. End of story.

Only that wasn't the end of the bloody story, was it? Do you remember when we found out how many Members around the world your mum had persuaded to do the same thing? I mean, do you actually remember the moment when we realised that if it seemed unbelievably horrific to watch thirty-eight women burn themselves to death, then it was nothing compared to the realisation that thousands and thousands of others had done it too? Actually, I'm sure you must remember. How could you forget? It was that policewoman who told us, wasn't it? We were in your dad's kitchen and she had just made some lame joke about how it was a good job there was always brandy available in a pub. We were all drinking this revolting brandy-laced tea when she told us that reports of suicides were coming in from almost every country where there was a branch of the Community.

How did we not guess that that was how it would end? Why didn't we realise what was going to happen? Why didn't we try and stop them?

I see now how your mother took advantage of people like my mum, people who were vulnerable, who felt they didn't have a place in society, unhappy, miserable, broken people. Rachel brainwashed them. Somehow, she managed to convince my mum that by sacrificing the rest of her life, my mum would be able to make the world a better place. But what I will never understand is why. Why did my mum have to try and do anything about anything? She had already been through so much.

And when it comes down to it, it didn't work, did it? What your mum and my mum and all those other women did to themselves did not make the world a better place. Sure, the Community does some good stuff, but you don't get something for nothing, do you? It comes at a huge, evil cost because Rachel of Chalkham's Community is bloody everywhere, controlling everything. The Community is benign if it likes you and deadly if it doesn't. It controls everything or, at least, it certainly feels that way. Is the world a better place because of your mother and her Community? I don't think so.

I detest your mother for what she did, but I don't hate you, Ems.

I wish you the best.

Tom

From: Olivia Taylor
To: Emilia Morris
Date: 24 August 2022

Subject: THAT DAY!

Dear Ems,

I was late to the party on the day of the Event. Nothing new there, eh? Sorry, I guess I shouldn't be flippant. Not about 'the Event'. You'd sent me a text and said you'd heard something big was going down with your mum at the Boar and if I could get out of work you'd meet me there. I guess I must have taken an early lunch or something, I can't remember now, and by the time I arrived, loads of people were standing around, the press were there and I had to park up the lane and walk back. I remember thinking, *What the fucking hell is Ems's mother up to this time?*

I was only halfway up the hill when they started the fires. I remember shouting. I remember smoke. I remember trying to run towards you, but it was muddy and I was wearing stupid work shoes. By the time I reached you, everyone was already burning and I couldn't tell which one was your mum. I remember you didn't speak. I remember your dad trying to pull your mum out of the fire. I remember how some of the people who tried to help caught fire and started burning themselves. I remember the cameras swinging from side to side. I remember the roar of the flames. I remember how hot it was. I remember Tom screaming and how it was only then that I realised that his mum was burning as well.

I remember how by the time the police made us all go back down the hill the flames had gone and the bonfires were just smouldering. I remember seeing bones. They were black. I remember how a few people were crying, but most people were completely silent. Your mum would have liked that.

That's it really, Ems. Most of the time I manage not to remember, but some days I catch myself thinking about it and then I do anything I can to try and stop myself remembering.

Love you, babes,

Livy xx

I asked Dad if he would be happy to write about his memories of that day, but he said he didn't know what words he was supposed to use to explain what it was like to watch the woman he loved burn to death. I loved her too, of course, and so I am just going to have to do my best to explain what it was like to be at the Chalkham Boar on the morning of 31 October 2011.

I'm not sure what it was about that particular day that made Dad and me think this protest might be different from usual. At any other time we would have just let Rachel get on with whatever she was doing without rushing out to watch. Maybe it felt different because they were at the Boar. I've often wondered why Mum chose to stage the Event there. She loved that place and right until the end she would walk there almost every day, but there's nothing in her notebooks that sheds any light on why she chose to die there. It may be because there was plenty of room for the thirty-eight pyres. And because of the annual Bonfire Night event at the Boar, the pyres were far less likely to attract attention. Or perhaps it was because they already knew from the crane protest that press helicopters would be able to capture clear footage of the burning women. It was probably a combination of reasons, but I like to think it gave Mum some comfort to die at a place that she loved.

Before that day I had never seen anyone die and I'd never seen a dead body, and right up to the moment Mum set light to her pyre, I honestly thought it was a stunt. A few minutes later, I had watched thirty-eight people die.

I explained in the preface how my mother didn't look at me. As far as I can remember none of them looked at anyone except each other. From what I can make out from the final entries in Rachel's notebooks, they had all been practising some kind of self-hypnosis (the first references appear in notebook #26, although I have no reason to think anyone – including Rachel – knew what they might eventually use the self-hypnosis for).

Certainly, everyone seemed unnaturally calm and I find a measure of comfort in Mum's final ever notebook entry. She doesn't sound frightened or nervous about what she is going to do. I suppose if I had to pick a word, I'd say she sounded resolute.

> *It is done. Around the world, Members are now living their final hours. Tomorrow the press will be invited to assemble at the Chalkham Boar for an announcement. We've been successful in keeping our plans silent and no one outside the Community appears to have any idea about the method we shall be using to make our 'announcement'.*

Detailed preparations have been put in place for the
first hours, days and weeks after it is done. New
leadership teams stand ready to grasp the opportunities
our actions will afford them.
I and my Members willingly choose permanent silence.
We do so freely in the belief that only by giving everything
of ourselves to our cause will our message be heard.
The Community will finally have a platform to do
everything that I want it to do.

(#29, p. 103)

I have no doubt that after the notebooks are published the Community will seize on Rachel's final sentence and claim that it refers to every policy it implements, no matter how controversial or abhorrent. It will say that these words are a direct validation of everything it does. Community detractors will argue just as fervently that it is just as clear that Rachel was simply referring to her messages of listening and hearing.

There is only one genuine certainty to be found in this message: the references to 'final hours' and 'tomorrow' make it indisputable that my mother wrote this entry the day before her death.

The rest of the notebook is blank.

I think about the Event every single day of my life. My memories never change. I am standing between Tom and Dad with Tom's arm around my shoulder. I am bored. There is a strong smell of petrol, and I'm assuming that the women are going to stay on their piles of wood for a while, being all silent and symbolic, before climbing down, setting light to them and retreating to a safe distance. I attempt to distract myself from the smell by trying to work out if the bundles of wood are positioned in the shape of letters, or maybe a giant Shelly, a message to the world that will be visible from the air when they're alight.

As well as being bored, I'm also annoyed with myself, wondering why on earth we've bothered to come. Mum doesn't care whether I'm here or not, so what on earth am I doing wasting my time standing around on the fringes of yet another of her silent protests? It's not like she needs our support – she's surrounded by women who revere her. I count the pyres. There are thirty-eight. I recognise many of the women on their piles of wood. Tabitha is on my mother's left and Libby, Tom's mum, is on her right. Behind Libby are the two journalists who came to expose the Community and never left.

What *is* Rachel's hold over them? What makes these otherwise normal women continue to carry out these stupid stunts? What can they possibly hope to achieve?

I've no doubt this protest will be like all the others. Silent. Well-intentioned. Pointless.

I'm about to tell Tom and Dad that I'm leaving when Rachel reaches into her pocket and pulls out a lighter. Tom can feel how restless I am and pulls me closer, kisses the top of my head. I've texted Livy and I look over my shoulder, wondering if she's here yet. When I look back, all the women are now holding lighters, although Mum is the only one holding hers above her head. They are silent, of course, and all of them are looking at my mother as she lowers her hand, flicks the lighter, cups her other hand around the flame and bends down towards the wood. I'm still completely convinced it's all just a charade and I'm wondering what the point of all this pretence is because at the moment it feels more like a piece of performance art than a protest.

Mum's hand is getting lower, she is having to twist her knees awkwardly to one side and her feet are wobbling. We watch the women. The women watch my mother. The reporters watch everyone, and still Mum moves the lighter towards the wood. And then, a second before the flame reaches the petrol, I understand she is not going to stop.

Mum is the first but the others follow. There is a collective gasp from all of us who are watching, and then the shouting starts. Tom runs towards his mother and Dad runs towards Rachel. I run nowhere. It is already too late.

Mercifully, for them and for us, the pyres are thoroughly soaked in petrol so the women are all dead within minutes. Mum's green dress catches fire almost instantly and disintegrates, leaving her naked. A few of them are screaming. Horrific, inhuman noises. But the rest of the women are silent and I don't understand how that can be. Surely the pain from their burning flesh is greater than their resolve to be silent? Two women topple forwards onto the grass. Then another collapses onto her pyre, curling like a foetus, then another topples and another and another. People tear off their coats, throwing them onto these blazing women. People throw themselves on top of the coats and the women, desperate to kill the flames. Everyone who is not burning is screaming and all the women are falling, until only Rachel is left standing and, in that moment it honestly seems like the flames are feeding her rather than killing her. She extends her arms, Christ-like, and I could swear the fire is coming from within her. Then my mother pitches forward in slow motion and falls, lying spreadeagled across the flaming wood. She convulses, once, twice and then is still.

After the Event

November 2011–Present Day

19.

On 2 November 2011, I was on the front page of *The Times*. It's funny, the tricks your mind can play, because looking at the photograph now makes me feel simultaneously as though it was taken both yesterday and a lifetime ago. It strikes me how much I look like Mum, more than in any other picture of myself. I'm in the doorway of the pub, closing the door, looking over my shoulder. My mouth is open – I was probably telling everyone to fuck off and leave us alone – and it's in my eyes that I see my mother. I look angry and I look frightened, which isn't surprising because I was both of those things.

In those first few days the press camped outside the pub, waiting for... I'm not sure what, exactly. I kept very few newspapers from back then, eventually shoving the ones I did keep into the same plastic IKEA box where Mum's notebooks spent the last ten years. At first, the reporting of the Event was confused: it had yet to coalesce into a coherent narrative, as they like to say these days. The dead women were described variously as martyrs, witches, victims, heroes, selfish, selfless, brave, stupid and, in one particularly pervasive – if completely misguided – description, as twenty-first-century incarnations of Joan of Arc.

The same edition of *The Times* – the one with my photograph on the front page – has an obituary of my mother on page sixteen. It's bland to the point of boring, which is ironic really, considering she had just organised one of the least boring protests of all time.

As I've said before, the actual details known about my mother's life are few and far between, but even so, some of what the article says – such as claiming she was born in Chalkham – isn't correct. The obituary lists some of the more prominent protests that Rachel and the Community had organised, but on the whole that article, like many others at that time, made it sound as if everything she had done had happened *to* her, rather than as a result of deliberate choices made *by* her.

I don't really have much recollection of those first days. Tom was there at the pub in the immediate aftermath and then he wasn't. His aunt came to collect him, took him back to her home in Manchester. I missed him badly, which really hurt, but I think we both already understood there was no way our relationship could survive what our mothers had done. The pub stayed shut, of course. Dad was pretty heavily medicated and his burned hands were wrapped in bandages. A doctor came several times, letting herself in through our back door. She offered me sleeping tablets, but I didn't take them – I was too scared about what I might see in my dreams. For those first few days, with Dad drugged up to the eyeballs and the world's press outside, our home was the only place I wanted to be, the only place I could be, really. I spent my time making my way through every drawer and cupboard in our house, emptying everything on to the floor, sifting through years of accumulated junk. I didn't sleep, other than in brief snatches, sprawled on top of the contents of our wardrobes. I told myself I was keeping busy, sorting things out, being helpful. I told myself a lot of things, but really I was searching for her.

Although my mother hadn't set foot in our house for eight years, she was everywhere. Apart from the few bits and bobs she had asked us to take down to the camp, Dad had never made any effort to clear out her things. I honestly think that right up until she died he never stopped hoping that Rachel would wander up the beer garden and step through the back door, calling, 'I'm home.' Well, that was never going to happen. But in those earliest of days after the Event, when it was impossible to imagine how I could ever pick up any semblance of my life and carry on, I spent my time chasing memories of my mother.

I found her in the most unremarkable of places. She was in the back of the airing cupboard, where her 'do not use them on pain of death, Emilia' spotless white towels were neatly folded, hidden under a spare duvet cover. I found her in an appointment card for the hairdresser's she used to go to. The card was in the third drawer down next to the oven, wedged under a box of staples, and it showed the dates for four hair appointments. The final date was scrawled in green biro, 22/05/03, the day before my thirteenth birthday. I sat motionless on the kitchen floor for a long time when I saw that.

'Look, Ems,' she had said, appearing in the doorway of my bedroom, 'I've treated myself to a bit of a lift, an I've-got-a-teenage-daughter-haircut in your honour.'

I remember looking up from my book (I was re-reading the first four Harry Potter books, ahead of *The Order of the Phoenix*, which was about to be published). The haircut suited her, and she'd had some sort of colour put in too. I thought she looked beautiful.

'Nice hair, Mum.'

'Thanks, baby girl. Can you believe you're going to be thirteen tomorrow? I hope you've been practising being all miserable and moody.'

I grinned. It had been a standing joke between us for a few months that my parents fully expected me to wake up on the morning of my thirteenth birthday in a foul mood and stay that way for at least the next five years. As it turned out, Rachel really didn't have anything to worry about – she'd miss out on all those years of my life.

Sitting on the kitchen floor, surrounded by the contents of the drawers, I wondered if, as the hairdresser was cutting her hair and they chatted about the weather and TV programmes and holidays, Mum already knew that it was the last time she'd go to a hairdresser, the last time she'd look at colour charts and choose something to give her 'a bit of a lift'. Had she already made up her mind to walk out on Dad and me the very next day?

The pub remained shut. The media were a constant presence outside our front door; police trampled all over our beer garden, cordoning off the camp and carting boxes to vans parked up in the street. Dad woke up only long enough to use the bathroom, force down a piece of toast, a cup of tea and another sleeping pill, while I carried on sifting through receipts and birthday cards and half-empty bottles of nail varnish and shopping lists and recipes for meals that had never been made. For six days we barricaded ourselves inside the pub. I did everything in my power not to let myself think of the blackened smoking remains up at the Boar. But that fragile bubble of security, well, obviously it couldn't last.

On the seventh day after the Event, Steven Trent came to find us and all hell broke loose.

Steven Trent. Such an innocuous-sounding name. Not one that you would think would come to assume multiple meanings. Of course, now there's the so-called Trent Test, the twenty-first-century yardstick for mass murderers: are they more or less prolific than Steven Trent? There's the whole 'doing a Trent', which is shorthand for a revenge killing. And recently I've even heard kids say to each other 'you're so Trent', which, as far as I can tell, basically means you're mad.

In the unlikely event anyone doesn't know what he did, Wikipedia is in this instance an accurate source:

> **Steven Phillip Trent** *(29 September 1959–7 November 2011) was an English mass murderer who killed seven people and an unborn baby on 7 November 2011 in the village of* **Chalkham, Hampshire**, *during a killing spree which lasted for three minutes and seventeen seconds. Five of Trent's victims were residents of Chalkham, one was a police officer and one was a freelance photographer from* **Idaho** *in the* **United States**. *Steven Trent, senior curator of the* **Military Weapons Museum** *in* **Boston, Lincolnshire**, *murdered all of his victims with a nineteenth-century* **cutlass** *which he had removed from the museum collection. Minutes before the attack, Trent left a rambling voicemail for his daughter, Charley Rose Trent, in which he said that he wanted to avenge his wife's death in the Event four days earlier, blaming* **Rachel of Chalkham (see also Rachel Morris)** *for his wife's decision to take her own life.*
>
> *In his message, Trent said that he had travelled to Chalkham with the intention of killing Rachel of Chalkham's husband, Nick Wright, her daughter, Emilia Morris, as well as anyone he happened to find on the street where Rachel lived 'because they should have stopped her'. Neither Nick Wright nor Emilia Morris, both of whom were inside* **The Wild Boar pub** *at the time, were harmed.*
>
> *Trent was killed by two Chalkham teenagers,*

Anthony Blake Howell and Robert Worthing, *who*
used kitchen knives to stab Trent multiple times. Both
Howell and Worthing were subsequently awarded the
George Cross[14].

Maybe it was because I was still in shock from seeing Mum
burn to death, but I didn't feel scared for myself as I stood in the
kitchen watching through the window as Steven Trent slaughtered
those people. Afterwards, of course, I felt horror and grief and
guilt and all the feelings you would imagine, but while he did the
actual thing itself, it felt like I was watching a particularly gruesome
film with great special effects.

Trent wielded the sharpened cutlass with tragic accuracy.
Lauren Martin, a forty-two-year-old part-time teaching assistant
was his first victim. She was practically decapitated, her head
flopping against her chest at an impossible angle while her blood
fountained onto a nearby car. Trevor Cleary was ninety-two and
the oldest resident of Chalkham. He was unsteady on his feet,
walked with sticks and stood no chance. Steven Trent's third
victim, Tim Rogers, a fifty-eight-year-old postman, turned his
head towards Trent just as he swung the blade which sliced
through Tim's cheeks leaving his mouth gaping from ear to ear.
Louise Morrison was thirty-one and thirteen weeks pregnant.
Steven sliced through her back while she was bending over Trevor
Cleary. Her spinal cord was severed. She and her baby bled to
death within minutes.

Carson Campbell, Jr was a fifty-four-year-old photographer
on holiday from Idaho. He was working on a book about England's
chalk figures and the Chalkham Boar was the final destination on
his four-week trip. He was due to return home to his wife and

---

[14] https://en.wikipedia.org/wiki/Steven_Trent

teenage twin daughters the following day. He tried to disarm Steven Trent and almost managed to get the cutlass away from him, but the handle was slippery with blood, and while Trent was wearing gloves which gave him some traction, Carson Campbell, Jr couldn't get a proper grip with his bare hands. Eventually Trent pulled the weapon free and slashed Carson's right thigh, severing his femoral artery. Carson was dead within minutes.

Thirty-nine-year-old Bethany Miller was making the first of her twice-daily walks around the village. She was recovering from a double mastectomy, having been given the all-clear ten days previously. She was still feeling exhausted by the smallest things, but she was making great progress and there was no reason to think she wouldn't go on to live to a ripe old age. That was until Steven Trent crossed the road to where she was standing rooted in terror. Trent stabbed her in the heart.

PC Theresa McNulty was outside our door, where a police officer had been stationed since a few hours after the Event. I never did know if they were there to keep us in or to keep others out. While she was frantically radioing for assistance, PC McNulty became Steven Trent's seventh and final victim (not counting Louise Morrison's unborn baby). PC McNulty was killed in the line of duty, preventing Trent from getting through our door. He sliced the blade through the right-hand side of her face and the force of his swing wedged the cutlass in her neck. He was still trying to pull the blade out of her flesh when Anthony Howell and Robert Worthing, three years below me at school, ran up and stabbed Steven repeatedly with knives they'd grabbed from the kitchen in Robert's house.

After that, Dad and I had to leave Chalkham.

We didn't want to go – it was our home, after all – but I do understand why we had no choice. We were no longer welcome in Chalkham. Steven Trent had come for Dad and me, and if we hadn't been living in the pub then those people wouldn't have died. The police said they couldn't guarantee our safety, that we needed to go into hiding for a while. We were allowed to take one suitcase each. A lifetime of accumulated possessions and half an hour to choose what to take. Much later, our belongings were returned to us – some poor soul had been dispatched to pack them into boxes. Goodness knows what they thought when they found the contents of our entire house spread all over the floor. Later still, my mother's belongings, including her notebooks, were also brought to our new home. But as far as the afternoon of 7 November 2011 goes, I was given thirty minutes to pack a suitcase for me and one for my father, then we were bundled out of the pub, into an unmarked police car, and driven out of Chalkham. To this day, I have never been back.

20.

When Mum's belongings were finally returned to us, they were brought to the flat in Basingstoke where Dad and I were taken after we left Chalkham. They told us it was a witness-protection place. It was tiny with a faint but persistent smell of bleach. The walls in every room were painted a depressingly dark green, the inside of the bath had a permanent brown ring, and the toilet didn't flush properly. There was one bedroom, which I made Dad take, while I slept on the pull-out sofa in the combination living room and kitchen. Although the sheets and pillowcases smelled clean enough, they were a horrible off-white almost-yellow colour, presumably where the sweat of many previous occupants had never quite been removed. There was a small television, but that was it. There was nothing else.

I begged them to bring me some books, and eventually one of the police officers handed over an old Asda bag. It looked as though someone had just gone to a second-hand bookshop and picked up the only titles they had heard of: *Great Expectations*, *Pride and Prejudice*, *The Great Gatsby* and *Vanity Fair*. Considering the dissertation for my degree had been on post-modern feminist literature, they wouldn't have necessarily been my first choice of novels, but by that stage I was grateful to have anything at all to read.

For a while, we were visited almost continuously by the police and security services, as well as numerous doctors and counsellors. We were given pills to help us sleep (which I still refused to take) and personal alarms that would have been ear-piercing had we ever had to use them (we didn't). Food was delivered, always by the same man in a stained blue overall who stared at his feet and sighed heavily each time he handed over the bags. There were armed guards outside the door at first, working on eight-hour shifts, and I could hear their walkie-talkies crackling, even during the night.

I had the distinct impression the police didn't know what to do with us. We had a family liaison officer assigned to us, as if we were victims of a crime, but Mum hadn't been killed, she had committed suicide, and although Steven Trent came to Chalkham intending to murder us, he hadn't got anywhere near me and Dad. Physically we were fine. Emotionally... well... that was another story.

I really don't know how to explain how difficult those first few weeks were. Dad carried on taking his own pills and, until I stopped him, mine as well. I wasn't sleeping, neither of us was eating – I just scraped the food into the bin and someone would come every few days and take the bags away.

When Gran died (thank goodness she hadn't lived to see what Mum did), I had experienced what I have to assume is a more normal form of grief. At first my loss – Gran's absence – filled me up. It was a filter through which I saw everything else. When the day was bright and sunny, I couldn't look at the sky without thinking how much she would have loved being outside in her garden on a day like that. Whenever I read a book, I'd wonder what she would have made of it – even though Gran was never a reader. But then, as the time passed, the filter became more transparent; I could see through it and I stopped reflecting my gran onto the world. In time, the grief retreated deeper inside me. It has never gone away and occasionally it reaches out and gives my insides a sharp twist and, for a moment, I'm back there in the first days all over again, but then it ebbs away.

I can't possibly know what anyone else's experience of grief is – all I can say is that the immediate flood and gradual retreat of emotion after my grandmother's death seems to chime with how other people feel.

Not so the grief at my mother's death. There were so many layers. I missed Mum, but honestly, I'd been missing her for eight years already, so the loss was perhaps the easiest emotion to bear. Far more difficult was my fury at how she had chosen to die. To do it in such a way that Dad and I were there to watch it happen. How could she be so fucking selfish? Didn't she care about what she was going to put us both through? The irreparable damage she would cause us? But of course, it wasn't just us. I was consumed by guilt, which was far more overwhelming and difficult to bear than my grief. All those dead women around the world. All those devastated families. All as a result of what Mum believed. And that's before I got started on the horror of Steven Trent. Whichever way I tried to look at it, no matter what the police said, what the counsellors said, that man was only there because of us. Us. Me and Dad. But instead of us… because of us… seven people and an unborn baby were murdered.

For a while there was no relief. The anger and guilt and horror were relentless. I would wake up thinking about death, spend all day thinking about death, fall asleep thinking about death and dream of death every single night. Every. Single. Night. I didn't have the concentration to hold a proper conversation. I'd lose the thread, repeat myself, stop mid-sentence and start talking about something completely different. I spent hours at a time imagining the future that those people would have had. I wrote letters to their families, which I never sent. I tortured myself with the idea that if I had found the courage to run out into the street, then maybe he would have just killed me and none of the others. I was suffocating, drowning under a tsunami of emotions, unable to move on from any of it.

And then they brought Mum's things to us and we found the letters. One for Dad, one for me. I've never read Dad's. He's so open about everything else, but that letter remains entirely his.

It wasn't an easy decision to include Mum's letter to me in this book. Like Dad, I was tempted to keep this one part of my mother for myself. But in my opinion, it's the most significant record of my mother's voice, more so even than the notebooks or the letter she gave me before I left for university, because when she put pen to paper that night she knew she only had hours left to live. She was vulnerable, unguarded. She knew she was going to be setting herself alight. And more than that, she knew that so many others, encouraged by her, were going to do the same thing. If what I'm doing here is going to stand as a true record of who Rachel Morris really was, then I have no choice but to include this letter.

My mother wrote to me on pages that she tore out of the final notebook (#29). The edges of the letter match the stubs of missing pages.

31 October 2011
2 a.m.-ish

My darling baby girl,
I'm in one of the Hearing Places. It is the perfect place to be. All I can hear is the rush of the river, my thoughts and, occasionally, an owl. It's a really clear night, it's cold, but I'm fully dressed, sitting inside a sleeping bag, with two blankets and a hat.

There are so many things I want to say to you. I turned the torch off a little while ago, and I saw a meteor burn through the sky above me. If I could wish anything for you, my darling, it would be that you always shine like a meteor in the blackest of nights. That sounds like one of those awful cutesy signs that I've always hated – you know, the ones that say things like 'Live Like There's No Tomorrow'. Well, for me there really is no tomorrow and one day there will be no tomorrow for you, either. Trust me, Emilia, everything is over so quickly. You must live, I mean really, truly, live your life. Don't drift, don't settle, don't accept anything less than whatever you need to be happy and fulfilled.

You've been angry with me for so long that I worry you will always feel that way. I am proud of you, Emilia. You are kind and compassionate and empathetic and clever – a first in your degree! – but it is for me that you reserve your hurt and anger and pain. My biggest regret, my only regret, about the last few years is that you don't yet understand that it's all been for you. I wanted – needed – to make the whole world see that it must be kind and compassionate too. It's no less than you deserve. It's no less than we all deserve.

Here's some advice: first, last and always, trust yourself. You understand yourself better than anyone else ever will. Don't be swayed or bullied or persuaded against your instincts. Listen to others – of course you must always, always, do that – but remember to listen to yourself as well, my darling. Be wise, be honest, be brave. This is how I have tried to live. Nothing is ever going to change unless the loud, the ignorant and the bigoted are forced to take notice of others. If we, the women of the Community, were not acting wisely, honestly and bravely, we could not do what we are going to do. Please, Emilia, for me, try and understand that.

There are some life lessons I feel I should pass on in case you haven't already figured them out for yourself...

~ Always wear pants with a cotton gusset
~ Life is too short for dry-clean-only blouses
~ Wine hangovers are the worst hangovers
~ If you aren't having at least as much fun as he is, he's not the one for you
~ You're perfect, just as you are
~ I love you
~ Walk for pleasure, as often as possible
~ Check all pockets for tissues before you put clothes in the washing machine
~ Never let anyone tell you you're not good enough
~ High heels are the devil's footwear
~ Blondie is the best band of all time. Fact.
~ Prince isn't bad either
~ Nor is Bruce Springsteen
~ Blue suits you better than any other colour
~ Always start a course of antibiotics by taking a double dose...
~ ... and always finish the course
~ Keep your body fit and your mind will follow
~ Wash new towels before using them, otherwise they'll shed like hell
~ Drink champagne whenever it's offered
~ Check your breasts regularly. If you find a lump, see a doctor immediately
~ Watching clouds is the simplest way to relax
~ Don't forget that you're allergic to prawns
~ Our world is so beautiful, but it is so fragile
~ Read always, read widely (although I think you've already figured this one out!)
~ Work isn't life and life isn't work
~ Your dad – Nick – is a wonderful person

~ *We love you*
~ *I love you*
~ *I love you*
~ *I love you*

It's not easy knowing I'm about to be the cause of so much upset for you and Dad. I cannot apologise for leaving you, because I have no choice, but I am truly sorry for the pain that I know you're going to feel.

Right now it sounds like there's a whole colony of owls just outside. I've always loved the sound of owls. You know that not one bit of me believes in any form of afterlife – neither God nor ghosts. But how about we do this? How about every time you hear an owl in the future you imagine that it's me, that I'm there, checking in with my baby girl? Too sentimental? Maybe, but it gives me a bit of comfort to think of you doing this.

It's not just the owls that are making noises at the moment. Every now and then I can hear crying. I don't know if it's the same person or different people. I understand their tears. What we're going to do is terrifying. But know this, what we're going to do will make a difference. It must. I don't know exactly how many women around the world will go through with it. Somewhere north of 25,000 Members have confirmed their intention to take part, and if even just a fraction of that number join me, it has to make the world listen. It just has to. Nothing like this has ever been done before. I hope, I really, really hope, that nothing like this ever has to be done again.

This night is passing so quickly. I don't want to leave anything unsaid. I wonder if you might be expecting me to tell you the name of your bio-dad, as some sort of end-of-my-life reveal. Whip away the curtain and expose the villain of the piece. If that's what you're thinking, then I'm really sorry, because it's not going to happen. I honestly don't know who he is. I went to a party at a friend of a friend of a friend's. I don't even know where it was. Someone else drove. It was outside London. The house was huge – maybe it belonged to someone's parents? I drank so much, far too much. You name it, I drank it. It wasn't the first time I'd done something like that. I don't remember anything after the first hour or so. Nothing at all. The next day I felt like hell but I had no reason to think I'd had sex. It was only after two missed periods when my boobs were really sore that it even crossed my mind that I might be pregnant.

I'm sorry if you're disappointed. I'm also sorry if you think badly of me for not knowing who your biological father is. But know this, Emilia, from the moment I sat in the toilet cubicle at work watching two blue lines appear on the test, I wanted you more than anything I'd ever wanted. I cleaned up my life, I took the very best care of both of us for the rest of the pregnancy, and then, once you were born, I brought you to live with the nicest, most caring man I have ever known. I wish with all of my heart that Nick was your biological father and I know he feels the same. As far as we are concerned, I chose him to be your dad and he chose you to be his daughter from the moment he met you.

Nick has always been the father for you that I never had, and I tried my best to be the mother for you that I never had either. I know I have never really talked to you about my parents, but there was so little to tell. They weren't bad parents. They didn't hit me or starve me.

They weren't cruel to me. Equally, they didn't love me or praise me or build me up. I was, as they used to say, 'a late baby'. You know how in novels the late baby is often the cosseted, cherished, longed-for surprise? Not so for my parents. They were perfectly happy as they were, moving every few years with my father's work, never getting too friendly with anyone. I'm not saying there was any great mystery about them, just that they liked the life they had made for themselves and then I arrived and disrupted it all. They never seemed to know what to do with me. They were never interested in the things I was interested in as a child – they didn't even pretend to like playing games with me or reading to me. I suppose I should thank them for giving me the strength to do what I've been doing for the last eight years because, if nothing else, being raised by my parents made me self-reliant and determined.

I keep imagining the sky is getting lighter, although it's too early for dawn. I must finish this letter and return to the others. They need me to help them be strong.

Do you remember that time, a few years ago, when you marched down here to see me and bellowed that poem you loved in my face? 'Ozymandias'. Do you remember? You said that I was Ozymandias, that I would soon be buried beneath the sands with no one to remember me. Well, you were right, my darling, I'll be gone very, very soon. The thing is, I don't care if no one remembers me, I really don't. I just hope they remember what we've done and why we've done it. The world is a terrifying place. We have to listen to each other. We must try, Emilia. There is no hope if we don't.

I must stop now and go to wait with the others. Be strong, my darling, shine brightly and dazzle the world.

I love you, baby girl.
Mum

Re-reading this letter takes me right back to sitting on the threadbare carpet on the bedroom floor in that horrible witness-protection flat in Basingstoke and how angry I was after I read it for the very first time.

Pants with a cotton gusset.

Pants. With. A. Cotton. Gusset.

My mother had decided to remove herself from my life forever but couldn't think of anything more important to say to me than what underwear I should use?

Also, it's mussels I'm allergic to, not prawns. She couldn't even get that right.

I couldn't see past my fury. I couldn't see anything other than my dead mother justifying her decision to kill herself and encourage thousands of others to do the same. For days, I fixated on the bit where she'd said, '*My biggest regret, my only regret, about the last few years is that you don't yet understand that it's all been for you*'.

The letter unmoored me. I'd already lost Tom; for a long time, my dad, understandably, had nothing of himself to give me; and my mother was dead. I loved her and I hated her. I didn't understand who she was; I didn't understand who I was. What did it mean, this huge, unimaginably awful thing that she had done? All my certainties had gone. I was twenty-one years old and my life was already over. I was desperate to leave that horrible flat in Basingstoke, but wherever I went, I would always be the daughter of the woman who had persuaded 21,078 women to burn themselves to death. My dead mother was suffocating me and I needed to find something to cling onto before I sank completely.

That's when the Community came calling.

21.

From: Nick Wright
To: Emilia Morris
Date: 7 September 2022

Subject: Thank you

Hi darling,

Just a short note to say thank you for coming to the hospital to see me yesterday. Please try not to worry, I'm going to be fine. As you said they would, someone from your publisher visited me this morning. They offered to rent me a flat, like they've done for you, but I said no. I'm staying in my own home and that's that.

I know you think I'm jumping to conclusions, but it's clear that the Community doesn't want you to write this book of yours. What if they sent the person who attacked me? If that's right, if that's what they'll do to me, I dread to think what they might do to you.

Please, for me, think seriously about abandoning the whole idea. That's all I really wanted to say, darling. I'm fine, a bit sore but fine. Everyone is taking great care of me. I'll be out of here soon and I'll see you then.

Love,

Dad

22.

Before the Event, back when the most notable thing about our family was my mum's silence, my father had put Gran's little cottage up for sale. The market was flat and there wasn't much interest at first, then two sales fell through before it finally sold a week before the Event. Dad had been intending to give me some of the proceeds, to help Tom and me get a foot on the housing ladder – back then it had still seemed possible that I could get an ordinary job and live an ordinary life – until what Mum did put paid to any chance of that. Dad's only source of income had been the pub, and he was in no fit state to run it, even if returning to live in Chalkham had been an option for him.

So, I told him that he should use the money from Gran's house to get himself somewhere to live and give himself time to deal with everything that had happened. That left me with the problem of myself.

I tried to ring Tom many times, but every time his aunt would answer the phone and, while always being unfailingly polite, she would say, 'I'm sorry, love, he's asleep,' or 'I'm sorry, love, he's just popped out to try and clear his head,' or 'I'm sorry, love, he's at the doctor's,' or 'I'm sorry, love, he's in no fit state to talk.' Eventually I got the message.

I tried calling other people too, friends from uni. Most of them didn't pick up, and I got the distinct impression that the ones who did were paranoid they would say the wrong thing to me. I didn't know how to explain that there wasn't a 'wrong thing' to say – they could have said anything at all and I would have been happy for the distraction from my own thoughts for a few minutes. But the conversations were so stilted and awkward that I eventually stopped calling my university friends, too.

Livy was different. Nothing had really changed between us after the Event, thank goodness, but she had just started work as a trainee solicitor at a large London law firm and her days (and many of her evenings) were suddenly filled with work. For the first time ever, Livy wasn't always at the end of the phone when I wanted to talk.

Ridiculous though it sounds now, I began to think that my father and I had been stuck in that horrible witness-protection flat as punishment. Punishment for me being my mother's daughter and for Dad being Rachel's husband. My life, which, prior to the Event, had been full of possibilities and choices, had narrowed to a space measuring no more than six metres by six metres, filled with suffocating quantities of anger, guilt and grief. I was obsessed by questions such as *Will I ever leave this place? Get a job? Meet anyone? Laugh ever again?* I could not see how any of these things were possible.

I'm not making excuses. I'm just explaining the state I was in when two Members came to see me. At the time I didn't think to ask, so I have no idea how they knew where I was. I can only think that the Community had contacts within the police, even back then. They arrived for the first time on an evening shortly before Christmas, when Dad had medicated himself to sleep so there was no chance of him hearing the doorbell chiming its off-key version of 'There's No Place Like Home'. Two women were standing in the hallway, both wearing Community hoodies and big smiles. One of them was only a few years older than me, late twenties at most, with thick black hair in a high ponytail;

the other one looked old enough to be her mother.

'Emilia?' the younger one asked. 'Emilia Morris?' They both smiled even more widely and stuck out their hands, which I shook, automatically. I had no idea who these people were.

Again, the younger one spoke. 'It's so good to meet you. I'm Soraya and this is Helen.'

'Sorry, what do you want?' I asked.

'We're from the Community. We just wanted to give you our condolences,' said the older woman, Helen. 'And to see how you're bearing up, ask if there's anything we can do to help. It must be such a difficult time.'

Soraya held up a white box. 'We brought cake.'

'Would it be OK for us to come in for a little while?' Helen asked. 'We'd love to have a chat and see how you're doing.'

One of Mum's favourite films was *Sliding Doors*. In one version of her life, Gwyneth Paltrow's character catches a train and gets home to find her husband in bed with another woman, and in another version, she misses the train and arrives after the woman has left. The two paths of her life diverge sharply from that point onwards.

This was my own *Sliding Doors* moment. I could have told them I was too tired or too upset to invite them in. I could have just thanked them for the cake and shut the door, and my life would have followed a completely different path.

But that is not what I did. At the time, I was just pathetically happy to have some company and so, with absolutely no concept of the consequences, I invited them in. I flicked on the kettle, swilled out three mugs and hunted around for clean plates while Soraya unveiled an enormous lemon drizzle cake. Then we all sat down at the little table where Dad and I had eaten so many depressingly silent meals.

I didn't know it at the time, but Soraya and Helen must have been working for the Outreach Sector. That particular sector would still have been in its early days, but Mum and her Community had long understood there was a virtually limit-less source of potential new Members to be found among the isolated, the depressed, the lonely, the disenfranchised (did it ever cross my mother's mind that, thanks to her, I might one day be one of these people?). Vocal critic and ex-Member of the Community Dr Martha Stephens's book *Silent Succour* (Lupin Press, 2017) is an in-depth and fascinating exposé of the Outreach Sector's unparalleled success in recruiting the vulnerable to the Community's cause by smothering them with compassion and understanding and, above all, by listening to them. Just like Mum wanted.

I am embarrassed to remember how I lapped it all up. But then again, I certainly hit all of their key markers: I was isolated, lonely and vulnerable. I was grieving, angry and depressed (although I wasn't ever formally diagnosed as such). I had no one to talk to, or at least that's how it felt, and no one who could possibly understand what I was going through.

Soraya and Helen had clearly been trained well and on that first occasion they mainly just listened, encouraging me to continue talking with occasional questions. They asked me about my feelings: *How do you feel about having to leave Chalkham? How do you feel about going back to work? How do you feel about people finding out you're Rachel's daughter?* After a while, they started dropping in some practical questions, such as had I thought about where I would like to be living and what type of job I would like to be doing.

They returned two days later and three days after that and, little-by-little, over the course of the half a dozen times that they came to see me, I began to shift my focus from what lay behind me and glimpse what could, possibly, lie ahead.

At first, they didn't really say much about the Community itself, but when they did begin talking about it, what they had to say was surprising. I suppose, in so far as I had thought about it (which wasn't very often), I had assumed that after the Event the organisation was as broken and directionless as I was. I'm sure I wasn't alone in thinking that with so many deaths there couldn't be many Members left. But as I listened to Soraya talking about how the Community was thriving, not just in the UK but overseas, too, it began to dawn on me just how wrong my assumptions were. There was so much more to the Community than the women who had chosen to burn.

Around that time, the press started speculating about the Community's new leader, the person they had dubbed the 'Designated Survivor'. Although everyone now knows her to be Sophie Turrell, for the first few weeks following the Event, her identity was shrouded in mystery. The deliberate secrecy enabled the Community to firmly embed the idea in the minds not only of the surviving Members, but also the public at large, that the organisation was still being guided in all things by Rachel and her legacy, while in fact this shadowy new figurehead – the Designated Survivor – began to steer the Community in an entirely new direction, step by insidious step.

Sophie Turrell featured significantly in the decisions I would make in the years that followed, but there in the flat in Basingstoke, I didn't give so much as a passing thought to who might have replaced Mum. Instead, as the three of us – Soraya, Helen and I – sat around the table, I asked Soraya what it was like living in one of the places she had been talking about.

'It's a bit like university halls of residence, but for adults, you know?' she said. 'I've got my own room, but without having to stress about rent or bills or anything. There's plenty of people to socialise with, but no one's on your back if you want to keep yourself to yourself. There's a gym and a canteen. It's great.'

'What's the catch?' I asked and Soraya laughed.

'There's no catch. I mean, obviously the pay is pretty poor, but that's because you get accommodation and food included.'

'Presumably everyone has to be silent?' I said.

Soraya shook her head. 'We're supposed to be silent at night, but during the day we're free to talk. We wouldn't be able to do our work otherwise.'

'So what *is* your work?' I asked. 'I mean, what sort of jobs are available?'

Helen answered that one. 'All sorts. We're preparing to launch a global consultation project, so we're recruiting for pretty much any role you can think of.'

'Are you interested?' Soraya asked.

'Maybe,' I replied.

And there it was.

I understand now that Soraya and Helen's entire purpose was to nudge me along until I reached this point. Looking back now, it's blindingly obvious that the Community would have been very keen to have Rachel's daughter as a Member. They wanted to keep me on side. To keep me inside.

I put up barely any objection; I felt genuinely grateful when Helen asked if I would like her to put in a good word for me with one of the senior managers in the PR and Communications Sector.

And so it was that in the second week of January 2012 I submitted my CV, had two Skype interviews with someone called Alice Corbett in PR and was invited to leave Basingstoke and travel to the outskirts of Slough to live and work as a fully fledged Member of Mum's Community.

23.

The best thing that ever happened to me was when Nick Wright took me in as his own daughter. How different – how much worse? – would my life have been if Dad hadn't done that? He's always put me first, just like he always put Mum first, and now I'm worried that I'm taking advantage of him if I insist on publishing this book.

As I write these words, my dad is in hospital with cuts, bruises, abrasions and four broken ribs, waiting for an operation to pin his shattered arm back together. He believes the Community did this to him. They wouldn't swing the baseball bats themselves, of course, but they have ways of getting things done, and we both know that even if they find the bastards who did this to my father, there won't be any link back to the Community.

Dad went through hell after Mum's death. I don't think any of his students – the ones who consistently vote him most popular arts and humanities lecturer year after year – have the faintest idea what it took for my dad to rebuild his life after the Event, to take a philosophy degree as a mature student, sail through his postgraduate studies and be offered a job at the university. They haven't got a clue and that, of course, is just how Dad likes it.

He always tells me he is proud of me, but I am who I am because of him.

Dad wants me to stop writing this book; he never wanted me

to write it in the first place. But now that it might be the reason he's in hospital, I have to wonder is he right?

According to the law, you can't defame the dead, which should mean anyone can say anything they like about my mother without fear of reprisal, but everyone knows that the Community is above the law and anyone foolish enough to publicly malign Rachel of Chalkham is putting themselves at risk of the Community's particular brand of 'reprisal'. It is in full knowledge of this that I say that I barely recognise the woman that is now so revered by the Community, and it is this gulf between their Rachel of Chalkham and my own recollections of my mother that is the principle motivation behind this book. Was Mum really the person they say she was: an inspirational genius, a giant on whose shoulders everyone else will forever stand? And if she was, why don't I see her that way?

Rachel was my mother and that gives me the right to write about her no matter what anyone says. If I abandon this book, the Community will continue to get away with its manipulation, misdirection, grandstanding, intimidation, bullying and control, and continue to twist stories about my mother until there's nothing of the real Rachel Morris left. If Mum taught me anything, it was to stand up for what I believe in. So, this is me, standing up. Telling the world about the Community.

24.

Dad found himself a place to rent in Winchester. In our last few days together in Basingstoke, we packed up what few belongings we had accumulated, although most of our things from Chalkham had gone straight into storage. I decided to take only what I could fit into a single rucksack. I liked the idea of arriving with almost nothing, starting somewhere new with little other than a toothbrush, underwear and my phone. Obviously, I took a bit more than that, but I was ruthless. Is it essential? I asked myself about each item, because if it wasn't, it wasn't coming. Consequently, most of my things were taken to Dad's new place. That was when I bought the IKEA box for Mum's notebooks and, together with the rest of my stuff, the box and its contents spent the next few years in Dad's spare room.

On our final night before we left Basingstoke, we ordered a takeaway and opened a bottle of wine. It was the most normal thing we'd done in a long time.

There were no wine glasses, so while I set out the food Dad got two plastic beakers out of the cupboard and filled them both. Before I'd finished opening all the cartons, he'd already knocked his wine back and refilled the beaker. I waited until we were sat at the table with the food laid out in front us before I spoke.

'You're OK with this, aren't you, Dad? Me going? You're sure you'll be OK without me?'

'I'll be fine.' He put a spoonful of rice onto his plate and had another large swig of wine.

'What're you going to do with yourself? Without the pub, I mean?' I asked.

'Ah, the pub. The pub. The pub. The fucking pub.' He drained his beaker and refilled it.

'This food is great,' I said. 'Here, try some of this.' I dug a spoon into the takeaway container nearest me and put some of it onto his plate. He picked up his fork and pointed it at me.

'The only time I ever actually enjoyed working in that pub was when your mum was there alongside me. The punters loved her; did I ever tell you that?'

'You don't need to, I can remember.'

He stared at me, like he was trying to work out if I was telling the truth, then he put down his fork and drank some more wine. The bottle was already almost empty, and he hadn't touched his food.

'Of course you remember. Sometimes I forget that she wasn't always living in a field, like a fucking garden gnome.' He poured out the remainder of the bottle, knocked back the wine, reached over to the counter and picked up a second bottle.

'Dad, I'm not sure you should drink so much, not with all the pills you're taking at the moment.'

Ignoring me, he unscrewed the cap and refilled his beaker, splashing a little on the table, then he picked up his fork again and had a mouthful of food, followed by a swig of wine, then another. 'You can stop worrying about me, Ems. It's not your job.'

'You would tell me if you wanted me to stay a bit longer? I could always put off the start date until you're settled in the new flat – I'm sure they'd understand.'

'Ha. I bet they'd understand.'

'What do you mean?'

He didn't say anything, and neither did I for a bit. I watched Dad, who was finally eating some food, even if he was washing down every mouthful with a big gulp of wine.

Eventually I said, 'What did you mean "I bet they'd understand"?'

'The Community. Why does it have to be the Community?'

'We've been over this, Dad.'

'You got a first in your degree. Any company would be lucky to have you.'

'How can I just go and get a job at some company? I'm Rachel of Chalkham's daughter, for god's sake. I'm a freak.'

The beaker was halfway to his mouth again, but when I said this he slammed it down on the table. 'Don't ever say that, Emilia. You're not a freak.'

'Maybe you don't think so, Dad, but that's how other people see me. I mean, apart from Livy, none of my so-called friends can even bring themselves to speak to me because I make them feel nervous or weird or something.'

'That's not true.'

'It *is* true. No one wants anything to do with me. Maybe they're wondering if I'm about to burn myself to death.'

'Don't say that.'

'Why not? It's probably true. To them I will always be the daughter of the woman who burned herself to death. That's Mum's legacy to me, isn't it? I'll always be known as Rachel of Chalkham's daughter. Just like you're Rachel of Chalkham's husband. The two people closest to her, the ones she was supposed to love the most. She has well and truly fucked up our lives forever. Thank you, Mum.'

'Don't say that about your mother.'

'Why not? It's true, isn't it?'

'She didn't do this to hurt us, Ems. She had no choice.'

'Of course she had a fucking choice. She could have refused to set light to herself. Nobody made her. It was nobody else's decision. It was her, all her, and she didn't give a fuck about us. She didn't give us a single thought. I fucking hate her.'

'The Community made her do it.'

'That doesn't even make sense, Dad. Mum and the Community are the same thing. Mum was the Community; the Community was Mum. Still is.'

'The Community is not your mother. It's something else. They twist everything. And now they've got hold of you, they'll twist you, too.'

'I don't even understand what you're talking about.'

He picked up his beaker and stared into it, then he reached for a third bottle of wine.

'Dad, you're really not supposed to drink this much and then take sleeping pills.'

He didn't reply, just unscrewed the cap, sloshed more wine into the beaker and immediately knocked back half of it. Drops ran down his chin. He pushed his plate away. He'd eaten hardly anything.

'This Community,' he said, 'there's something wrong about it. I mean *really* wrong. Evil.'

I took a sip of my wine; it wasn't particularly nice.

'So, because it feels wrong to you,' I said, 'you're saying I should turn down a great job, accommodation…'

'There'll always be room for you in my home. You could come to Winchester.'

'We're just going round in circles. What would I do in Winchester?'

'You'd find a job. You could commute to London.'

'But this is what I said before. I don't want to get a job where all I am is the freaky daughter of Rachel of Chalkham. If I join

Mum's Community I think I'll be able to... I don't know... hide in plain sight, I suppose, have an easier time of it anyway. Not be such a weirdo.'

'You're not listening to what I'm saying,' Dad said, and then he laughed a weird high-pitched giggle. 'What an irony. I'm talking, you're not listening. Seems your mother was right.'

'For god's sake, Dad,' I said, 'you're drunk. You're not saying anything that makes any sense.'

I got up and cleared away the plates. I reached for the third bottle but Dad grabbed it first, pouring wine into his beaker until it overflowed.

'Sit down, Ems,' he said, and after a couple of seconds he added, 'Please. Please sit down.'

First, I filled a pint glass with water and placed it in front of him, then I sat down, folded my arms and looked at him. Alcohol didn't flatter my father: his cheeks were bright red, his teeth were stained purple, dribbles of wine tracked down his chin, and bits of rice clung to his jumper. It was several days since he had last shaved or washed his hair.

But through all the dishevelment I recognised the same devastating collection of emotions in Dad that I was feeling myself.

How could I even think of leaving him?

Somehow, despite his alcoholic fug, Dad knew what I was thinking. He sat up a little straighter, swiped at his jumper, brushing rice onto the floor, and wiped his chin on the back of his hand.

'I'm only going to say this once, Ems. You must do whatever you think is right for you, and if that means working for the Community, then so be it. I'll always love you and you'll always have a home with me,' he paused, drained the rest of the wine in one swallow and continued, 'but that doesn't mean I agree with what you're doing. Your mother and the Community are not the same. You do understand what I'm saying, don't you?'

No, I didn't understand, but we were going round in circles and I just wanted Dad to stop drinking, and so I said, 'I understand.'

He nodded and reached for the bottle again, but it slipped out of his hand, caught the side of the table and smashed on the floor. Ignoring his protestations, I helped Dad to bed, left him with a large glass of water, then slowly picked up all the pieces of glass and mopped up the wine on the floor. Despite my efforts, there would be a permanent stain on the beige lino. I thought about the next people to occupy the grim little witness-protection flat and how they would look at the stain and wonder what had happened.

Dad's story is not mine to tell; all I'll say is that it took him a long time to pull himself out of the pit that Rachel had kicked him into. He almost didn't make it. My father was broken, not only by the Event and its aftermath, but also from the preceding eight years of holding our lives together. There is nothing he has ever said or done that I don't forgive him for.

Having said that, neither Dad nor I was remotely capable of making rational decisions back then. What I had said about hoping to be able to hide in plain sight in the Community was true and, to some extent, it made sense, but what didn't make sense, on any level, was how I could hate my mother so ardently on the one hand and on the other cheerfully go and work for the organisation that she herself had set up.

Now, I realise that the explanation I gave Dad was only part of it. So too was the eagerness with which I succumbed to the slick persuasion deployed by Soraya and Helen. I was looking for answers. I wanted an explanation. I wanted to find something, anything, that would make sense of what had happened.

I was searching for my mother.

25.

I left Basingstoke the next day.

I caught the train and had to change at Reading to get to Slough. Dad insisted on walking me to the station, although he looked awful and must have felt even worse. Neither of us mentioned what had happened the previous evening, but I hugged him for the longest time before I went through the ticket barriers.

'You sure about this, Ems?' he asked quietly, but not so quietly I couldn't hear the tremor in his voice.

I nodded, not trusting myself to speak.

'Just remember, you'll always have a home with me. Always. OK?'

He held me at arm's length and shook my shoulders gently until I nodded again. Then I was on the platform, then on the train, and although I'd already spent three years at university, going away had never felt like it did that day. I wanted to stay with Dad; I wanted to protect him from all the bad things. But where would that get either of us? He had to put himself back together again and so did I, and then we both had to find a way to navigate this post-Event world.

I know I walked from the station at Slough, but my first clear memory after leaving Dad at the ticket barrier in Basingstoke is finding myself standing outside Unit 15 in the middle of a light industrial estate. It looked just as you might imagine a place like that would look: constructed from large panels of grey metal, overbearing, functional, boring and identical to everything else around it. Apart from a yellow 1 and 5, there was no signage or any other indication of what was inside. I pushed a doorbell next to the small door and waited, not entirely certain that I was even in the right place.

The door opened to reveal a young woman a few years older than me – nearer thirty than twenty – wearing jeans and an oversized neon-pink hoody with a huge black *Shhhh...* logo. Her hair was twisted into a messy bun, held in place with a biro, and she was holding a clipboard. I only got as far as 'Hi, I'm Emilia' before she cut me off.

'You're Emilia Morris. Oh my god... I can't believe you're here... Oh my god... I've been dying to meet you... Come in.'

She stopped gushing long enough to stand back and let me enter before shutting the door behind me. Without daylight, the only illumination in the little reception area was a harsh overhead strip light. On first sight, there wasn't much to recommend the place: a water-dispensing machine with no water and a terracotta pot containing something that might once have been living but had been as deprived of water as the dispenser.

'You're Emilia,' she said again, pointlessly, 'and I'm Lucy, welcome to Unit 15.' I couldn't help thinking that she sounded like someone out of a bad science fiction movie. She pointed at a side room. 'Let's go in there.'

Relieved to get the weight of my rucksack off my shoulders, I dumped it on the floor and slid into one of only two chairs in the room. The walls were covered with framed magazine covers, mostly pictures of my mother. In several of them, she had been photographed in the camp, and it was weird to be surrounded by images of somewhere so familiar. I suddenly missed Mum so desperately that it took my breath away and I forced myself to turn my gaze away from the pictures and back to Lucy.

'So, you're her daughter?' she said. 'Wow. I mean... just... wow. We were told last week that you were coming.' She waved towards the pictures and then at me. 'You look like her. I can't believe it... her actual daughter...'

I had considered changing my name when I joined the Community. I could have used Dad's name – called myself Emilia Wright – but there had been so many photos of me splashed all over the media and online that I was bound to be recognised. I decided that if I tried to hide who I was, I'd just get even more attention when people figured it out. In the end it had seemed simpler just to stick with Morris, deal with it upfront and hope that the interest would fade when everyone realised how completely ordinary and un-Rachel-like I actually was.

Lucy giggled and I sincerely hoped my presence wasn't going to have this effect on everyone in Unit 15. She cleared her throat and managed to say, 'Right, I'm going to do your induction, give you a quick tour and then I'll show you where your bedroom is.'

'Where do we sleep?' I asked, expecting to have to travel to some sort of hostel.

'Oh, didn't they say? We live here.'

'In a warehouse?'

'Well, it's more than just one warehouse. Although it's just called Unit 15, this unit is linked to Units 16, 17 and 18, which is where the bedrooms are. And on the other side of the street, we've got Units 19 to 22, which are also connected. You'll see when I show you around. They're not actually like warehouses at all. None of our facilities are.'

'There are more of these places?'

'Of course,' Lucy said, and this time she giggled as if I had said something really stupid. 'Loads. I've personally only been to the ones in Coventry, Plymouth and... um...' She looked up, as if expecting to find whatever she was trying to remember written on the ceiling. 'Cardiff. That's it, Cardiff. But they're all over the place – new ones keep being opened.'

This was the first indication I had of the scale of the Community's post-Event strategy, part of which involved buying up large warehouses and converting them into live/work units. I later found out that by the time I joined in February 2012 there were already a dozen of these cavernous hubs across the UK. And it wasn't just the UK. I can't put a figure on it, but similar activities had been going on in almost every country where the Community had a foothold. Although it couldn't be clearer from Mum's notebooks that she hadn't conceived of the Event until a few months before it happened, there is no doubt that plans for ramping up the scale of Community operations had been put in place long before then.

'OK,' Lucy said, sliding a booklet across the table to me. 'First things first, this is your induction pack. And these –' she opened it to the first page '– these are our silent times.'

I was expecting to have to be silent. I had been steeling myself for it and a little part of me was even looking forward to it. Silence would mean less 'wow' and 'you're *her* daughter' and 'what was *she* like?'.

'So now we're PE,' Lucy said, but then she paused, flushing, and I guessed it had occurred to her that since I had actually been at the Event, I had no need to be reminded that we were *post*-Event.

She pressed on. 'In PE, the requirement for silence in Community camps and facilities has been relaxed in order for us to more effectively work towards achieving the Community's goals.' Lucy had obviously learned her spiel off by heart. 'However, to remind ourselves of the importance of listening, and to remember and honour the Sacrifice of Our Members' – I could practically see the capital letters – 'we're silent between 11 p.m.

and 7 a.m. Of course, that doesn't apply to the Hearing Places, where you can speak at any time that you have a designated time-slot.'

That threw me. Just the words 'Hearing Places' conjured up so many memories of my mother: all the times I'd gone to see her only to find her shut away in a Hearing Place with someone; and the image, which was so vivid that I often had to remind myself it wasn't an actual memory, of Mum sitting in a Hearing Place on the final night of her life, writing my letter.

Lucy was looking at me curiously and I managed to say, 'You've got Hearing Places here?'

'Of course,' she said. 'They've recreated the original campsite as closely as possible. We can't copy everything exactly but it's the symbolism that matters. Out the back, in one of the old loading bays, we've got a firepit, and every other day we gather out there for Silence Sessions, just like Rachel... I mean... your mother taught us.'

'It's fine, call her Rachel,' I said.

Lucy waffled on at length about mealtimes, she showed me a floorplan of Units 15 to 18 and 19 to 22, explained how to book a slot at the Hearing Places, went through the schedule of daily group activities – some of which we were encouraged to attend, such as the firepit gatherings, and others that were entirely voluntary, like the yoga classes. Unit 15 was beginning to feel like a cross between a girls' boarding school and a military training camp and at any other point in my life I would have just walked out of there. Back then, though, I had no choice but to stay, or at least that's what I had convinced myself of, and so I stayed.

Lucy stood up. It was time for my tour. Leaving my rucksack where it was, I followed her out of the room, back through the little reception area, out of the door and across the road to Unit 19, where there was an identical reception area complete with matching dead plant. Lucy led me into a gloomy corridor where the lights must have been linked to a movement sensor because they only clicked on as we walked, so it was impossible to see very far ahead.

'So, this is corridor A,' Lucy said, looking over her shoulder. 'All the corridors are numbered with letters if you see what I mean.'

I did see, but that didn't stop her pulling the induction booklet out of my hands and leafing through it until she found the floor plan. She pointed at a green line with the letter A marked at regular intervals. 'See this line?' she said.

'Yes.'

'The A means that it's corridor A,' she said, and it occurred to me that perhaps Lucy had been chosen for the induction role because of the obvious pleasure she took in obsessively regurgitating mundane information.

'Right. Got it,' I said.

She traced a blue line, one with the letter B marked on it. 'And this here,' she said. 'This is corridor B.' Her finger moved to another line, picked out in purple. 'And this one is corridor C.'

'I think I understand the numbering-by-letter system,' I said and smiled, but Lucy just frowned a little, presumably considering whether to continue through the entire alphabet. Thankfully, she decided against it, and we carried on wandering along the gloom of corridor A, lights flicking on too late to make much of a difference. I wondered if I'd somehow become stuck in a Kafka novel, doomed to endlessly roam dimly lit corridors, all numbered by letter, never arriving anywhere, with only an officious admin assistant for company, and I was beginning to seriously reconsider my decision to join the Community when Lucy finally stopped in front of a door which had the word Canteen written on it.

'Let me guess,' I said. 'Is this the canteen?'

Not even a flicker passed across her face. 'It certainly is,' she said, pushing the door open.

To my immense relief the cavernous room was flooded with daylight, which was pouring in through huge skylights in the roof. At one end were large serving stations, while the wall at the other end was covered with several oversized televisions. Between the two walls were numerous tables, most of them empty, although here and there a few women were chatting over tea and cake. They looked up when we came in, a couple of them nodded and smiled, and I got the impression that most of them recognised me, although no one actually said anything to me.

'The mealtimes are in your booklet,' Lucy said, holding out her hand, presumably so she could find the page and read them all out to me. Slowly.

'It's fine, I'll look at them later,' I said.

'If you're sure?' she said, and I nodded vigorously.

'Of course, you're free to come and go as you please and eat out, but the bus service into town is pretty poor in the evenings. The times are in your booklet.' Her hand sneaked back out, and I clutched the booklet more tightly.

'Yes, I suppose you can look them up later, too,' she said. 'Anyway, three meals a day are provided, plus snacks are available all day. All food preferences can be catered for – just tell the cooks. We do ask that you don't eat in your room – there was a problem with rats a little while ago.' She shuddered. 'They came from the pet-food wholesaler on the other side of the estate, and it took ages to get rid of them, so now we're only supposed to eat here in the canteen.'

My guided tour probably lasted less than an hour, but in my memory it feels like I trailed behind Lucy for days, watching ever more hair slip from the biro failing to hold up her bun. She was certainly thorough, I'll give her that, determined to show me everywhere and explain everything in mind-numbing detail. She pointed out the Hearing Places, which were housed in former offices in Unit 22 ('unfortunately not wooden huts like the original ones, but it's the symbolism that matters'); the loading bay firepit outside Unit 20; and the Communications Office in corridor C in Unit 21 – where I would be working – which was flanked by the Membership Office and the Legal Affairs Office. There was also a first aid room, a hairdresser, even a small shop, all of which were in corridor B in Unit 20. I would soon come to realise that the place in Slough wasn't even the largest of the Community's facilities, but at the time I was staggered by how well organised, well funded and permanent it was.

Eventually, we retraced our steps, recrossed the road and went back into Unit 15, where I picked up my rucksack and trailed behind Lucy along more gloomy corridors until we finally arrived at my bedroom, which was housed in Unit 18. The room was small with a bed, a wardrobe, mirror, desk and chair. The room was functional, which was probably the most positive thing you could say about it. For decoration, if you can call it that, there was an old *Shhhh…* poster. Black background, bright red lips with a finger pressed to them. There had always been loads of them lying around the camp and it felt strange to see it here in my new bedroom. Later that night, before I went to bed, I would rip it off the wall and shove it in a drawer, where it remained for the whole time I was at Unit 15.

After reminding me that I'd be collected from the reception area in Unit 19 at 8.30 the following morning for my induction with the communications team, Lucy finally said goodbye. My solitude lasted all of five seconds before the door reopened. Assuming she'd forgotten to tell me something, I waited for Lucy's messy bun to appear, but the head that came round the door was instead framed by an enviable afro.

'Hi. I'm your neighbour,' the young woman said, stepping into the room and waving her hand towards the right-hand wall. 'On that side. Please tell me you don't snore; these bloody walls are like cardboard and the woman who used to be in this room had sleep apnoea. Well, I assume she did because it sounded like a bloody jumbo jet was taking off in here every single night.'

'I don't snore. At least, I don't think I do.'

'Hallelujah,' my new neighbour said and stuck out her hand. 'In that case, I'm delighted to meet you.'

I shook her hand. 'Pleased to meet you too, I'm—'

'Emilia Morris,' she said, before I did.

I pulled my hand away. 'Yes. That's right.'

She slapped her palm on her forehead. 'God, I'm sorry, it must be annoying when complete strangers behave like they know you.'

'You could say that.' I heaved my rucksack onto my bed and unclipped the straps.

'I'm Casey Banza, by the way. I knew you were arriving today or tomorrow. Have you come far? I mean, I heard you had to leave Chalkham after the Trent murders.' She looked stricken. 'God. Sorry. Have I done it again? My mum always used to say that as far as I was concerned tact was just a word that came between table and tadpole.'

'Your mum? Was she…?' I left the question unspoken.

She nodded. 'Yes. Not at Chalkham, though. She burned at Abingdon. That's why I'm here, really, for Mum. I joined up before Christmas. I finished uni last year, hadn't got a job – well, not one I actually wanted to be doing – so I thought, why not do a couple of years with the Community? It'll look good on my CV and I feel like I'm doing something proactive in Mum's memory.'

I started pulling stuff out of my rucksack. 'Where did you go to uni?' I asked, more out of politeness than because I really wanted to know.

the Hear the People consultation. They've been recruiting like mad for it.'

'Is that what you're doing?' I asked.

'Nope. I'm in climate health. I did a geography degree and I want to be a meteorologist, so I figured a couple of years or so in the Climate Health Sector would be good for my CV.'

I have to admit that I only realised how much the Community was focusing on climate health after Rachel's Goals had been announced. Now I've read the notebooks I understand that Rachel believed it was vital for people to listen to the planet, not just to each other. Everything was linked, she believed, even if we didn't realise it, and that meant nothing could truly be healthy unless *everything* was healthy. Nowadays, of course, the Community is only too happy to use 'climate health' as the justification for all sorts of dubious programmes.

Pushing my empty rucksack under the bed, I picked up the booklet that Lucy had given me. 'According to this there's a Guided Silence Session at the campfire tonight,' I said.

'I don't usually bother going.' Casey clapped her hand over her mouth. 'Shit. I don't mean any disrespect to your mother, or my mother, or any of them. It's just, we're encouraged to do these things, but it can all feel a bit intense, know what I mean?'

I grinned at her. I knew exactly what she meant. 'Totally. I'm not interested in sitting round a campfire outside a warehouse. Even if it is the symbolism that matters.'

Casey grinned back at me. 'Let me guess… the scintillating Lucy showed you round? She certainly loves her symbolism. But look, I'm glad you're not annoyed – I wouldn't want to piss off the famous Emilia of Chalkham.'

I frowned, uncertain whether she was joking.

'Too soon?' she asked.

And as I stood there, it occurred to me that it really wasn't.

'Cambridge. What about you?'

'Bristol,' I said, with a sudden pang of nostalgia for my old student flat in Redland. Life had been so uncomplicated. I knew who I was and what I was doing, or at least, that's what it had felt like. I had Tom and my friends, I enjoyed my degree and, although plenty of people knew about my mother, it was no weirder for me than being the daughter of a politician, say, or an actor.

'So what sector are you going to be working in?' Casey's voice broke into my thoughts as I shoved clothes into the wardrobe. Tidiness has never been a strong point of mine, and when a blouse slid off a hanger, I left it in a heap on the floor of the wardrobe.

'Communications,' I said. 'I'm a PR assistant. I did English at uni, so I suppose they hope I'll be able to string some words together.'

'Are you going to be working on the Hear the People consultation?'

'I don't know – guess I'll find out tomorrow.'

My interview had been less of an interview and more of a chat with someone who had introduced herself as 'Alice from PR and Communications'. I had been surprised that she didn't ask me more questions about my suitability for the role, but perhaps they were never going to turn down Rachel of Chalkham's daughter.

'You're bound to be working on the consultation,' said Casey.

'What makes you say that?'

'Well, they've made such a big deal about it, haven't they? How we're going to spend twelve months asking people around the world how we can achieve Rachel's Goals.'

She did air quotes around the last two words, then pointed at a couple of posters pinned to the wall opposite my door.

Both of them were typical of the messaging that the Community favoured back then: a jarring combination of in-your-face colours and highly stylised font. The poster on the left looked brand new and on a vivid pink background in thick black letters it said *Rachel's Goals*. Underneath that were the three 'goals' which had apparently been set out by my mother for the Community immediately prior to her death. They had been publicly revealed (with great fanfare) only four days before I arrived at Slough.

Dad and I had been sitting side by side on the sofa in the Basingstoke flat watching the announcement of the goals, which was made from a field as near to the Chalkham Boar as anyone was allowed to go. It was remarkably noisy for a Community event. It had the air of a concert and in fact a female K-pop band (I forget their name) did actually knock out a couple of high-tempo songs to kick the whole thing off. Various celebrities wandered on and off the stage to have their say about how my mother's actions had 'deeply inspired' them and 'profoundly moved' them and shown them 'what true sacrifice looks like'. Community supporters around the world participated in a mass Silence Session via video link and huge screens either side of the stage cycled through pictures of crowds gathered in more than two dozen countries.

Leaders of three UK political parties took turns assuring us that not only had they 'listened' and 'heard' (cue raucous applause) Rachel of Chalkham, but that her actions were bringing about a 'transformation in the relationship between people and policy', an end to 'decades of localised political navel-gazing, as we lift our eyes and open our ears' and, rather startlingly, 'the beginning of a bold global journey where we say "all aboard at Listening Junction for the one-way train to Hearingsville"'.

That was a catchphrase that never caught on.

Eventually, as it was getting dark, 'Learn to Listen' by the Ramones was played at a volume which was ear-bleeding. As soon

as it began, Dad went into the bedroom, pulling the ⟨ behind him. I didn't know the song, so it took me a m⟨ realise that it was about how, if you didn't learn to list⟨ get burned.

Listen or burn.

You've got to give it to the organisers, it was a bold ch⟨ it was so inappropriate that it was actually funny. I'⟨ admitted this before, but I'm pretty sure that sitting there⟨ to a song about listening and burning was the first time I'd⟨ since Mum's death.

Finally, with fireworks going off and an interminab⟨ roll and videos of near-hysterical audiences around the ⟨ huge backdrop was unfurled, revealing Rachel's Goals: '*E⟨ International Conflict, Restore Climate Health, Solve Populatio⟨*

Four days later I was looking at a poster of these same ⟨ a poorly lit corridor in a converted warehouse on the o⟨ of Slough.

Next to it was a smaller flyer – in lime green – and by ⟨ I have an identical one here in front of me which I found ⟨ was searching through yet another box of belongings that ⟨ to Dad's when I left Slough. I certainly didn't save the fly⟨ any sort of sentimental reason – I appear to have used the ⟨ it to write a shopping list, although goodness knows ⟨ considered a shopping list important enough to keep. At th⟨ top, the flyer says '*Delivering Rachel's Goals*'. Underneath ⟨ says '*Plans for a Mended World*', then it sets out the step⟨ Community was planning to take to achieve the goals. Step⟨ listen to people. Step two: hear their problems. Step ⟨ understand their needs. Step four: deliver solutions.

Casey pointed at the flyer. 'They're calling steps one and⟨

Instead, it was the first time for as long as I could remember – months and months, probably – that someone had taken the piss out of me rather than treating me like a victim (which I desperately didn't want to be) or a heroine (which I absolutely wasn't) or a fragile little teacup that might shatter if it wasn't handled with absolute delicacy.

'It's only too soon if you want me to develop a very loud snoring habit,' I said, and for good measure, I picked up a pillow and threw it at her.

'Too soon?' I asked.

She laughed and her laughter was generous and infectious and I laughed, too.

'I happen to have a rather fine vintage of Tesco own-brand gin next door,' she said. 'Although, of course, if you'd prefer to sit round a symbolic campfire…'

As I followed Casey out of the room, I realised that although I wasn't feeling happy, exactly, I was definitely feeling that I had made the right decision by joining the Community. And if nothing else, I was looking forward to a large gin.

26.

In their ground-breaking and controversial study *Community, Cult, Culture* (Global Press, 2018), Dr Sara Lenz and Professor Melanie Overbury explore how pre-Event symbolism came to assume a ritual significance to the post-Event Community.

For example, by mid-2012 onwards every new Member joining the Community was assigned a Shelly by L&H (the Listening and Hearing Sector). Shelly was not a large rubber ear, but a real pair of ears attached to a human mentor. For the first three months of membership, the new Member was able to talk to their designated Shelly, who would listen without judgement. Thereafter, Members could speak to one of a large pool of Shellys (called Camp Shellys) who were available for listening to anyone. After twelve months of membership, Members were eligible to apply to L&H to become Shellys themselves.

Lenz (a neuroscientist) and Overbury (a social anthropologist) interviewed a number of ex-Members (including two anonymous ex-sector-heads) and demonstrated how a powerful combination of neurological and cultural factors generated an effect among Members which Lenz and Overbury labelled the 'Dopamine Dream'. Being part of the Community made people genuinely feel good about themselves – just by becoming a Member you were doing something positive to make the world a better place.

The Community reinforced the Dopamine Dream over and over again through multiple channels: in e-newsletters delivered weekly to millions of mailboxes, splashed across adverts in magazines and on billboards and television, and on the shirts of the multiple sports teams they sponsored. By 2013, it was virtually impossible to go anywhere without seeing someone wearing a T-shirt or baseball cap emblazoned with *I'm listening. Are YOU?* The original lips and finger logo (already considered 'retro' by then) was printed on banners hanging from their buildings and the fences which surrounded the construction sites of their new Conflict Resolution Academies and on the flags planted in the ground in front of booths at conferences and festivals around the world.

Everywhere, all the time, Members were encouraged to feel morally superior to non-Members – *if you're not with us, you're against us* – and Lenz and Overbury's research revealed that after only two months of membership, 84 per cent of new Members instinctively felt that Members were 'more trustworthy' than non-Members, and after six months a staggering 67 per cent said that they felt 'as close or closer to other Members than their own families'.

The 'membership for all' question came to a head in early 2013 – although, as I've previously mentioned, the debate about opening the Community to men started well before the Event. Anecdotal evidence suggests that between 250 and 1,200 men around the world burned themselves to death on 31 October 2011 in solidarity (or possibly suicide pacts) with their partners. These men have never been included in the official headcount, nor are their names mentioned in the 'Celebration of Silence' held on each anniversary of the Event. Most commentators agree that the decision to permit men to become Members was inevitable (how could the Community promote listening for all, if they only heard half the population?), and in the first fifty days following the adoption of universal membership in April 2013, unofficial figures indicated a 15 per cent rise in global membership and a 25 per cent rise in donations as men (often *rich* men) rushed to show their support.

Lenz and Overbury devote an entire chapter to the decision to allow men to become Members, concluding that while the Community began as a genuinely benign movement, transitioning into a cult around two years before Rachel's death, the shift from cult to culture coincided with the opening of membership to all.

Inclusivity may have swelled membership numbers and enriched the coffers, but at the time of writing, the current board is entirely composed of women, all but two of the sector heads are women, and the majority of Members are still female. I don't know how they did it, but the Community appears to have achieved the best of all worlds.

Whether you consider it a cult or a culture, there is no doubt that the Community was a club, and one which huge numbers of people wanted to join. Humanity, it seemed, was looking for a new direction and believed the Community would provide it. In the post-Event aftermath, millions of people flocked to join, adding their voices to the demands that their politicians, their armies and their enemies stop talking and start listening.

In many ways I was no different; although, of course, I had my own unique reasons for joining. When I started working for the Community in 2012 I got everything I'd hoped for: employment, a home, companionship, plus the space and time to begin to heal. I kept my head down, worked hard and few demands were made of me. Casey and I quickly became good friends, and I visited Livy and Dad as often as work would allow.

The Community cannot have been as happy with its side of the bargain. When I joined, I wasn't really in any state to question what the Community wanted from me, and it took a few weeks for me to understand that they were hoping to mould me into a proxy for my mother. No one wanted me to lead the Community, of course; preferring instead to wheel me out at events as a flesh and blood link (the *only* flesh and blood link) to their precious Rachel of Chalkham. Unfortunately for them, I wanted none of it, and after the third occasion when I was persuaded to take a day away from my job in PR only to spend hours hanging around the Albert Hall in London in order to stand at the back of the stage during a long Guided Silence Session, I made it absolutely clear that I would not be doing it again.

They kept asking and I kept refusing until they accepted that they would not be able to persuade me to represent my mother in this way. At that point, I assume I was allowed to remain a Member because they preferred the idea of me being unco-operative inside the Community, rather than uncooperative outside the Community.

After working at the unit in Slough for twenty months, mainly on the Hear the People consultation, I was promoted to a new role as a National Communications Manager and my life changed again. At the time, I didn't question why I was being sent abroad to set up a programme providing free contraceptives, but looking back now I have no doubt that I was promoted into a role they were relatively confident I could perform, but where I would be tucked away, out of sight and out of trouble.

I didn't think twice about accepting the job. Slough was great, but it was... Slough. Going abroad would be an adventure, a chance to get far away from everything that had happened while, at the same time, perhaps, allowing me to see Rachel's legacy for myself. We had listened to people. We had heard them. We were delivering solutions. Maybe my mother might even have been proud of me.

Before I arrived in the Democratic Republic of the Congo, I

had only ever spent time in Chalkham, Bristol and Slough. Goma City could not have been more of a contrast: with a population of one million, it is sandwiched between Mount Nyiragongo and Lake Kivu, a body of water so vast that when you stand on its shore you could be looking across an ocean. Nyiragongo is an active volcano, its most recent eruption having been in 2002 – only eleven years before I arrived – when the lava flow which covered 13 per cent of the city was so deep that all that remained of many two-storey buildings was just the top storey. I was warned before I left Slough that the volcano could blow again at any time (as indeed it did in May 2021, when more than a thousand homes were destroyed and thirty-two people lost their lives).

In the city itself, poverty, filth, disease and malnutrition were everywhere, and less than a year before I arrived, rebel fighters had taken temporary control of Goma before being ousted. Everywhere I went there were men armed with machine guns and bullets slung across their chests, most of them so young that I was sure they should have been in school. Something else I was warned about before I left Slough was that if I wanted to photograph anything in DRC I had to obtain a photography permit, and even if I had a permit, I must never try to photograph anyone armed with a gun. I never did.

Not long after I arrived, one of the local Members took me to see the border crossing with the Rwandan town of Gisenyi. By European standards Rwanda was poor but DRC was so much worse. On the Rwandan side, the buildings had roofs that stood a fighting chance of keeping the rain out, but on the Congo side, there were rarely four walls, let alone a watertight roof. On the Rwandan side there was a proper tarmac road, but in Congo there was just mud.

Every day hundreds of Congolese people queued up to cross

the border. Because there were so many of them it could take a couple of hours to get from one side to the other, even though essentially they were just walking past a sign. Once they were inside Rwanda, many of them just squatted down right there in the road only a few metres from the border with piles of manioc, bananas, kola nuts and something that looked like burnt fingers which I later realised were caterpillars – a local staple. They laid out the food in neat piles on scraps of cloth to try and tempt people who were marginally less desperate than themselves, and at the end of the day they traipsed back into Congo to sleep and to look for more things to sell.

I found all of this galvanising, just as I was supposed to. *This* was why I was here. I could help these people. What the women of Congo had told the Community they wanted was effective contraception and I was here to provide it. Back then, as far as I was concerned, it was really that simple. Arrogance or ignorance? Maybe both.

Our compound was a forty-minute drive from Goma airport, depending on quite how gridlocked the traffic was. It was surrounded by a black wall made of volcanic rock and armed guards were stationed by a barrier. Every time a vehicle arrived the guards would use angled mirrors on long handles (like huge dentists' mirrors) to inspect the underneath of the vehicle's chassis before raising the barrier.

Within the perimeter, three houses were constructed entirely of concrete inside and out – it was a brutalist architect's dream – and like all non-Congolese Members, I had my own room. During the three years I was there, as many as two dozen Members might be staying in the compound at any one time, although generally there weren't as many as that. As in Slough, we shared bathrooms, which included two flushing toilets. I mention this because I quickly became obsessed with the toilets (or lack thereof) in Congo. In my defence, I can still smell the putrid long-drops all these years later.

What made the whole 'bathroom' experience even worse was that it was acceptable for men to nip behind a bush in the lovely fresh air, but if I tried to do the same thing someone – usually a man – wearing a suitably appalled expression would shepherd me towards the nearest shack where not only would the nauseating smell rising from the putrid hole-in-the-ground literally stick to my clothes, but I had to contend with my near-phobic fear of the mutantly gigantic flies buzzing around in their millions. I am not exaggerating when I say that if it wasn't for flushing toilets in our compound, I would probably have flown home within the first month.

Behind our houses were smaller wooden buildings with corrugated iron roofs, which is where the Congolese guards and drivers and cooks slept (most of whom, although employed by the Community, were not Members). From the outset, I hated people doing things for me that I could do for myself: cooking, cleaning, driving – there were even women who took away my dirty clothes every evening and returned them washed, ironed and folded the following morning. Early on when I suggested to a local Member that I should do my own laundry, she jabbed her thumb at several people in the compound, saying, 'How will they eat if they don't work? How will their children eat?' It was my 'duty as a foreigner', she informed me, to give work to as many local people as possible.

The din from the road was our constant companion, and as far as I could tell it was mandatory for drivers in Goma to lean heavily on the car horn every twenty metres or so. Likewise, it appeared to be forbidden for those of us inside the compound to actually stand beside anyone we wanted to speak to – instead, everyone preferred to bellow from building to building. Music blared from competing sound systems, unless there was a power cut, in which case the generator kicked in, drowning out everything else. Only when the generator itself failed was there anything approaching silence. In an email that I sent Dad a couple of weeks after I arrived, I wrote, 'You'd hate the noise here but I love it. I mean, I really love it. I like how it makes me feel anonymous. Like I'm just a tiny cog in an enormous wheel, and as long as I keep on turning, nobody has any reason to pay me the slightest bit of attention. I like that.'

Most of my emails to Dad and Livy were written in the early evening, which meant they generally ended with a reference to Alain and his drumming. By day, Alain was one of our drivers, but every evening, while the rest of us ate, he would play the drums. I never did work out if there was a connection between drumming and eating, but once I got to know Alain, I decided it was probably just that he enjoyed having a captive audience. I still love the sound of Congolese drums, but they always make me feel hungry!

I was considerably less enamoured with the humidity – it was impossible to ever get completely dry, and within seconds of having a shower, I would be covered in a thin sheen of sweat. However, I would have taken the humidity over the mosquitoes any day. Mosquitoes were the second worst thing about living in Congo (after the toilets!) and a significant proportion of my emails were devoted to my hatred for the tiny, deadly bastards that lay in wait hoping to stab me with their evil little proboscises.

When I found out the Community was sending me to Congo, the first person I told was Casey. Her job in the Climate Sector mainly involved putting together spreadsheets of soil-sample data, and the furthest she had travelled for work was to the Met Office's Hadley Centre in Exeter. At some point she had decided that she no longer wanted to be a meteorologist, and when she heard where I was going, she set about persuading the powers that be that she too should be sent to DRC. As Casey has proved over and over again in the years since then, if she puts her mind to something, she generally succeeds, and when I flew to Goma from Heathrow (via Schiphol in the Netherlands and Entebbe in Uganda), Casey Banza, newly appointed Infrastructure Manager, was sitting right alongside me.

Until we left Slough, Casey was just about the most upbeat and positive person I knew, the first to joke around and always up for a laugh, even though she, too, had lost her mother in the Event. If I had to choose a word to describe her attitude towards the Community at that time, I suppose I'd say 'irreverent'. Other than Livy, Casey was my closest friend, but almost as soon as the wheels of our plane touched down at Goma International Airport, things between us began to change.

One of her roles was to organise the weekly Firepit Gathering which, although not mandatory, all Members were encouraged to attend. There was a template for how these things were conducted so that anyone could go along to a gathering wherever they were in the world and it would feel familiar. Ideally, we were supposed to sit or lie near an actual firepit to remind us all that the Community started around a firepit in Chalkham (as if I could ever forget), but if a firepit wasn't feasible, there were permitted replacements such as a tree, to 'represent the attendance of the planet itself' at the gathering, or an empty chair, to 'represent Members who were absent' because of 'their great sacrifice'.

Each gathering started with a Silence Session (of course), followed by Listen and Hear, where the group would listen to what anyone wanted to say. There was no obligation to speak, just an expectation that those present would listen to and hear whatever may be said. I rarely spoke at L&H, but from the beginning Casey was surprisingly vocal, going on about how we weren't doing enough and how more needed to be done to honour those who had burned. Afterwards, when we were alone, I would ask her what 'more' she thought we should be doing, but she would just say that I couldn't understand, that I would never understand, because *you're Rachel's daughter.*

Like me, so many people lost their mothers in the Event, but it wasn't until I moved to Unit 15 that I realised just how many new Members were joining the Community because their mothers and sisters, their aunts and friends, had burned. Rather than turning away from the Community in the face of so much death, countless people turned towards it, perhaps needing to make sure the sacrifices of their loved ones weren't in vain. But while everyone else was free to grieve their dead however they wished, I was (and still am) set apart by virtue of being my mother's daughter.

The Community was so focused on behaving as if Rachel of Chalkham was still with us, guiding all our actions, that most of the time my mother was as much of a presence in my life – more so, in some ways – as when she was alive. Even in the Democratic Republic of the Congo, it was impossible to get away from her and often it was as if she had never died. Sometimes, I would fantasise that she had been killed in a car crash or succumbed to terminal cancer when I was a child. Something that would have been shattering for me at the time but would mean that memories of my mother were confined to me, Dad and a few others, rather than belonging to everyone.

Casey knew how much I hated being treated differently because of my mother, and before we arrived in DRC she had been scrupulous about not falling into that trap. It was one of the first things that had drawn me to her. But once we were in Goma, it felt as though in Casey's mind, I – her friend, confidante and next-door-room-mate – had been replaced by someone who was, first and foremost, Rachel of Chalkham's daughter.

I found this really upsetting, but I was so busy with work that in the beginning I tried to ignore the changes in Casey's behaviour.

Because I lived and breathed the implant programme for more than three years, it's easy to forget that not everyone is as familiar with it as I am, but when the Community carried out its consultation, women in many countries (including DRC) spoke about the oppressive expectation placed on them to bear as many children as possible. The Community listened, and one of its earliest multinational initiatives was a programme offering free contraceptive implants which would remain effective for seven years. This was intended to improve women's health, career opportunities, financial independence and chance to escape poverty (or so I was told at the time).

It seems extraordinary now, but when I arrived in Congo the sum total of my qualifications for the role was two years' experience in the Slough PR & Comms team, a spreadsheet full of statistics such as 'only 7.8 per cent of women in DRC use contraception' and 'less than 1 per cent use the pill', and a well-thumbed copy of what was then and still remains one of my favourite books of all time – Barbara Kingsolver's *The Poisonwood Bible*, which is set in Congo around the time of its independence from Belgium in 1960.

I may have been completely underqualified but I was committed, organised, focused and, even though I say so myself, incredibly hard-working, as evidenced by the copious emails that I sent to my (London-based) manager, Laura Williams. Within weeks of arriving I had organised workshops and induction sessions with local Members, had begun the process of recruiting nurses and health-care assistants and visited the site of proposed clinics. Our first clinic was in Goma itself, but within weeks we opened two more (in Bukavu and Mpala) and thereafter searched for sites the length of both Lake Kivu and Lake Tanganyika (with a preference for premises already used as part-time medical centres or ophthalmology clinics). I also began a never-ending battle to persuade the Chef des Douanes (head of customs) at Goma airport to release the many shipments sent to Congo by the Community.

I was given a budget by head office and worked with local Members to put together what we euphemistically called an 'incentive': every woman who had a seven-year implant would receive a Community-branded tote bag containing a $5 pay-as-you-go phone voucher, a sack of rice, a bag of assorted seeds, water purification tablets and a Community-branded water bottle. I am well aware that commentators outside the Community have long referred to this incentive as a bribe, and all I can say is that I honestly didn't see it that way back then.

Of course, the main challenge was convincing the women to come to the clinics, and I suppose that was where I could bring my whole two years of experience in communications to bear as I self-importantly reported back to Laura how we were targeting existing health facilities, marketplaces, water-pump stations and other gathering areas. In one email, I included an image of a poster that I was intending to use in the campaigns. It depicted two families. The family on the left consisted of two parents and five children standing beside a traditional mud and stick house with glassless windows and a dilapidated palm-frond roof. By contrast, the family on the right consisted of two parents and one child and they were standing beside a concrete house with gleaming glass windows. The father in the second picture was resting his hand on the bonnet of a small car.

I conceived of the idea, approved the photography and authorised the use of that poster. I didn't question what I was doing. It felt right. More than that, it felt important.

27.

Unfortunately, we had to replace our first translator within only a few days of her starting work when we became aware that she was handing out religious 'tracts' covered in Bible quotes about a woman's duty to 'go forth and multiply'. She was specifically targeting Congolese Members, telling them that the implants were against God and anyone helping us could look forward to spending eternity in hell. By the time we found out what she was doing, three of our team had already resigned.

In her place, we recruited a young woman with the wonderful name of Scholar Mbuya. Scholar was from Muhongo, a small town about 140 kilometres from Goma on the edge of the Kahuzi-Biéga National Park. She and I worked together to localise training and PR material for the programme and Scholar's English was excellent, thankfully, since I had arrived in Congo with rusty GCSE French and non-existent Swahili. At first, I found the number of different languages spoken in DRC absolutely baffling. Everyone spoke French, and in the regions I covered, most people also spoke Swahili, but additionally I would frequently hear what I would come to recognise as Lingala and also, to a lesser extent, Kikongo. There were others, too, although I never learned to distinguish them from each other. English was most definitely a minority language, and little of it was spoken outside the compound.

Scholar was a few months younger than me and by contrast to

the sweating, soggy mess that I generally was, she had flawless skin and cheekbones to die for, usually topped by a vividly colourful purple, green and orange head wrap. When she first joined us I was a little in awe of her because before moving to Goma she had been a ranger protecting mountain gorillas in the Virunga National Park. It sounded like a fabulous job until she told me about her youngest brother, also a ranger, who had been killed by poachers the previous year when they had shot him in the back and left him to bleed to death in the forest. By the time his body was found, several animals had already got to him. Her brother had been the eleventh ranger killed by poachers in Virunga that year. Her next oldest brother (Scholar was one of nine children) was also a ranger, but she had given in to her mother's pleas for her to move to the city and get a safer job.

When Scholar started working with us it was still possible to be employed by the Community without formally joining it (these employees were called 'Adjunct Members', a term which was later dropped when the policy changed to require all employees working on the delivery of policy initiatives to be full Members). Scholar was an Adjunct Member. She had heard of Rachel of Chalkham and the Community (who hadn't by then?) but it was refreshing to realise that she had little interest in either of them. When we got to know each other better, Scholar told me she had applied for the job for three reasons: she had promised her mother she would stop being a ranger, she wanted to improve her (already excellent!) English, and when her twenty-five-year-old sister announced she was pregnant for the fourth time Scholar decided she wanted to help make contraception available to women in her country.

I loved going on site visits with Scholar because she would chat virtually non-stop about whatever caught her eye. Thanks to her, I now consider myself something of an expert on both the life cycle of the plantain, which grows in vast plantations all over the region, and the ubiquitous charcoal ovens which, although vital for making fuel, litter the landscape, belching out dirty, polluting fumes. Scholar had a real talent for identifying any bird that flashed past, no matter how fleeting the glimpse, and she would frequently interrupt herself to call out 'lilac-breasted roller' or 'namaqua dove' or 'white-backed vulture'. It occurred to me, shamefully, that had we been driving through England instead of Congo, I would not have been a fraction as knowledgeable about my own country and its wildlife.

Every now and then, Scholar would ask me about Rachel. She became genuinely interested in learning more about the Community, and perhaps because she was so generous in sharing her own knowledge with me, I didn't mind Scholar's questions in the way I did when other people wanted to talk to me about my mother. Having said that, our conversations often went round in circles because she frequently asked the same things, unable to make sense of my confused answers, which was hardly surprising since I couldn't make any sense of them myself.

'You joined the Community because of your mum?'

'No. Although, if she hadn't died, I wouldn't have joined.'

'So you joined because she died?'

'No, not really.'

'To remember her better?'

'No, not that.'

'So why *did* you join?'

'It's complicated.'

As my first Christmas in DRC approached, most of the Members in the compound decided they would spend the day at an extended Firepit Gathering which Casey was organising. Thankfully, I had another offer, because Scholar had kindly asked me if I would like to spend Christmas with her family. I jumped at the chance, although I was a little daunted by the idea of meeting Scholar's mum and all her brothers and sisters, mainly because at that point my French was still poor and my Swahili practically non-existent. I knew *Krismasi njema*, though, which is 'Happy Christmas' in Swahili, and hoped to stumble my way through everything else as best I could.

Scholar's brother Fortuné arrived at the compound in an old jeep to collect us and Scholar was insistent that I take the front seat next to him. I assumed she was being polite until I realised that the passenger door was only kept shut by an arrangement of frayed bungee cords tied to the gear stick, and that the back seat would almost certainly have been the safer option.

Fortuné drove like a maniac; he shared Scholar's ability to identify a spotted redshank, say, or the lesser sand-plover at one hundred paces, even while driving; and he was the most handsome man I had ever seen.

Scholar and Fortuné's whole family, and in particular their mother, Andréa, was so kind to me that first Christmas – as soon as we arrived I was absorbed into a cheerfully boisterous mass of family and friends. (Later, after we returned to Goma, Scholar told me that many of their neighbours had popped by because they were curious to see the white foreigner she had brought home for Christmas.) Although I understood barely anything that anyone said to me, everyone seemed friendly, and my face muscles ached from all the smiling I was doing.

Almost from the moment we got there, Andréa plied us with food. There was *fufu*, of course – a staple food in DRC, which requires a herculean effort to pound manioc into a puree – spiced with a tomato and fiery *pili-pili* pepper sauce. There was also a delicious okra soup, a ferociously hot bean stew and deep-fried dough balls the size of my fist. But that was not all. Andréa's oldest son had brought a goat. Thankfully, by the time we arrived it had been killed and prepared and was already being roasted. During my time in Slough, I'd become a vegetarian, but that Christmas was one of many times in Congo when I ate meat so as not to be rude and, I have to say, the poor roasted goat tasted wonderful.

It was the first time Scholar had been home since starting work in Goma, and as we sat in the sunshine, eating and drinking, her family continually talked over one another, no one ever letting anyone else finish a sentence. Fortuné stayed close beside me, translating bits and pieces of the conversation.

'Your English is really good,' I said, then immediately worried he might think I was being patronising, but he just said, 'Thank you. I work as a ranger, but sometimes also as a guide. As a guide it is good to speak English.' He nodded towards his sister, who was still in full flow. 'Scholar's English is better than mine. It is her dream to visit America.'

'What about you?' I asked. 'Where would you like to go?'

Before he could answer, a football flew over my head and thumped into Fortuné's shoulder. Behind us a young boy was laughing. He must only have been eight or nine, and he was dwarfed by a Manchester United shirt that came almost to his knees; when he turned to run away I saw '11' and 'Giggs' on the back. Beside me, Fortuné had got to his feet.

'Albert,' he called, scooping up the ball and holding it under his arm. 'Arrêtez-là.'

The boy stopped. 'Je suis désolé, Fortuné.'

'Viens ici, Albert.'

As the boy trotted towards us, Fortuné said to me, 'Albert is my oldest brother's youngest son.'

When he reached us, the boy smiled hopefully and said, 'Vas-tu jouer au football avec moi?'

Fortuné looked down at me. 'You play football?' he asked.

I hadn't kicked a ball since I was about five years old, playing with Dad in the beer garden, but when Fortuné held out his hand, I let him pull me to my feet. 'Of course.'

Within minutes the two of us, Albert and his four brothers and sisters, and several other children of varying ages who had appeared – as if summoned by a referee's whistle – were involved in a chaotic, dusty, fast-paced game right there on the road. When cars approached, the match moved fractionally towards one side, leaving just enough room for the vehicle to speed past. I wasn't sure who was on my team, the kids found it hilarious on the rare occasion I managed to actually kick the ball, and they screamed with laughter when I missed an open goal. I was running out of steam when the ball landed at my feet for the final time but I somehow managed to pass it to Albert, who ran the length of the makeshift pitch and slotted the ball past his older brother. Little Albert threw himself onto his knees, flung his head back, pointed over his shoulders with both thumbs at the name on the back of his shirt, then thumped his own chest, yelling, 'Geeg-sy, Geeg-sy.'

That night, wrapped in my sleeping bag with its fancy in-built mosquito net, listening to Scholar's family settling down around me, it struck me that this was perhaps the first time I had really been able to imagine what it might have been like to have had a different childhood to my own, one with a noisy, loving, hectic family. It wasn't something I had ever experienced, and neither had anyone I'd ever been close to. There was Tom and his poor bereaved alcoholic mum, and Livy's mother who spent our entire childhood mired in bitterness towards her ex-husband, and then there was me. The girl with the father who worked to the point of constant exhaustion and the mother who lived silently at the bottom of the garden. Not exactly a recipe for happy families.

The next morning – Christmas Day – Andréa, most of her

children and their neighbours, dressed in their colourful *pagnes* – wax print fabrics – joined a festive procession snaking towards their local church, Our Lady of Seven Sorrows. Scholar, Fortuné and I declined to join them, a decision that caused Andréa to shake her head vigorously and suck her teeth in the direction of her two recalcitrant children. Scholar went to visit a friend of hers who had just had a baby, which left Fortuné and me alone. When he asked if I'd like to go for a walk I didn't hesitate.

As we walked along a rutted clay path running behind their home, I said, 'Maybe we should have gone to church. Your mother obviously wanted us to.'

'It is difficult,' Fortuné said. 'Scholar and I don't want to upset our mother, but we do not believe in what the Church says.'

'Neither do I,' I said. 'But I wouldn't have minded going if it made Andréa happy.'

'The Church will have much to say about your work here. Contraception. The Church will not like that.'

I laughed. 'Someone already gave out leaflets condemning us all to hell.'

Fortuné did not join in with my laughter. 'Many people do not think it is the right thing.'

'What do you think?'

'Things must change, but what you are doing is difficult.'

'I'm not sure any of us think it will be easy, but it's going well so far. We've already recruited a few nurses, and they're training health-care assistants to administer the implants, plus we've already found several clinics.'

'The problem is not the nurses or the clinics.'

'So, what *is* the problem?' I asked, somewhat sulkily. All this gloom and negativity was a bit depressing. Where was the cheerful football-playing Fortuné from yesterday?

'I mean the way people think in our country. It is complicated.

It is not just about giving contraception to women. Scholar knows this, but she won't listen.' Then he did laugh. 'I don't think your mother Rachel would be happy with Scholar.' He pronounced my mother's name with a soft *ch* – Ra-*shell*.

The path, which had been getting steadily narrower, was now heading straight for a forest. Although Muhongo was right on the edge of the Kahuzi-Biéga National Park, I wasn't yet used to how, outside of the permanence of cities, settlements felt fragile and temporary, as if only a brief moment of inattention is all it would take for them to be overrun by the forests that surrounded them.

At that point, I hadn't been into a forest in Congo. I'd seen plenty of them from the window of a jeep, but most of the places I'd visited up until then were dotted along the shores of either Lake Kivu or Lake Tanganyika.

'Wait a minute,' I said, stopping to pull my socks up and over my trousers, stretching them tight so they almost reached my knees. Fortuné laughed.

'What?' I said, defensively. 'I've been told about all the horrible things that could bite me. Mosquitoes are bad enough, but I don't want army ants marching up inside my trouser leg, or a button spider snacking on my calf, or hookworms making their way to my intestines, thank you very much.'

'OK,' he said. 'But I'm not sure socks will protect you from adders.'

I very nearly turned around at that point, but then Fortuné smiled and all thoughts of snakes left my mind.

The forest air tasted damp and earthy, fertile somehow. There wasn't a path as such but Fortuné seemed to know where he was going, and our feet crunched through bark, dried twigs and dead leaves. He touched trees as we passed, naming them for me, and his words sounded like an incantation: mahogany, sapele, ebony, limba, wenge, iroko. After a few minutes I began to recognise the dark ridged trunk of the ebony tree, the paler smoother iroko and the slim elegance of the sapele. We must have walked for no more than fifteen minutes before Fortuné stopped in what I suppose could be described as a clearing, although really it was just a patch of scrub.

For a moment we stared at each other. Goodness knows what Fortuné made of the overheated mess facing him, but he looked beautiful, like he'd been sculpted from the heartwood of one of the ebony trees we had passed.

He gestured to the ground. 'Will you sit for a minute?' he said.

'But the ants... the snakes...'

'You will be safe, I promise.'

When I think about it now, I realise there was never a time when I didn't trust Fortuné, even when he suggested that I sit in a forest full of creatures that would have loved nothing more than to feast on my sweaty skin. I made sure my socks were still pulled up to my knees, and then I sat.

'Close your eyes,' he said.

'What? No... I...'

'Please. Close your eyes,' he said, and again there was that smile.

Then, 'Listen,' he said. Nothing else. Just... listen. So I closed my eyes and I listened.

At first, I heard nothing... no voices, no traffic, nothing. My hatred of silence began to uncurl itself and I put my hands on my stomach to push it back. I forced myself to listen, properly listen, and gradually layers of sound began to emerge. Cicadas buzzing. Mosquitoes whining around my head. Turacos, beautiful birds to look at that, to me at least, sounded like asthmatic old men wheezing over their cigars. A red-faced woodland warbler trilling somewhere above me. Then... was it...? Again, in the distance... there. An elephant trumpeting.

I felt dizzy, like I was spinning away from myself, and without opening my eyes, I pushed my palms flat against the ground and felt the earth beating, pulsing through my skin, throbbing up my arms and into my chest where my heart matched the beat. Our heartbeats – mine and the forest's – were the same.

I have no idea how long I sat there, listening to the forest and to myself. All I know is that when I opened my eyes, Fortuné was sitting on the other side of the clearing, his smile wide and generous, and I understood that he was sharing something precious.

He handed me a bottle of water and waited until I'd drunk my fill before he asked, 'What did you hear?'

My eyes filled with tears and I swallowed hard a couple of times before I said, 'Everything. I heard everything.'

'Did you hear yourself?'

I nodded.

Fortuné reached for the water and tipped his head back. I wanted to reach out and touch his throat, rest my fingers on the vein pulsing in his neck, slide my hands up to stroke his face. But I stayed where I was. He put the cap back on the bottle.

'I have come here since I was a boy,' he said. 'At my home there were so many people always talking. I came here to listen to this,' he threw one arm out wide, 'but also to this.' He tapped his temple. 'I believe when you listen to the forest, you also hear yourself.'

Before that day, I'm sure I would have dismissed that sort of thing as hippy nonsense, but with my fingertips still pulsing from the beat of the earth, it was as if cogs that had long been disconnected inside me suddenly clicked together and slowly began to move.

'I think, maybe,' I said, hesitantly, feeling my way cautiously towards what I wanted to say, 'this is what my mother meant. That if we listen, properly listen, so we hear everything and if we keep listening then, in the end, we can hear ourselves, too. Does that make sense?'

Fortuné nodded. 'Your mother was wise.'

'Maybe she was,' I said uncertainly.

Fortuné stood. 'Rain is coming,' he said, holding out his hand.

I let him help me to my feet, and as we walked out of the clearing, it felt like my steps were lighter and I was standing taller. For as long as I could remember, carrying my mother around with me had been an actual physical burden: my back ached almost continually, my neck was stiff, my shoulders were sore. Since arriving in Congo it had become worse, although that was probably because of what Alain the driver called the 'Congo-shake', as we bounced around inside vehicles with no suspension over potholes the size of small ponds. The Congo-shake may have made my aching back worse but I never doubted the cause.

But there in the forest, with Fortuné, I glimpsed the possibility of a future free from the burden of Rachel. Maybe I didn't have to always lug my past around with me. I was a part of the world and the world was part of me and maybe I didn't have to bear my burden alone.

Of course, it wasn't as simple as that. I couldn't just shuck off the weight of my mother in one go. But I could begin to lay it down, piece by tiny piece.

I am still in the process of doing that; this book is part of that process.

28.

The tranquillity I had found in the forest lasted for precisely as long as it took me to go down with a bout of what Casey and I called the 'Goma-trots'. To be fair to the cooks in our compound (headed up by the marvellous Mama Em, of whom more later) we never once got the Goma-trots from their food – it almost always followed a visit to a remote village alongside Lake Tanganyika where we would be served bushmeat, a catch-all term for any dead animal that would fit in a cooking pot.

I spent the first three days of 2014 running between my bedroom and the bathroom (the flushing toilet *really* came into its own then), and when I finally emerged several pounds lighter and with a craving for Jacob's Cream Crackers that almost drove me onto the first plane back to the UK, I was greeted by the news that Fortuné had applied for a job as a guard at the compound. When Scholar told me this, she raised her eyebrows in a way that I assumed was supposed to be meaningful.

Spending a few days apart over Christmas hadn't helped things between Casey and me – we were bickering frequently, which was horrible, particularly because the arguments were petty, resolved nothing and almost always degenerated into a stand-off about our mothers.

So many times, Casey would say, 'My mum died in the Event too, you know...' and I would inevitably reply, 'I *know* she did...'

'Because it seems like you think everything is about *your* mother,' she'd say.

This was really unfair because I had never once suggested that everyone else who died was somehow less important than Rachel. Other people may believe that, but I don't.

However, rather than just leaving it alone, I'd usually be stung into replying, saying something like, 'You *know* I don't think everything's about Mum.'

'I'm just telling you how I feel,' Casey would say, and idiot that I was, I would take the bait.

'I hardly ever even mention my mother.'

'That's not the point.'

'Well, what is the point?' I'd ask.

'The Community wouldn't exist without Rachel,' Casey would say. 'She started all of this. She's bloody amazing, but the *point* is that it's *your* mother that everyone remembers, whereas *my* mum is just one of the anonymous twenty-one thousand.'

'*All* their deaths were important, Casey.'

'Really? I joined the Community to make sure my mum's death *meant* something. But what are we doing? Doling out contraceptives.'

'What's wrong with that?' I would say. 'We're helping women live better lives.'

'It's not enough. There's got to be more.'

'More what?' I'd ask, genuinely perplexed.

'I don't know, but there's got to be something that'll make everyone else's sacrifice as meaningful as Rachel of Chalkham's. Otherwise, what was the point of them dying? What was the point of my mother leaving me? Did she do it just so I could set up clinics to hand out contraceptives? I don't think so. I'd rather have my mother back, thank you very much.'

It is only now that I can see how living in Goma gave Casey

the distance she needed to begin to come to terms with losing her mother. Casey had joined the Community within weeks of the Event. She convinced herself (and me, when I arrived at Unit 15) that she was doing it for the work experience, to build her CV, but once we were in DRC it quickly became obvious that that wasn't the reason. Like Casey, so many people joined the Community because they were grieving for their mothers and sisters and aunts and friends, and were desperate to find meaning and purpose in their deaths. It has taken most people a very long time – in some cases years – to find any measure of peace about what happened on 31 October 2011. Plenty of others are still searching for a way to make sense of the Event and, tragically, for a minority, suicide has been their only relief.

Casey's own search for meaning and purpose in her mother's death has taken her very far away from me, and in the noise of our bickering in Goma, I heard the sound of our friendship fracturing.

Every month I had to compile a progress report which I emailed to my boss, Laura, and by the time of March 2014's report, I was proudly announcing that we had successfully completed preliminary certification of seven clinics: two in North Kivu, three in South Kivu, and one each in Maniema and Katanga. When fully operational, each clinic was expected to employ a minimum of ten health-care assistants (HCAs) with the capability of administering implants to six women an hour, seven hours a day, six days a week. At maximum capacity, we expected to be able to administer a total of 2,520 implants per clinic per week.

In my emails and phone calls to Dad, I avoided telling him about anything that might worry him. For example, I never told him about the young men patrolling the streets of Goma armed with sub-machine guns. In the end I got used to the sight of them; they faded into the background, like furniture. I didn't tell him about the checkpoints that popped up overnight between our compound and the clinics and how I never went anywhere without a copy of both my passport's identification page and the page with my entry visas. I carried authorisation letters from the Community and from the Congo government, stamped and stamped and stamped again until no one could possibly read the faded type underneath. I had papers from the police – the PNC – for not only Goma and North Kivu (the province that Goma is in) but also for the other three provinces that fell under our remit: South Kivu, Maniema and Katanga. I had boxes full of receipts for 'entry' fees, 'registration' fees, 'travel' fees, 'right to pass' fees, 'you want me to raise this barrier, I need a fee' fees and 'no legitimate right to charge fees but you are a foreigner so give me money' fees.

Every now and again, the LRA rebel group's activities in the north of the country would make the news back home and Dad would fire off a worried email to me. I would reassure him that there was minimal risk to us. I never told him that what was reported in the UK was only a fraction of what we heard about in DRC. I didn't tell him about our mandatory weekly 'briefings' either, when we would be given the best available information about what were euphemistically called 'hot spots' to avoid, and how we would run through our hostage strategies in case we were kidnapped.

It would be disingenuous of me to pretend that the Democratic Republic of the Congo wasn't a dangerous place, but that didn't mean I didn't love being there, and Dad didn't need to know all the 'bad' stuff, or how, almost from the outset, our implant programme appeared to stoke yet more unrest, or that the Community's only response was to increase the numbers of guards in the more 'vulnerable' areas.

Dad was (and remains) an obsessive sender of links to websites that *you should read* and *I know you'll find interesting* and *this one's a good one*, and judging by the quantity of links he sent while I was in Congo, it would be easy to think that he did nothing but hunt down anti-Community articles, which he'd send sandwiched between doom-laden homilies like *the Community has a much bigger agenda at play here than anyone will admit* and *I know how committed you are to your work out there but never mind Rachel's Goals, what are the Community's goals?* and *birth control is just the tip of the iceberg.*

For the whole three years that I was in Congo, Dad kept up a near-constant stream of accusations about how the Community was self-serving at best or sinister and controlling at worst. These days, I understand Dad's concerns in a way I couldn't or, perhaps more accurately, *wouldn't* back then. My father not only blamed the Community for Mum's death but when I swanned off to live in Congo without so much as a backward glance, he believed he was losing me to the Community, too. As far as I was concerned, when I left the UK my relationship with Dad went into a sort of stasis, and I assumed that exactly the same person I had waved goodbye to at Heathrow Airport would be standing there waiting for me whenever I chose to return. My father couldn't have felt more differently. He was terrified that the Emilia who had practically skipped through passport control might never return and all the articles and blogs and news sites that he sent me were his way of trying to remind me of who I was before the Community got its hands on me.

When we discussed this the other day, I admitted to Dad for the first time how his constant negativity about the Community had had the opposite effect than he had hoped for because, and I don't feel good about admitting this, within weeks of my arrival in Congo, his emails had begun to wind me up so much that I had to steel myself to even open them. I convinced myself that he was just trying to make me come home. Every now and then it crossed my mind that he might even be jealous: there was I, in Africa, having an incredible time, helping people, loving life, while he was still struggling to move on. I'm ashamed of such unkind, uncharitable thoughts. My father deserved better.

Most of the time, in my emails to Dad, I confined myself to the other things going on in his life: his new home in Winchester, the philosophy degree he was doing, old friends he had been in contact with, that sort of thing. But every now and again his obsession with ferreting out anti-Community articles would wind me up sufficiently that I would feel the need to reply in a pious, preachy tone that now makes me cringe. When we talked about this recently, Dad dug out one of those emails.

From: Emilia Morris
To: Nick Wright
Date: 5 June 2014

Subject: STOP WORRYING!!!

Hi Dad,

Will you please stop worrying about non-existent threats! I'm totally fine. I'm more likely to be charged by an elephant than attacked by a protester (but for god's sake, don't start worrying about elephants – that won't happen either!). I know how the protests against the implant programme are being reported, but those reports are blatantly biased and anti-Community. It's unfair of you to say that I'm just parroting Community PR in my emails to you. It's also quite amusing because here in Congo, I write the PR! The Community is changing the world for the better. You have to see that, surely?

One of the major issues that came out of the consultation was too many people and too few resources. That's what people said they need help with, and that's what we're developing programmes to address. As far as my specific programme is concerned, I don't understand why you say the consequences haven't been properly thought through. No one is forcing anyone to have an implant. They're a game-changer for women out here and I don't understand why you see it as a bad thing. Congo is a poster child for how we can help countries address the burdens and inequalities suffered by women.

Since you like reading articles so much, here are some you really should take a look at:

https://www.zatimes.com/2014/04/12/africa/community-initial-successes-in-congo-signals-reframing-of-overpopulation-crisis

https://www.aljazeera.com/news/2573482/Rwandan-President-officially-opens-Communitys-first-African-Conflict-Resolution-Academy

https://www.eatlessmeat-savetheworld/strategic-partnership-with-Community-focuses-on-animal-welfare-and-farming-practices

The Community is doing so much good work, and I honestly don't recognise the organisation you seem to think it is. What about all the seemingly intractable conflicts they're helping to resolve? And there's the Beijing Accord – 156 countries have committed to improving agricultural practices and enforcing standards in their food chains! I accept that the Community hasn't done these things single-handedly, but it has played a significant part. For every article claiming it's a sinister sect infiltrating governments around the world, I can send you at least two more that say what fantastic results we're achieving.

I think it might finally have cooled down enough for me to get some sleep, and the battery on my laptop is about to die, so I'm going to stop now.

Love, E x

Maybe if Dad had been less obsessive, I might actually have read the things he sent me. Maybe if I hadn't been so convinced that my point of view was the only one worth having, I might have stopped to consider whether my father had reasons to be concerned. But I didn't read the articles and I didn't listen to my dad.

Ignoring my father wasn't all I was doing during 2014, though. I was also falling in love.

29.

Before I embarked on this project of writing about my mother, I promised Fortuné I would spare his blushes. He does not want a starring role in this or any other story that might be written. However, there is no avoiding the significance of our relationship, not only while I was living in DRC but also with everything that happened subsequently, and it is impossible to tell this story without talking about him, at least a little.

Despite Scholar's knowing looks, it didn't cross my mind that Fortuné had come to work at the compound because of me (later on he told me I was the *only* reason he applied for the job, although I'm not sure I ever really believed that). Regardless, it took me less than two weeks to memorise his rota, and unless I was away on a site visit, I would loiter by the main gate when his shift was finishing.

In the early days, we would walk a few hundred yards from the compound to a shop with a single cracked window held together by a faded poster of Thierry Henry. In the gloom, an old man with no teeth and black gums sold SIM cards, cigarettes, a selection of food and cold drinks. I can still taste the *akara* – fried bean fritters – Fortuné and I ate while sitting on plastic stools under a faded awning that might once have been yellow or green. Accompanied by the noise and fumes of the passing traffic, we talked, shoulders touching, speaking words for our ears alone.

While night engulfed day – there was no dusk in Congo, no

gentle fading, but a swift 'dethronement of light', as I wrote to Dad in one of my more poetic emails – I told Fortuné about the Event and how, when I was least expecting it, I would smell the petrol and taste the acrid smoke and see their bodies toppling and collapsing in on themselves as the fire took hold. It was difficult to find the words to tell him about Steven Trent and more difficult still to talk about my mother, but I told him about my guilt and shame and fear and anger. I told him, too, how Casey and I rarely talked about anything but work anymore, that I missed her friendship and didn't know how to put things right. Fortuné listened to me in the same way my mother had listened to others: he did not fidget, or fiddle with the label on his drink, or prepare to speak as soon as I fell silent.

Fortuné talked, too, but his stories are not mine to tell, except for one occasion, when rain was sheeting off the awning, transforming the red dust beneath our feet into a morass of sticky, cloying mud, and his breath landed on my cheek, carrying words he is happy for me to share. They are about his brother Nicolas, the one who was murdered by poachers after only eight days as a ranger.

When Nicolas was four years old and Fortuné was eleven, Nicolas would follow his older brother everywhere, 'like a baby goat, bumping against my legs'. One of Fortuné's jobs was to collect water, and twice a day he would take a large plastic container that had once held motor oil and walk twenty minutes to the pump. Nicolas would go too and he wanted to help his brother, but once the container was full of water, the little boy would become upset because he couldn't even lift it, let alone carry it. Fortuné told him that there was another job, equally important. He gave him an old water bottle and told his brother that he must fill it with fresh air.

For two years, while Fortuné pumped water into the container, little Nicolas would unscrew the cap on the water bottle and spin in circles, collecting fresh air which he would carry home for their mother. He would hand over the bottle with great solemnity, and Andréa would carefully unscrew the cap and, holding the bottle under her nose, she would take several deep breaths. 'L'air est très bon, merci beaucoup, mon petit fils,' she would say, and Fortuné said that every day when he heard those words Nicolas would smile his biggest smile.

While he was telling me this story, Fortuné curled and stretched his fingers compulsively until I put my hand on top of his. He turned his hand over and laced his fingers through mine. His hands were always warm, as if he carried the sun's heat within them.

'I have given you a memory of Nicolas,' he said, 'and now you carry my brother with you too.'

I chose Fortuné and he chose me.

His arms became my home, his kisses my nourishment. Fortuné was my luck.

Mpenzi was what he called me. Darling.

In the early months, laughter drew us together. Like when Fortuné did ridiculous impressions of Alain's flamboyant drumming or of Mama Em flapping her arms and clucking loudly in her futile efforts to chase away the chickens that were forever wandering into her kitchen. In the years since my art A level, I'd developed a love of caricature, and Fortuné used to pick out a shop owner or one of the guards at the compound and say 'draw him' or 'draw her' and then chuckle almost maniacally at the likeness (or, just as frequently, the *un*likeness) which emerged from my pencil.

Fortuné also continued what his sister had begun, revealing his country to me experience by extraordinary experience.

In August 2014, his cousins invited us to visit. They lived near Bukavu, about three hours south of Goma. After driving alongside Lake Kivu for most of the way, Fortuné turned onto a tiny track, barely wide enough for the jeep. Less than two minutes later we were in the middle of what I can only describe as a butterfly blizzard. One second the track was clear, and the next there was a wall of butterflies.

There must have been millions of them. We couldn't see the front of the jeep, or behind, or to the sides, and we crawled along, making sure the butterflies had as much chance as possible to get out of our way as they parted and instantly closed up again behind us. Fortuné had only seen something similar once before, when he was a boy, and after a few minutes we decided to stop driving. It wasn't until I got out and stood on the track that I realised the butterflies were all identical: black with yellow blotches and a smudge of blood-red on their wings.

Later I found out that they were the *Papilio demodocus* butterfly which, despite the rather lovely English name of citrus swallowtail, are considered a pest, because they lay their eggs on the leaves of citrus plants. But pest could not have been further from my mind as I stood in the middle of the swarming butterflies, unable to see the track, or the sky, or Fortuné.

'Where are you?' I shouted. 'This is incredible.'

Then he was beside me, reaching through the blizzard for my hand, leaning close.

'The sound of butterfly wings is one of the rarest sounds in the world,' he said. 'We are so lucky.'

Until that point, I had thought I could hear water, perhaps a fast-flowing stream at the side of the track, but I was wrong. Instead, there were so many butterflies vibrating around us that they had transformed into a giant amplifier, something that only happens when millions of butterflies beat their wings together.

That day, on a road between Lake Kivu and Bukavu, they were beating for us.

The butterflies started to land on me, first on my hand, which Fortuné was holding, then along my arms, down to my feet, on my face and up in my hair – they kept on coming until I was completely enveloped. Each butterfly was weightless, dancing around a little, shuffling up to make room, before closing its wings revealing a pale underside, but still with the vivid blood-red spot. The rushing-water sound of millions of butterflies swarming around us suddenly made me think of my mother and how she had loved to listen to the River Chalk tumbling past her camp after heavy rain.

And the whole time Fortuné and I were standing there, I knew the butterflies were trying to work out what I was, this strange being that had appeared from nowhere, as if they were deciding whether or not to allow me to remain in their midst.

The following month we went to see the mountain gorillas (yes, the actual gorillas in the mist!). I had been dying to see them ever since I'd arrived in Congo, but the combination of frequent reports of poachers and my work schedule meant that the time had never been right. But, finally, when I'd been in Congo for almost a year, Fortuné arranged a visit with one of the rangers he had worked with.

It was eight hours from Goma to Virunga National Park and we left at midnight, driving through the night to meet Fortuné's friend Fabrice early in the morning. Gorillas sleep somewhere different every night and the group we were going to see were a couple of hours' walk away. Virunga is a tropical rainforest, and when it rains there, it's less rain and more apocalyptic deluge, so although I was wearing every bit of waterproof clothing that I possessed, I was drenched within minutes. The walking itself was really hard because there weren't any proper paths so almost the whole time we were wading (or in my case, slipping) through mud or streams or muddy streams.

But that wasn't all. We took the shortest route to the gorillas, which meant making our way through, under or over whatever was in our way. Fabrice and Fortuné both had machetes to cut back anything that was completely impenetrable, but I felt like I was on an army assault course. Thankfully, I only had to drag myself through the forest, whereas the guys not only had machetes and backpacks, but were also carrying rifles to warn off any wild forest buffalo that might take an interest in us.

I don't know why it hadn't occurred to me that, being mountain gorillas, you'd have to climb a mountain to find them, and we walked for what felt like about a hundred hours uphill and the whole time I was being driven ever so slightly insane by the relentless rain drilling onto the hood of my jacket.

Eventually, abruptly, Fabrice stopped walking and held up his hand. I was still trying to make out what he'd seen when he started forward again, slowly, trying to make as little noise as possible. Looking past his shoulder I saw a dark shape between two trees and I thought *gorilla*, before realising it was just a large rock. We kept on sneaking forward, threading through the trees, single-file, Fabrice in front of me, Fortuné behind me, until we finally emerged from the trees into a small clearing and there they were.

Gorillas.

Thirteen of them.

In the mist.

Seeing them for the first time was so overwhelming that I promptly burst into tears.

Because it was raining, the family were huddled together in and around a large stand of trees, trying to get some shelter from the dense canopy. Although they looked as pissed off with the rain as I was, they didn't seem to be at all bothered when we materialised in front of them. On the journey to Virunga, Fortuné told me that some people believed that gorillas were descended from a group of humans who had become so fed up with the behaviour of other humans that they had gone to live in the forest, where they became hairier and hairier over time until they ended up as gorillas. Scientists believe that gorillas most likely think that humans are another species that live on the mountains, who they happen to see quite regularly and who are neither friend nor foe. As far as gorillas are concerned, humans just 'are', in the same way that they themselves 'are'.

For the first twenty minutes or so, we stood in the torrential rain, just watching them. Most of the gorillas had their arms crossed over their chests, hands gripping their shoulders, not moving, although occasionally one would shift a little closer to another. I wondered if they were cold. While we watched them, Fabrice explained that this family were called the Hirwa family after their silverback. *Hirwa* means 'lucky' and Hirwa himself had been extremely lucky because after being chased out of a previous family by the resident silverback, he left with two females and gathered several others on his travels through Virunga and was now the head of a family of eighteen. He himself had his back to us, totally ignoring us, although every now and again one of his family looked in our direction, checking if we were still there.

Without warning, the rain stopped, and as is the way in the rainforest, within minutes the pale washed sky was completely cloudless and the temperature was rising rapidly. The smell of the forest after rain is my favourite smell in the whole world. Occasionally I have bought a candle lured by the promise of an 'authentic woodland scent' and I can categorically say that they smell nothing like the Congo rainforest after a downpour. There, everything steams – animals, insects, people, mud, trees, flowers – their odours mingling in a thick rising mist smelling of earth and life, sweet and clean. It smells like nothing else, and yet it smells of everything.

As soon as the last raindrop had fallen, Hirwa's entire family roused themselves and went to find food. They walked as a group, the older ones giving the youngsters piggybacks. At one point Hirwa's eldest daughter, who was carrying one of her siblings on her back, meandered away from the path the rest of her family were on and headed straight towards me. I tried to back up and give her space, but there was a spiky bush behind me which was too thick for me to force myself into. From where he was standing a few metres away, Fortuné said quietly, 'You are safe, *mpenzi*. Just be still.'

Fabrice said, 'Her name is Ishimwe and she is carrying her little brother, Gikundiro.'

Ishimwe kept on coming, knuckling the ground, both her and the little one rocking gently from side to side. Unlike their father, with the saddle of grey fur proclaiming him the silverback, Ishimwe and Gikundiro were entirely black, their dense coats fluffy where they were drying after the rain.

Then they were alongside me, so close I could have picked out the strands of grass and twigs caught in Gikundiro's fur. Ishimwe stopped, and she and her brother tilted their heads to look at me. They stared at me and I stared at them. Their eyes were human eyes. As they considered me, gravely, I wished I knew what they were thinking. I smiled, Ishimwe blinked, Gikundiro wound his fists more firmly into the fur on his sister's back, and she turned away from me and carried on knuckling softly through the undergrowth.

We didn't have to follow them far before the whole family settled down to eat. Gorillas are vegetarian, which is pretty incredible when you consider that the silverbacks weigh around 220 kilograms, and they immediately focused on the task of ripping up shoots and tearing off fistfuls of leaves and stuffing them into their mouths. Nothing was going to distract them and the loudest sounds in the forest at that moment were ripping and chewing and swallowing.

There were two exceptions to all the eating.

The youngest of Hirwa's children were twin boys, an extremely rare occurrence among gorillas – Hirwa was lucky in more ways than one. These eighteen-month-old boys were chasing each other round a small tree, hanging on for extra propulsion, until without any warning the one being chased would suddenly spin around and start chasing the other one and they'd go round and round the other way. That continued for quite a while until they got bored (and possibly dizzy!) and decided instead to annoy their dad.

At first, Hirwa was quite happy to let them climb all over him, but at some point he clearly had enough because he pushed them both away and they ran to their mother instead, who was enjoying a post-brunch snooze. They barrelled into her arms, snuggling close. She kissed each of her twins on the top of their head, wound her arms tightly round them and they all went to sleep.

'Just like us,' I said, talking to myself really, but out of the corner of my eye I saw the look Fortuné and Fabrice gave each other. 'What?' I asked.

'These animals are not like us, *mpenzi*,' Fortuné replied. 'We want to own the forest, to own the animals. The gorillas do not want to own anything. They want to live *with* the forest, not be its master.'

With Fortuné knitting my wounds together stitch by patient stitch, I was learning how to appreciate what I had and let go of things that no longer needed to be part of me, loosening my grip on the past. I was calmer, less angry, and for what felt like the first time in my life, I wasn't continually obsessing about my mother, instead able to consider her from far away, as if from the wrong end of a telescope.

So, I can't help but ask myself: if I had known back then what I know now, would I have made different choices? I like to think so. I hope so. The truth is I'm really not sure, because I was so incredibly happy.

But you know what they say: if something feels too good to be true… it probably is.

30.

I received the phone call at 11.37 on 7 November 2014.

I know because I wrote the time in the Protests and Disruptions Report for Laura. I also gave a statement to the PNC – the Police Nationale Congolaise – for all the good that it did.

I was in the compound at the time, working on a new advertising campaign with Scholar, and the clinic was in Bukavu, a five-hour drive away, so by the time we arrived there was only about an hour of daylight left. People were milling about outside and when I got out of the jeep some of them started waving and shouting. I spotted Isa, the clinic's senior nurse, among the crowd. Scholar and I made our way over to her.

'Ça va?' I said. Isa shook her head. Of course she wasn't. Stupid question.

I turned to Scholar. 'Can you ask her to tell us what happened?'

Isa spoke for a minute or so and I only understood snatches of what she was saying. Then she stopped talking and burst into tears.

Scholar turned to me. 'The man came with his wife. After the injections, Falonne, the health-care assistant, handed over the incentive bag to his wife but the man took it and emptied everything on the ground. He said he was looking for the key for the car. He said that because he had agreed for his wife to have the implant, he wanted the car that we had promised on our poster. He was shouting for the key. He slapped his wife and said she had stolen the key. Falonne tried to stop him. She told him there was no key because there was no car, that the poster was just a picture, not a promise. He accused Falonne of stealing the key. He punched her, she fell over, and hit her head on a rock.'

When Scholar stopped talking, Isa wiped her eyes and, grasping my hand firmly so I had no choice but to follow, she walked towards the clinic. Falonne's body was just outside the door. Someone had covered her face and most of her body with a colourful *pagne*, which I realised with a jolt was identical to the blue, orange and neon-pink flowery fabric that Scholar's mother, Andréa, had worn to church at Christmas. The cloth wasn't large enough and Falonne's bright blue trainers were sticking out of the bottom.

'Why is her body still here?' I asked.

Isa spoke to Scholar, who said to me, 'They cannot find relatives to remove the body. Falonne has four children, but they are very young and her husband was killed by the LRA in the north last year. They are trying to find a brother or a sister, someone to take the body away.'

Isa said something else and Scholar translated. 'She asks what we will do for the children.'

I wish I could say that I understood the significance of what happened that day, that this was not an isolated incident but the first of many tragic consequences that were a direct result of both the implant programme and my own decisions.

I was devastated, of course, for Falonne's children and for Isa and all the staff at the clinic, but at the time, I convinced myself that because the man was known for having mental health issues, it was a tragic one-off. I included details in my next Protests and Disruptions Report, arranged for Falonne's children to receive the compensation authorised by head office several weeks later, and applied to the head of the Sub-Saharan Sector for emergency funds to recruit more guards.

I should have asked questions. I should have asked why more hadn't been done to understand the challenges of rolling out a contraceptive programme in Congo. I should have asked why we weren't listening to the objections. I should have asked whether we were doing the right thing, injecting women with implants that would leave them unable to have children for seven years.

I am ashamed to admit that I wasn't yet ready to ask those questions.

Four weeks after Falonne's death, the tension that had been building between Casey and me exploded.

Two American Members – Alyssa and Jess – had arrived to spend a week with us. They had come from Quiet Corner, Connecticut, to undertake a feasibility study into extending the DRC implant programme into neighbouring Burundi. On the first evening, Alyssa, Jess, Casey and I ate together, then, after Alain's customary final flourish, and with the mosquitoes swarming, hunting for exposed flesh, the four of us settled down for a chat over some bottles of Primus lager. At first, we talked about meaningless stuff. *The Hunger Games: Mockingjay – Part 1* had just come out, and as a big Katniss Everdeen fan, I was dying to see it, but Alyssa had watched it before leaving the States a couple of weeks earlier and said I wasn't missing anything. After our two visitors had filled us in on Brangelina's marriage and Gwyneth and Chris's conscious uncoupling, we all opened another beer and the conversation moved on to the latest Community conspiracy theories.

Almost from the day of the Event itself, Members have claimed

there are hidden signs and coded messages in absolutely everything to do with my mother. What we were discussing that
night has since become part of the Community's 'origin story',
accepted as inviolable truth by most Members. I'm referring,
of course, to the idea that Rachel deliberately chose 31 October
2011 as the date of the Event because the United Nations had
announced some weeks beforehand that that was the day on
which the world's population would reach seven billion.

'It's obvious why Rachel... Rachel of Chalkham, I mean...
you know, your mother...' said Jess, stumbling over her
words.

'Call her Rachel,' I said. I found the breathless, tongue-tied
uncertainty that people developed when they were talking to
me about my mother intensely irritating. I always referred to her
as Rachel and wished everyone else would just do the same.

'You guys do know why Rachel picked that date for the Event,
right?' Jess said.

Casey nodded. 'Yeah, I read about that.'

I had a swig of beer, then said, 'It's just before Bonfire Night
in the UK, so I guess she thought they were more likely to get
away with building their pyres.'

Casey rolled her eyes at the two Americans. 'Emilia doesn't
like talking about this stuff. She prefers to think that nothing ever
means anything.'

'That's not right,' I said. 'Just because I don't want to look for
"meanings" in every single thing... coincidences happen... stuff
just *happens*. We don't need to waste our lives looking for
explanations.'

'Really?' said Alyssa. 'You honestly think there's no significance
to the Event date?'

'I honestly do. It's just another date, like all the other dates.
Nothing more than that.'

'See?' Casey asked the other two. 'She always refuses to discuss it.'

Jess looked at her watch; Alyssa knocked back the rest of her beer. I got the impression that, although they agreed with Casey, they were reluctant to be drawn into our argument.

'Why do you all think everything has to *mean* something?' I asked. 'God knows the Event itself meant enough.'

'Why are you so bothered with the idea that the date *does* mean something?' said Casey.

Alyssa pulled another Primus out of the crate next to the table. Jess swatted a mosquito, leaving a tiny red blotch on her shirt sleeve.

'Here's what I think,' Alyssa said, picking her words carefully. 'There were always reasons behind Rachel's choices. That's why the Interpretative Sector puts out all those webinars – so we can better understand her choices.'

'That's rubbish,' I said. 'Rachel just picked a date. End of.'

'Hang on a sec,' said Casey, opening her laptop and scrolling through pages of bookmarked articles. 'Let me just find this thing I read…' She searched for a few seconds longer then turned the screen towards me. 'Take a look at this,' she said.

I glanced at it, recognising the Letters from the Silent Shore website, that one with the weird logo where little alphabet characters complete with fins and gills and stubby proto-legs are crawling out of the sea onto a deserted beach. The specific blog Casey was showing me had the headline: 'The Fate of Humanity Is a Numbers Game'.

'That site's full of wacko conspiracy theories,' I said. 'Complete waste of time. I don't know why you bother even looking at it.'

'It's not very Community-minded to be so judgemental, is it?' Casey said. 'Some of these bloggers talk a lot of sense. Here, listen to this.'

She pulled the laptop towards her and started reading.

'"Overpopulation is the greatest issue facing humanity. Many of the issues that the Community is fighting to address, such as climate health, deforestation, rapacious agricultural practices, not to mention inequality in education, opportunity and employment, would all be resolved if rising global population was halted and reversed. We urge each and every Member to push for absolute focus on programmes to facilitate the immediate reduction in population numbers. This is what Rachel of Chalkham wanted. She chose 31 October 2011 as the date for the Event because she understood that 7 billion people is too many people."'[15]

After she finished reading, Casey looked at me expectantly. 'See?'

I shrugged. 'See what? It's just a stupid blog.'

'God, you're so annoying,' she said. 'Rachel knew that reducing population is *the* most important thing. We should be focusing 100 per cent on it. Contraceptive implants are just the start, but it's nowhere near enough. There's so much more we need to do. You do get that it's all part of a much bigger picture, right?'

'No. No I don't get that at all,' I said. 'We're providing contraception to women who don't otherwise have access to it. That's it. That's the beginning and the end of what we're doing here.'

'Oh, so you'll happily hand out implants to these women, but you don't think we should be looking at other ways to reduce the population. Typical. You're such a hypocrite.' Casey's voice was loud.

The two Americans were peeling the labels off their bottles of beer, avoiding looking at either of us.

'I'm not a hypocrite,' I said, 'but you're well on the way to becoming a fanatic.'

---

[15] https://lettersfromthesilentshore/overpopulation/27849325

'Bullshit. I'm a committed Member. But you wouldn't know what that even means, would you? Committed Members will do whatever it takes to deliver Rachel's Goals, not pick and choose cosy little jobs that make them feel good about themselves.'

'What's that even supposed to mean? You seem to have forgotten that what Rachel wanted more than anything else was for everyone to shut up, so why don't you just shut your mouth?'

'Fuck off.'

I stood and stalked towards the house. Pulling the door open, I paused, looked back at Casey and shouted, '*You* fuck off.'

It was like being back in primary school, except with swearing.

After a few days, once we'd both calmed down and Alyssa and Jess had left, Casey and I had more Primus and got drunk enough to pretend we'd forgiven each other. However, there is no doubt that that argument marked a watershed moment: we may have both been working for the same organisation, we may have been living in the same place, but we had embarked upon starkly different paths.

31.

I suspect I'm giving a skewed impression of my time in DRC. It wasn't all childish arguments, terrible tragedies and once-in-a-lifetime experiences. In the main, after the frenetic pace of the first few weeks and months, my working life took on its own routines, as work generally does, and frankly many of those routines were downright tedious.

When I think back now, it feels like I spent most of my time in Congo dealing not with the marketing campaigns, or the clinics, or the staff, or the clients, but with paperwork. I've already mentioned the monthly reports that I was required to put together for Laura, but they were just the start, because wherever I went, whatever I did, there were forms for absolutely everything.

For example, in addition to the regular batches of contraceptive implants sent from a production plant in South Africa, the Community regularly dispatched staff uniforms along with the branded tote bags and water bottles that formed part of the incentive offering. They also sent 'care packages' to those of us who were expats: everything from magazines, books and sweets to Community-branded clothing. Every single parcel and box and container required forms to be completed in triplicate as an absolute minimum, not to mention the hours and often entire days at the airport I spent 'negotiating' with the Chef des Douanes – chief of customs – to release the shipments into our custody.

I would always ring ahead, but every single time, without

fail, whenever I arrived the Chef des Douanes would make me wait for at least ninety minutes before he'd deign to see me. Each time he would behave as if he'd never met me before and force me to go through the pantomime of explaining that I would like to have my shipment released to me, 's'il vous plaît, Monsieur le Chef des Douanes'.

Mr Customs Chief would sigh heavily as if I had broken his heart and shuffle through thousands of forms on his desk but somehow always fail to find the ones relating to my parcel. He'd leave the room, and I would wait for another unspecified period of time until eventually he would return and, with more theatrical sighing, find that the missing forms had been there under his nose all along. Every single time he would hand over even more paperwork for me to complete, and as he watched me fill tiny squares with letters his sighs became so dramatic that forms fluttered on his desk. He would scrutinise the newly completed paperwork, then ask for my passport and leave the office again to photocopy the passport, despite having copied it dozens of times before. When he returned, he would staple the photocopy to the sheaf of forms and wait in silence for me to push an envelope containing pristine US dollars across the desk. Only then would he finally pick up the phone and authorise the release of my parcel.

Imagine my absolute joy whenever a shipment turned out to be a box containing nothing more than a stack of Community newsletters, intended for distribution around the clinics.

When I wasn't form-filling and dealing with overbearing bureaucracy, I spent a lot of my time having to manage the issues caused by the high turnover of staff. Although we did a fairly good job of hanging on to the nurses who supervised the clinics, the HCAs – the people responsible for administering the implants – regularly left after only a few weeks. I understood that it was difficult for them: the Community offered a permanent job with a guaranteed salary, but all too often their families and friends who disagreed with the contraceptive programme would bring too much pressure to bear and the HCAs would quit, at which point we'd have to begin the whole recruitment and training process all over again.

Having said that, the longer I was in Congo, the less of an issue the high turnover of HCAs became. During the three years I was there, our most successful month was July 2014, when almost 3,500 implants were administered across all four regions: North Kivu, South Kivu, Maniema and Katanga (which, by the way, make up less than 50 per cent of the total area of DRC); but by September 2015, the monthly total had dropped to 643 implants. It hadn't escaped my attention that this coincided with an increase in the protests against the programme, and my Protests and Disruptions Report for October 2015 contains details of '*two clinics closed due to vandalism*', a shortage of implants as a result of '*the hijacking of the vehicle transporting them to Maniema*' and '*sixteen attempted attacks on staff*' of which '*twelve were prevented by the security guards*', '*three resulted in cuts and bruises*' and in one an HCA '*suffered broken ribs*'.

For an organisation that usually makes every effort to splash their branding across anything and everything, it is worth noting that as early as January 2015 the Head of Sub-Saharan Security had advised us not to use vehicles with any markings associated with the Community. She also suggested that when we were stopped at roadblocks and checkpoints it might be prudent to claim we worked for the World Food Programme.

Despite this, I rarely felt unsafe, although I did often feel unwelcome. Back then, I accepted it as the price I had to pay to, as Laura put it in her emails, 'help people who aren't able to help themselves'.

★

The annual Africa Forum was one of the highlights of our working year, and in late 2015, Casey, Scholar and I travelled to Kigali in Rwanda for that year's event. Within minutes of arriving at the hotel, I emailed Livy to say, *'I'm in a hotel and I have a flushing toilet OF MY OWN. I am in heaven.'*

The Community loves Rwanda. And little surprise: it was the first country in the world to have a majority of female MPs; the first country to ban plastic bags, back in 2008; and of course Kigali, Rwanda's capital city, was the location of the Community's first Conflict Resolution Academy in Africa, which had enormous success brokering dialogues in places like South Sudan, Central African Republic and Somalia, not to mention DRC itself.

Before the conference began a few of us went to a church in Kibuye. During the Rwandan genocide twenty-one years earlier, many Tutsis had fled there hoping for sanctuary and, in their memory, beautifully wrapped bunches of flowers lined the path leading to the church. To the left of the main door was a window, but it was only when I got up close that I saw there were shelves on the other side of it. Piled on the shelves were skulls of some of the eleven thousand men, women and children who were slaughtered in and around the church on 17 April 1994.

Above the window in large metal letters were just two words, in English: *Never Again.*

I have thought of that church and those words often. Rwanda isn't perfect. No country is – not when it's at the mercy of the whims of the people who govern it. But what struck me looking at those skulls, there in Kibuye, was that there was no attempt to hide the past or pretend that it was something other than what it was. Instead, it seemed to me, the memorial signified a nation trying to live with itself and learn from its tragedies. There was, I believed, a lesson there for me. Perhaps for us all.

The Africa Forum was much the same as any other conference.

For three days we were stuck inside, with no daylight, starved of fresh air, doing our best to look alert, interested, engaged. I spent hours in a dull workshop on 'Targeted Communications' run by my old boss, Alice Corbett. Outside of the mandatory seminars, there were optional 'interest group sessions' covering a wide range of subjects, from lobbying national governments for regulation of animal welfare and agricultural practices to practical demonstrations of effective 'Social Media Silence Sessions' designed to highlight the benefits of listening without judging.

Casey spent all her free time with a group calling themselves Further, Faster, which, as far as I could tell, was made up of hardcore ultra-fanatical Members pushing the overpopulation theory about the date of the Event and holding workshops to 'deconstruct' Rachel's 'final silence', whatever that meant. They were also working on strategies to persuade the Community to implement their group's proposed population-management programmes which were, according to them, 'vital for the future of humanity'. In an effort to build bridges, I tried talking to Casey about it, but she just kept saying that I hadn't yet 'fully embraced Rachel's legacy' and that if I just 'allowed myself to listen, I would hear'.

What Casey expected me to hear wasn't clear but, of course, allowing voices to be heard was at the core of Rachel's beliefs. The problem is that by allowing all voices to be heard, a platform is given to voices that would do better to remain silent.

Did my mother really not see that silence cannot wholly be a force for good? That as a protest it is as nuanced and flawed as anything else? Surely she anticipated the ill-intentioned voices that emerged from the silence? Rachel filled twenty-nine notebooks with her thoughts but in not one of them does she offer a suggestion for dealing with voices that don't deserve to be heard. Her lack of responsibility is breathtaking.

The Community would have us believe that they are delivering Rachel's legacy exactly as she intended. However, if my father and I can achieve anything by the publication of her notebooks, we hope it is the realisation that nothing, *nothing*, being done in Rachel's name today was ever mentioned by my mother.

Back then, in Rwanda, I dismissed the Further, Faster group as outliers, the sort of fringe group that all large organisations seem to spawn. Casey was wasting her time. No one was taking them seriously, I thought. Nothing to worry about.

On the second day, Scholar and I attended a presentation by a Congolese Member based in Kinshasa who had been researching cultural resistance to the implant programme in DRC. We were the only two who turned up for her session.

Professor Ruth Ngoy (who left the Community shortly afterwards) is now a leading expert in the field of fertility economics, and her presentation was both impressive and persuasive. As part of her research, she had interviewed couples in situations both where the women had had the implant and where they had not. She also quoted extensively from respected peer-reviewed articles from around the world.

I still have the notes I took during Professors Ngoy's talk:

- *Widespread belief that women 'owe' their husbands as many children as possible in return for the bride price paid by their husband's family*
- *Men encourage wives to have multiple children to ensure that their wives become physically unattractive to other men*
- *Women believe if they have many children then their husband is less likely to divorce them*
- *High proportion of both men and women believe women who use contraception are more likely to become prostitutes or suffer from sterility and disease.*

Her conclusion was blunt and unequivocal:

> *Research demonstrates the complexity and multiplicity*
> *of reasons for the sustained opposition to the implant*
> *programme in the Democratic Republic of the Congo.*
> *The Community is not doing enough to listen to the*
> *people who hold these views or to address their concerns.*
> *Without a change of approach and a return to listening*
> *and hearing and addressing issues rather than merely*
> *continuing to arm ourselves against protesters, all*
> *indications are that the opposition will only get worse.*

On our final evening in Kigali there was a mandatory Guided Silence Session, which Sophie Turrell flew in from London to lead. It was several years since she had last been referred to as the Designated Survivor. She was now Chair of the Board.

The official version of Sophie Turrell's life is well documented. *Designated: The Remarkable Rise of a Survivor* by Terri-Rose Price (Community Press, 2017) details how she was born in Stroud in 1974, went to an independent girls' school, graduated from Oxford with a first-class honours degree in politics, philosophy and economics, joined the civil service, married at twenty-seven, divorced at thirty-two, at which point she went to Chalkham to join the Community. Of course, Sophie's life is more complicated than that potted history makes it seem, and Price's book details at length the sexual abuse which Sophie suffered at the hands of her maternal grandfather for twelve years from the age of three.

Sophie has always maintained that it was not until she spent time with Rachel in the Chalkham Hearing Place that she felt able to speak about the abuse for the first time and that it was Rachel's talent for listening that enabled Sophie to acknowledge and accept what had happened to her. She mentions this frequently, as if she believes it somehow gives her a greater insight into Rachel herself.

Nowadays you can't turn on the television or go online without seeing endless footage of Sophie Turrell getting in and out of the Community's private jet, shaking hands with waiting dignitaries, hobnobbing with political leaders, launching Community initiatives and opening new Community facilities with trite little speeches about it being another step along the road to achieving Rachel's Goals. Sophie's reach is great, which is why my publisher's lawyers have warned me to confine myself to referring only to my personal encounters with her and only where it is essential to my story.

Sophie has always claimed to have been present when The52 attacked the camp, the day Robert Kenny fell into the firepit, and occasionally she refers to scarring on her left hand which she claims is as a result of pulling my mother away from the flames. All I will say is that I was there that day, and I don't remember my mother ever being near enough to the fire to have been 'pulled away'. In fact, I don't remember ever seeing Sophie Turrell in Chalkham, although that's not to say she wasn't there – by the time I was at university, my visits to the bottom of our garden were infrequent and fleeting.

According to Price's biography, Rachel handpicked Sophie to replace her.

> *In Sophie Turrell, Rachel of Chalkham finally found an individual uniquely placed to seize the opportunities which would arise in the aftermath of the Event... seize them, capitalise on them and push the Community forward as far and as fast as possible. Sophie's superior intelligence, her vision for what the world could be if only people talked less and listened more, her resilience and her willingness to put her entire self into the task of*

delivering Rachel's legacy meant that she was the
obvious – quite possibly the only – choice to be made
when Rachel was selecting her Designated Survivor. It
was with a heavy heart, and a great deal of persuasion,
that Sophie agreed not to burn in the Event, but instead
to assume the mantle of Designated Survivor. In the
months prior to 31 October 2011, Sophie was constantly
by Rachel's side, using her prodigious intellect to master
the skills necessary to run the post-Event Community[16].

This is the official version. I don't know if it's the truth, but I don't know that it's not, and I've been told in no uncertain terms that I am not to speculate.

What I *can* say is that there is not a single mention of Sophie Turrell in Rachel's notebooks.

I can also say that it seems to me that when there's a power vacuum in an organisation, it's not necessarily the most deserving individual that steps in or the individual who was intended to pick up the reins. Often, the person who assumes power has other qualifications. They might be the most ambitious, or the most ruthless, or selfish, or, when it comes down to it, just an arch political manoeuvrer.

But to be clear, I am not, absolutely not, implying that the official account of Sophie Turrell's ascendency to the position of Designated Survivor is false. I am definitely not suggesting that.

At the end of the Guided Silence Session in Rwanda, one of Sophie's entourage (by then she was always accompanied by several women who looked like they might previously have been professional wrestlers) handed her a magazine. Sophie stepped onto a small makeshift platform and held the magazine over her head.

[16] Price, Terri-Rose, *Designated: The Remarkable Rise of a Survivor*, Community Press, 2017, p. 36.

'This month,' she announced, '*The Atlantic* magazine devoted a whole edition to us. It declares 2015 the Year of the Community, the year that Rachel of Chalkham's Community cemented its position on the world stage.

'Each and every one of you has contributed to our astonishing success and I hope you will indulge me while I mention just a few of the stand-out moments... As you all know, in January the Climate Sector launched the Leaf not Beef campaign and *The Atlantic* has this to say about the adverts.'

She read directly from the magazine, '"Recent multimedia adverts released as part of the Leaf not Beef campaign are unsparing in their message. No one who saw them will ever forget the images of ravenous cattle rampaging through cities abandoned by humans in the wake of food-chain-related pandemics. The call to consumers to avert such potential catastrophes by forfeiting all meat (not just beef!) has been staggeringly successful and the Leaf not Beef campaign is already credited with an eight-hundred-fold increase in the number of people identifying as vegetarian around the world. Moreover, our Community has been working with the World Health Organisation to establish an international task force recognising that to maintain public health and avoid global health crises it is essential to reduce meat consumption, tackle animal welfare and improve agricultural practices."'

There was an approving murmur around the room – less than two months later all Members would be required to sign the Leaf not Beef pledge but, of course, vegetarianism had always been strongly encouraged and all Community-owned facilities were designated meat-free zones.

'But, as you know,' Sophie continued, 'that was just the beginning. This year, we have received three major awards. First, we had the honour of receiving the Mother Teresa Award for promotion of peace, equality and peaceful coexistence, which was awarded in recognition of our policy of listening and hearing. Shortly after that, we received the Conrad N. Hilton Humanitarian Prize for our coordination and oversight of the Tropical Reforestation Programme which, to quote *The Atlantic*,' Sophie turned a page in the magazine and read, '"reaps immeasurable benefits not only to the environment but also for the indigenous peoples to whose guardianship these areas have been returned".

'And then it's no exaggeration to say we landed the big one when we received the Nobel Peace Prize for our Conflict Resolution Academies' efforts to, and I am quoting the Nobel citation directly here, "eradicate violence, for contributions to brokering constructive dialogue in conflict-affected areas and seeking resolution to intractable conflicts and for acting as a driving force in prevention of war and conflict".

'Each and every one of you has played your part. The Community is its Members, its Members are the Community, and you should all give yourselves an immense round of applause because it is thanks to you, each and every one of you, that we have received these awards.'

Everyone clapped and Sophie smiled and nodded, looking for all the world as if we were applauding her, not ourselves. Eventually she patted the air with her hands, and we quietened down.

'Together we have already achieved many extraordinary things and it is gratifying that our efforts are being recognised. Make no mistake, though, there is much more we must do to fulfil Rachel's Goals. We all know what the goals are, but why don't we remind ourselves? Number one?'

'Eliminate international conflict,' we shouted.

'Number two?'

'Restore climate health.'

'And number three?' called Sophie.

'Solve population crisis,' we bellowed back.

'Every single one of you here today has a part to play in fulfilling Rachel's Goals. If you're not with us, you are…?'

'Against us,' we cried.

'Where is Abigail Okafor?' Sophie said.

Near the back of the room, someone I didn't recognise raised her hand and called, 'I'm here.'

Sophie pointed at her. 'Are you with us, Abigail?'

Abigail waved both her hands above her head and called, 'I'm with you.'

'What about Sue Lawrenson – where are you?'

Sue identified herself with a yelp of excitement.

'Are you with us, Sue?'

'I'm with you.'

This call and response went on for a while. There seemed to be no particular category of Member Sophie was choosing, and she recalled names effortlessly, without a prompt. She ended with a woman I vaguely knew called Afiya Odongo. When Sophie asked, 'Are you with us?' Afiya didn't immediately respond, but instead made her way towards the platform. Two of Sophie's entourage stepped in front of her, but at a word from Sophie they stood aside. Sophie handed over the microphone and, turning to face the room, Afiya yelled, 'Hell yeah, sister, I'm with you.'

After the laughter subsided, Sophie thankfully only had a little more to say.

'Those who are not with us are against us. Those who are against us are not listening. They do not hear. They are deaf. Only we listen. Only we have the solutions. In the last month three of the world's richest philanthropists have thrown their influence and money behind the Community's programmes and I am predicting that even greater success awaits us in 2016. Rachel would be so proud of you all. Our journey continues tomorrow, but if Rachel was here with us tonight, she would be celebrating.'

On cue, large doors in one of the walls were folded back, revealing a room with tables loaded with glasses of wine and platters of food. To one side, complimentary tote bags branded with the *Shhhh…* logo were stuffed with Community baseball caps and T-shirts, together with pamphlets on a variety of subjects from 'Answering 10 Common Criticisms of the Community' to 'Persuasive Listening Skills'.

Among shiny, smiley faces, I could see Casey standing with her Further, Faster group chanting, 'Let's do more, let's do more.' Other Members, overcome with emotion, were wiping away tears. I thought about Sophie's unquestioning conviction that she had insight into Rachel's thoughts. I did not share her certainty. This all seemed a world away from Mum's message of listening and hearing.

Why was it that only Scholar and I had bothered to attend Professor Ngoy's presentation? Why did no one else think it worth hearing what she had to say? As my fellow Members started heading towards the food and wine, and the intro to 'Uptown Funk' (which had even reached Rwanda) boomed from speakers around the room, I thought about the 35,000 implants our programme had administered so far. I thought about the increasing backlash against the programme in Congo and everything that Professor Ngoy had said. I still believed we were helping women… but at what cost?

I didn't stay to celebrate or pick up a complimentary tote bag. Instead, I went to my room, packed my suitcase ahead of our flight back to Goma the following day, texted Fortuné, sent an email to Dad and went to bed, where I lay awake for a long time.

A few weeks later, I emailed Laura the following.

From: Emilia Morris
To: Laura Williams
Date: 5 February 2016

Subject: Opposition to the programme

Dear Laura,

Further to our Skype call yesterday afternoon, I'm sending you this email to set out my concerns about the opposition to the implant programme.

Our staff continue to be targeted and the numbers of incidents are increasing. Across the four provinces there have been twenty-seven attacks in the last six weeks.

As I mentioned when we spoke, among certain sectors of Congolese society there is strong cultural and/or religious opposition to the contraception programme. This opposition has been there from the beginning, but the more widely we roll out the programme, the more vocal (and, often, more violent) this opposition has become.

While I appreciate that the additional security guards will help to ensure our safety and that of our clinic staff, I would welcome your guidance on how to deal with the issues that lie behind these protests. I assume we should be listening to and hearing the protesters, and trying to find a resolution that works for them, too, rather than just arming ourselves against them?

In putting the needs of one part of society first, I think we failed to appreciate the distress that the programme would cause among other sections of society, who genuinely believe that what we are doing is contrary to either their religious beliefs or their cultural beliefs. I would appreciate some assistance in how to handle the objections and reduce the increasing number of violent incidents happening at our clinics.

DRC cannot be the only country where the programme is encountering opposition, and I wondered if it might be worth asking the board to set up a forum for Members from all countries currently rolling out the implant programmes to share our experiences about how best to deal with these issues?

In recent months we have also seen a sharp increase in the numbers of women returning to the clinics to ask for their implants to be removed. Last week 256 women across the four provinces requested contraceptive removal. As you know, HCAs are only trained to insert the implants, not to remove them, so they can't perform the necessary procedure. Additionally, of course, all clients sign a waiver before having the implant, so they have no right to ask for it to be removed. However, I would be grateful for your advice about how to deal with these women who are claiming that they did not understand what having an implant would mean and/or that they have changed their minds and now wish to have a child.

Kind regards,

Emilia

Laura never responded directly to this or any of the other emails that I sent in a similar vein. Instead, she sent copious emails about 'targets' and 'success strategies' and 'programme optimisation' and told me over and over again what an important job I was doing and how well I was doing it. I am ashamed to admit it, but because I loved so many things about my life in DRC, I found it too easy to ignore my doubts and suspicions, to believe what Laura was saying, accept her praise and continue to do my job.

The only thing in my favour is that finally I was asking questions.

32.

In April 2016 I came down with a dose of malaria. I had taken an anti-malarial drug every day for the first eighteen months that I was in DRC, but when there was a temporary issue getting hold of more tablets I stopped bothering and (stupidly) just relied on trousers and long-sleeved shirts to keep the mosquitoes from jabbing me with their ravenous vampire mouths. It was a tactic doomed to failure.

Thankfully, I don't remember very much of the nearly three weeks that I spent in bed. When I emerged from the fever, several kilograms lighter and as weak as the proverbial kitten, there were two notable pieces of news.

Four days after I got sick, a car bomb exploded outside our North Goma Central Clinic on Boulevard Kanyamuhanga. Clinic had finished for the day, so thankfully there were few people inside. No one was killed but four people suffered severe burns (one of our HCAs and three passers-by) and more than a dozen others had burns, cuts and bruises of varying severity. Nobody had claimed responsibility; and it was conceivable that those responsible weren't even targeting the Community, that it was just a coincidence that the car was detonated outside the clinic, as unlikely as that seemed.

I hadn't told Dad about the malaria because I didn't want him to worry, so when he heard about the car bomb on the news back home he was frantic when I didn't answer my phone or reply to his emails. In the end he managed to get hold of Alice Corbett in London, who contacted Casey, who asked Fortuné to Skype my father and reassure him that I was fine. Having told Dad that I was nowhere near the clinic when the bomb went off, Fortuné then broke the news that I was, instead, very poorly, feverish and drugged up to the eyeballs. I have no recollection of this, but apparently Fortuné stood at the foot of our bed holding up my laptop while I waved at Dad so he could see for himself that I was safe.

A week after the car bomb, Scholar resigned.

I was devastated when I found out.

Casey was the one to tell me, and although I wouldn't go so far as to say she was happy to break the news to me, she certainly didn't feel the need to sugar-coat it. She breezed into my room with a folder full of work notes, which she dumped on my bed before saying, without any preamble, 'Scholar's bailed on us. I always said she wasn't committed.'

If Casey ever had said that about Scholar, it was never to me.

'What?' I said, trying to push myself upright. As far as I knew, it was the first time Casey had been to see me since I'd been ill, and I was still a long way from feeling anything like myself.

'Scholar's resigned.' Casey sat on the end of the bed and patted my leg. 'Good luck to her. If you're not with us, you're against us.'

It wasn't just my body that wasn't working as it should, my concentration was terrible and my thoughts seemed to be fighting their way through a lake of treacle.

'Scholar's leaving?' I finally managed to say.

'That's what I said,' Casey replied. 'You all right? You look a bit dodgy. You're not going to be sick are you?' She picked up an incongruously dainty teacup that had, for some reason, been left on the floor beside my bed and held it out. 'If you're going to throw up, do it in here.'

I didn't take the cup. I wasn't going to be sick.

'Jesus, you're crying now. Look, you know I don't do illness. I'll leave you to have a sleep. I'll come back tomorrow, see if you're feeling up to talking through the work stuff.'

She gave me another pat on the leg, scooped up the folder and breezed back out of my room.

It would be wrong to blame the malaria for how upset I was: Scholar was such a big part of why I had fallen in love with Congo, not to mention Fortuné, and when he came to check up on me a couple of hours after Casey left, I was really annoyed that he hadn't told me. He, in turn, was furious with Casey.

'Scholar was waiting until you were stronger, *mpenzi*. This was not Casey's news to tell. Always that woman speaks without thought for others. This was Scholar's news and she wanted to tell you.'

Scholar herself came in later that evening and even in the state I was in, I could see how distressed she was.

'I wanted to tell you myself,' she said, reaching for my hand. Her skin was cool on mine.

'Why are you leaving, Scholar?'

Every part of me ached, even my eyeballs. I closed my eyes and tried to find a cool patch on the pillow.

'We will talk about it when you are better. I'm here until next month. We'll talk when you are feeling stronger.'

It was another five days before I was feeling well enough to venture out of my bedroom for the evening meal. The weather was warm and dry, but I was taking no chances and had a thick blanket with me. Mama Em had made me a huge pot of *muamba nsusu*, a spicy chicken and peanut stew which wasn't allowed since all food served in Community facilities was supposed be vegetarian, but Mama Em generally operated in accordance with her own set of rules.

'Au revoir, paludisme,' she said, dumping a huge pot on the table in front of me. Bye-bye malaria. I wasn't about to argue with Mama Em, and after so long eating barely anything, the *muamba nsusu* tasted amazing. Mama Em came out several times to check that I was eating ('Dieu merci, Dieu merci,' she said when she saw my empty plate).

As ravening hordes of mosquitoes came to pay their respects to me and bats occasionally brushed the backs of our heads, Scholar and I finally talked.

'I can't believe you're leaving,' I said. 'I'm going to miss you so much.'

'We'll still see each other. I'll come back to visit you and Fortuné, and you'll come to Muhongo...'

'It won't be the same.'

'No.'

'But you like this job.'

'I thought the implants were a good thing,' Scholar said.

'They *are* a good thing. How else can women have any control over their bodies? Or their lives?'

'This is not the right way.'

'What do you mean?'

'It was like that professor said in Kigali,' Scholar replied. 'All these women who want contraception are in a locked room begging to escape, but rather than unlock the door and let them out safely, we're blasting the door open with a bomb. We are not caring about the damage we cause to them.'

Why had the task of providing free contraceptives to women become so complicated? Professor Ngoy's talk had really got me thinking, too, but I didn't believe it was as straightforward as my friend was making out.

'Surely it's more damaging for the women to continue to have so many children?' I said.

'Things must change, of course,' Scholar replied, 'but we should be helping women to make changes themselves, not giving them an injection and expecting their problems to disappear.'

'But they want the implant.'

'Do they?' she said. 'I don't think so. They want control over their bodies. Control over their pregnancies. Why do these implants have to last seven years? And why aren't we training HCAs to remove the implants if they're asked? Better still, why aren't we giving women contraceptives to take every day like the ones you brought from home for yourself? If we gave them those contraceptives, they could stop taking them whenever they want.'

'It's because of the economics,' I said, uncomfortably aware that I was just quoting Laura. 'By using an implant that lasts for seven years, the Community can offer them to so many more women around the world.' I stopped myself from repeating something else that Laura had once said in an email to me: *this way we don't have to rely on these women to remember to take a pill every day*.

Scholar looked at me, her gaze just like Fortuné's: steady, unguarded, unencumbered by a need to fill the silence that ballooned between us.

Eventually she said, 'You're quoting the Community. Is that what you really believe?'

'Of course. What other reason would there be?'

'Maybe to make sure that it is only countries like mine that stop growing in population?'

'Countries like yours?' I said, confused.

'Where are these implant programmes, Emilia? African countries. Asian countries. Non-white countries.'

'But that's because they're the countries where women asked

for contraception. You're making it sound like the Community has another reason for giving women the implants.'

'Maybe they do.'

'What are you saying?'

'Did the women of my country say, "I don't want to have children for seven years?" No. They said, "I want to decide for myself when to have children." That is different.'

'But I came here to help the women of your country and now you're accusing me of… well, I'm not sure what you're accusing me of, but I came to *help*.'

'I am not accusing you of anything, Emilia. I understand that you came here wanting to do good. The Community brought you and Casey and others to my country and told you that you are helping us, that you are *saving* us, but you are tools of the Community and the women of my country are their victims.'

'I can't believe you think that.' I felt tears pricking my eyes and realised the malaria hadn't quite done with me yet. When I shivered, Scholar reached out and tugged up the blanket, covering my shoulders, tucking me into the chair.

'The implant programme is not about giving women control of their bodies,' she said. 'It's about the Community controlling women's bodies.'

'But why would they want to do that?'

Scholar reached over and laid one finger gently on my cheek. She sighed. 'That I don't know.'

I was exhausted suddenly, too tired even to get up from the table and go to bed, which is where I wanted to be. Scholar leaned over and kissed my forehead.

'I am leaving. I think, one day, you will too. But we will always be friends.'

★

I am not here to defend myself against the fact that despite everything – Dad's unceasing cynicism, Casey's growing fanaticism, Professor Ngoy's case studies, Scholar's disenchantment, even Fortuné's doubts right from the start and the increasingly violent protests – I continued along the same path. I continued to supervise a programme that prevented women from having children for years; continued with wilful blindness to do what the Community asked me to do.

Instead, I am here to give an account of my experiences, whether they reflect well on me or not. However, I do believe that some of my inability to see the whole picture, or for a long time to even realise there was a picture to see, was because I had become increasingly distracted by the relationship between my mother and the Community.

Some of the more fanatical Members, including Casey and the rest of her Further, Faster cohort, had become obsessed with promoting Rachel as a sort of modern-day saint who should be put on a pedestal and worshipped. They referred to her as the *Blessed Rachel of Chalkham*. This attitude was spreading, and even more moderate Members tended to talk about my mother as if she was superhuman. Occasionally this veneration – if that is the right word – was extended to me, which I hated and would complain about vociferously to Fortuné whenever it happened.

Not long after Scholar had left, Fortuné and I were lying on our bed one evening waiting for Alain and his drums to summon us to dinner. The humidity was exhausting and the ceiling fan gave little relief as it circulated damp air around the room. I propped myself up on one elbow and said, 'I forgot to tell you. When I was at the clinic this morning, one of the HCAs, Marie, asked me if I would pull some hairs out of my head and give them to her.'

Fortuné tugged gently on my hair, but he didn't say anything

– he didn't need to, I always finished stories once I had started them, whether he wanted to hear them or not.

'I was so surprised that I almost did pull some out, but then I asked her why and she said, "Je veux quelque chose qui appartient à la fille de la bénie Rachel de Chalkham."'

'She wanted something belonging to Rachel's daughter?'

'Yes! And not only her, but she said her *maman* and her bloody *tante* did too. She had a whole list of people waiting for strands of my hair. Can you believe it?'

'And did you give her your hair?'

'No, I bloody didn't. Why on earth would someone want my hair?'

'To feel closer to Rachel?'

'That's weird. In any case, I don't even recognise who they're going on about most of the time when they talk about the *bénie* Rachel. Blessed Rachel. What does that even mean? It's like they think she's a saint or something.'

Fortuné shrugged. 'People love your mother. They love that she wanted to listen to them. To hear them. Love makes you do strange things, you know.' He smiled at me in a way that I knew all too well.

'They don't love Rachel,' I said, ignoring his invitation. I wasn't in the mood and, besides, the humidity was getting worse – surely it had to start raining soon?

'They didn't even know her,' I continued. 'They love their idea of her. That's different.'

Realising that I wasn't going to let it drop, Fortuné put his hands behind his head and said, 'People believe Rachel is the Community, *mpenzi*. They love the Community and so they love Rachel. They do not see a difference.'

He reached for a book by the side of the bed. Written in French, it had been left behind by a Member who had stayed in the compound the previous week. Fortuné's reading could best be described as unselective. He read anything that crossed his path, refusing to abandon a book no matter how poorly written or how boring the subject matter. 'There is always something to learn,' he would say when I asked him what he could possibly find interesting in a book on, say, the biography of a long dead Portuguese physicist.

He showed me the cover of this particular one. 'In English, the title is *Ten Steps to Achieving Rachel's Better World*. Let me read some sentences for you, *mpenzi* – maybe they will explain better than I can.'

He found the page he wanted, read the passage through to himself first, then began to translate. 'For many Members there is no difference between the Community and the…' He paused. 'I don't know this word in English. The *beginner* of the Community? Is that right?'

'The founder,' I said.

'*D'accord*… There is no difference between the Community and the founder of the Community. The Community is following Rachel of Chalkham in everything that it does. Her… *esprit*…?'

'Spirit?' I offered.

'*Bien*… her spirit gave life to the body of the Community. Her ideas gave life to the head of the Community. In all things the Community is the living *héritage* of Rachel of Chalkham.'

'I think you mean legacy, but it's bullshit.'

Fortuné looked hurt and I said, 'I don't mean your translation. I mean what these people say is bullshit. There's no way that all the Community programmes around the world were my mother's idea. There are so many memos supposedly containing 'Rachel's solutions' and 'Rachel's ideas' and 'Rachel's thoughts' that she literally would have done nothing but write these memos her whole life. And how likely is it, really, that she sat there at the bottom of our garden in Chalkham and wrote a memo about introducing contraceptive implants in the Democratic Republic of the Congo? I mean, *really*?'

When Fortuné didn't answer, I continued. 'Here's another. How likely is it that my mother came up with a plan to bring about a democratically elected government in Afghanistan? I mean, really? No one ever questions the Community when it announces yet another of Rachel's policies. Everyone just credits my mother with the ideas and accepts that everything is part of some grand plan dreamed up by the Blessed Rachel of Chalkham.'

Fortuné didn't speak – he just curled and stretched his fingers until I slotted my fingers between his and held his hand, stilling it.

'Why does this make you so angry, *mpenzi*?' he asked.

'What they say isn't true. It's a lie.'

'Does that matter?'

'What do you mean? Of course it matters.'

Finally I heard the sound I'd been waiting for and I practically sprinted to the window. The first drops of rain were hesitant, one here by the window, one over there across the yard, but within thirty seconds they had become a deluge. I pushed the window open, taking care not to touch the glass, which had been cracked ever since I had moved into the room. In the yard, two of the guards were unrolling an awning above the tables and chairs where we would soon be eating.

I stayed where I was, enjoying the breeze, which was blowing rain through the window and onto my back, cooling me down.

'So many people believe my mother is something she was not,' I said, picking up our conversation.

'That is true of all famous people,' said Fortuné. 'Think of Cristiano Ronaldo...'

'Mum wasn't a bloody football player.'

'*Mpenzi*, it is not me you are angry with. Why don't you listen, like your mother said?'

I went over to the bed and gave him a kiss. 'Sorry. Go on. I'd love to listen to you talk about football.'

Ignoring my sarcasm, Fortuné said, 'Cristiano Ronaldo is the most famous football player in the world, but all these people who wear his name on their backs, who shout for him when Real Madrid is playing, you think they really *know* him? The Ronaldo they shout for is an *illusion* – you understand that word?'

'Illusion, yes, same word.'

'So, Ronaldo the footballer is an *illusion*. He is not Ronaldo the father, or Ronaldo the son...'

'Or Ronaldo the holy ghost?' I offered, but my attempt at humour fell flat.

'Look,' I said, 'I understand what you're saying. I really do. People in the Community feel like they *know* my mother, even though there's only a handful left who actually did. But I hate how everyone makes out she was this wonderful person when she really wasn't. And how they lie about her having all these ideas. Every time they announce a new programme, it's always "Oh, here's another great plan of Rachel's". Like I said, it's bullshit.'

A thump resonated around the yard. And another. It would take more than a downpour to keep Alain from his drumming. It was time to eat.

When I think about this conversation, and so many others, I can see that I was reaching for something that wouldn't become clear to me until I finally read Mum's notebooks. Back then, in Congo, I thought my anger stemmed entirely from the glorification that Rachel was receiving. Adulation I believed she did not deserve. I was annoyed too, by how their view of my mother bled into people's treatment of me. Not all the time and not by everyone, but when it happened, I hated it.

Now, of course, I understand that everything was so much more complicated, not least Rachel's arrogance in assuming that those who were left behind would know what she intended them to do after the Event. But even if she had made her plans clear, her assumption that everyone who followed her would remain true to her intentions was negligent at best and murderous at worst. The long history of humanity's manipulative, power-grabbing nature meant it was inevitable that if Sophie Turrell hadn't stepped into the void left by Rachel, then someone just like her would have done. Someone ambitious, ruthless and self-serving. Why didn't Mum anticipate that? Why didn't she see that this Community of hers had the potential to mutate into something terrible? Why didn't she make any attempt to stop it happening?

In chapter 18, I quoted the last words Rachel wrote in her notebooks: 'The Community will finally have a platform to do everything that I want it to do' (#29, p. 103). If my mother was here with me now, I would ask, 'So what *did* you want the Community to do?' and then, regardless of her answer, 'How *dare* you take no responsibility? How *dare* you be silent?'

This is why there must be absolute honesty about the relationship between Rachel and the Community. This isn't about me, and in many ways, it's no longer even about my mother. This is about the Community. It *must* be about the Community because although what it is doing began with Rachel, it ends with them, and it is *only* by speaking the truth that we can have any hope of holding the Community to account for the devastating programmes it continues to implement in my mother's name.

33.

In June 2016, an anonymous whistle-blower leaked what they alleged was a confidential Community board memorandum to the investigative journalism website DogWhistle. Within minutes of it appearing on the website, Dad sent me a link.

> *We in the Community recognise that overpopulation is a twenty-first-century pandemic...*
>
> *Decades of evidence prove that incremental measures to reduce population don't work. Any sustained fall in birth rates is inevitably followed by a rise. A dramatic, permanent decline is required...*
>
> *Those of us who are self-supporting due to our intelligence, initiative and self-control are forced to share resources with those less competent than ourselves....*
>
> *Radical population-management programmes are urgently required. Simultaneously, the Community should bring pressure to bear for a cessation of current charitable endeavours in countries with high per capita birth rates. The work of these charities only serves to perpetuate the status quo...*
>
> *Only by deploying radical population-management programmes can the weight of overpopulation be lifted from our shoulders*[17].

[17] Extracts from the alleged board memorandum, published at https://webarchivetool.dogwhistle.community-whistle-blower

The Community vehemently denied the legitimacy of this so-called 'confidential memorandum', subsequently putting so much pressure on Craig Lorcan, DogWhistle's founder, to disclose the name of the alleged whistle-blower that Mr Lorcan left his home in Brighton, drove 250 miles up the A1, checked into a room in the Premier Inn Pontefract North and swallowed sleeping pills washed down with a litre of vodka. His death is yet another that the Community has not accepted responsibility for.

At the time, I accepted the Community's denial that the whistle-blower was genuine. I chose to believe its assertions that the memo was fake. I cannot excuse this. All I can say is that by then I had been a Member for almost five years, I was steeped in Community propaganda, and although I had begun questioning elements of the contraceptive programme, I was not yet giving much thought to the Community's broader aims. Besides, even then, the Community's voice was so loud, much louder than the DogWhistle website, that it was easier, I suppose, for me to simply accept what it said.

Having said that, from June 2016 onwards, my emails to Dad and Livy begin to reflect a long overdue change in tone. I had begun to feel as though some of the Community's achievements were at risk of being undermined by the radical views of the Further, Faster group, particularly since their ideology seemed to be becoming more mainstream.

Casey's latest obsession was with euthanasia or, as she insisted on calling it, 'planned death'. She went on and on about it and genuinely appeared to see no difference between managing population through contraception and encouraging people to agree to a planned death. 'No one would be forced to do anything,' she said. 'We just want to offer people an alternative option.'

In an email to Dad dated 25 June, I wrote, *I'm certain that the reason for the Further, Faster fascination with euthanasia is their fixation on this supposed link between the date of the Event and Mum's own suicide. According to them it proves that Rachel believed suicide was the solution for all sorts of different issues, including overpopulation, but I don't think Mum ever believed that, do you?*

I've already made this point, but it bears repeating: the notebooks make no mention of euthanasia being a 'solution' to anything. My mother committed suicide. So did more than twenty-one thousand others. But I believe that rather than 'proving' that Rachel believed in suicide as a panacea for the world's problems, her silence on the subject in the notebooks proves she did not. Nowhere does she encourage people to take their own lives. The women who died in the Event did so because they wanted people to listen to each other. They wanted people to be heard. They did not want people to start making plans for their own death.

On Tuesday 19 July 2016, Casey and I were scheduled to travel together to Kalehe, a town on the shores of Lake Kivu, seventy-five miles south of Goma. We were planning to open a new clinic there and had arranged a meeting with local officials, a visit to the proposed premises and interviews with several nurses. However, Casey and I had had another one of our arguments and I really wasn't in the mood to sit next to her all the way to Kalehe and back while she harangued me with her Further, Faster nonsense, so I had arranged a not-entirely-necessary early morning meeting at the North Goma Central Clinic. I suggested to Casey that she go as planned to meet the local officials, and as soon as I finished my meeting, I would travel to Kalehe and see her there.

On that Tuesday morning, I and my driver Joseph, who had only been with us for three weeks at that point, left the compound around the same time that Casey and Alain set out for Kalehe. Joseph pulled out into the traffic and we trundled along in nose-to-tail gridlock, eventually hitting the main RN2 road, where the speed was even slower, so by the time we finally turned right onto Boulevard Kanyamuhanga and Joseph pulled up outside the clinic, I was nearly an hour late for my wholly un-necessary meeting. Apologising profusely to Kristel Kipoyi, the clinic manager, I rushed through a list of questions, and forty minutes later I was back in the jeep with Joseph and we were heading to Kalehe.

Once we left Goma City, our route on the N2 skirted the western shore of Lake Kivu. After more than two and a half years of living in Congo, it was a trip I was very familiar with. Kalehe was just over halfway along the lake from Goma en route to Bukavu, where one of our largest clinics was located. The idea of the new clinic was to make it easier for women in the mid-lake area to receive implants without persuading them to travel north to Goma or south to Bukavu.

I've said before that Lake Kivu – one of Africa's Great Lakes – is huge. DRC's border with Rwanda runs down the middle of it, skirting round Idjwi, which is itself the tenth largest lake island in the world, with a population of nearly a quarter of a million. If I had to sum up the Democratic Republic of the Congo in one word, I think I would choose oversized. Everything is on an enormous scale: forests, rivers, lakes, wildlife, population, natural resources. That particular day, as Joseph drove us along the N2, I wound down the window and, letting the sun flood in, I propped my arm on the door, rested my chin on my hand and stared towards Idjwi, wondering how feasible it would be for us to open a clinic over there on the island.

When we were half an hour away from Kalehe, I texted Casey: *30 mins away. Where R U?* She replied immediately: *Just finished meetings. About to head to premises. C U there?*

K! I replied, hesitating for a few seconds before adding *xx.*

Neither Joseph nor I had ever been to Kalehe, and the only information we had was that we were looking for a newish concrete building roughly halfway along a street with a Seventh-Day Adventist church at one end and a market at the other. Kalehe is not large, but we drove around aimlessly for a while, and when we arrived at the same junction for the third time Joseph was really apologetic.

'Pas de problème,' I said. 'Mais, stop and I'll walk.'

He pulled over to the side of the road and I got out, happy to stretch my legs. There was one street we hadn't yet driven down, off a road which was itself off the main through-road, and I headed in its direction. I took the second left, walked a little way then turned left again and found myself outside a squat whitewashed building with a sign proclaiming it as a church of the Seventh-Day Adventists.

The road was a pitted, pockmarked clay track lined with the usual jumble of tumbledown shacks selling drinks, food, tobacco and SIM cards. Phone company names – Airtel, Vodacom, Africell – were painted in faded letters on metal and wooden signs fixed to the roofs. At the other end of the street a market was in progress, vendors and their produce jostling side by side.

About fifty metres along the street I recognised one of our jeeps. Alain was leaning against the door. There was no sign of Casey – she must already have been inside. I waved at Alain but he didn't see me and I hurried towards him.

My memories of what happened next are fragmentary, like individual frames from a film which I can't run together in my mind.

First: the blast. Even on that cloudless day, the detonation is blinding. The flash spreads out, not up, red in the centre, turning orange, yellow, fading grey to white at the edges. I see it before the crack-boom tears the air. The blast echoes around the street, bouncing off buildings.

For a single moment there is silence. Just… silence.

Then the screaming begins. People from the far end of the street are running and I too am running, towards Alain, who is no longer leaning against the jeep but is face down on the ground. I reach him; he is enveloped in thick smoke. I am coughing. Everyone is coughing. People are screaming. More people are running.

I kneel beside Alain. He is alive, but his arm is trapped beneath twisted metal. It is hot to touch. I am shoved sideways, voices yelling at me, 'Dégage du chemin, dégage du chemin,' and I move out of their way.

I am staring at a building about thirty metres beyond where Alain is lying. No, I am staring at what used to be a building. Casey. Is she inside? I pick my way over glass, metal, masonry, everything slippery with blood. Where is Casey?

Someone screams. It is me; I am screaming for Casey. I can taste metal. Each cough makes it worse. Something is burning. Flames flick behind the demolished shopfront. I feel the heat. I must find Casey. The flames reach for me and I step towards them.

Then, I am sitting on the road. Joseph is with me.

Later, I find out that he stopped me entering the building. He had been driving around looking for me and was at the end of the street when the bomb went off. He abandoned the jeep and sprinted towards me. No one else was paying me any attention, and he reached me just as I was about to walk into the fire. He slung me over his shoulder, carried me to the road, stumbling across flesh and wreckage. He stayed with me while the building I had been trying to enter collapsed.

Casey was carried out, and although I didn't see her, both she and Alain were alive when they left Kalehe, driven to the hospital in Goma in the back of a truck, propped between recycled motor parts. Casey and Alain owe their lives to Armandine Sifa, one of the nurses we were scheduled to interview. She heard the blast from about a kilometre away, suspected what had happened and ran as fast as possible towards us. Armandine had trained as a trauma nurse in France. She accompanied Casey and Alain in the back of the truck, and without her, both of them would almost certainly have died before they reached the hospital.

Incredibly, only one person did die that day. Adhylia Odia. The suicide bomber. Although a group calling themselves the Anti-Community Global Alliance claimed responsibility – they had been behind several attacks in other countries, all in contraceptive-implant clinics – the bomb itself was detonated by a nineteen-year-old woman from Bukavu who had heard from her cousin in Kalehe about our plans to open the clinic. Although no one knows how the contact was initially made, the Anti-Community Global Alliance provided Adhylia Odia with the explosives which she strapped to her body and detonated.

Odia was in the doorway when she blew herself up, which is why the blast reached Alain in the street, and also why Casey, who was in a room at the back of the building, survived.

I had the length of the drive back to Goma to pull myself together enough to be able to face everything I had to do.

I spoke first to Dad and then Fortuné (who was visiting his mother, Andréa) to reassure them that, whatever they might hear, I was completely fine. I spoke to the head of the Sub-Saharan Security Sector and then, at her suggestion, to the British embassy in Kinshasa (who promised to send someone to Goma on the first available flight). I spoke to both Laura and Alice back in London, and Alice's boss, and even, briefly, with Sophie Turrell, all of them wanting to make sure I was clear what to say in the interviews. ('We deplore this attack, which is against everything that our Community stands for. Our thoughts are with those who are injured. These cowardly perpetrators want to stop us listening to people, but they will not succeed. We are still listening and we hear you.')

Within the space of three hours, I appeared on BBC News 24, Sky News and CNN and then, with the aid of a translator, fumbled my way through interviews on France TV and Congo's RTNC. I comforted the other Members in the compound and the guards on the gate. I held Mama Em's hand while she cried big fat tears. I had a Skype call with a medical repatriation flight company and a further two calls with the head of the Security Sector to arrange for yet more guards, more guns, more protection. I spoke to two different surgeons in Goma's HEAL Africa Hospital, and several hours later, I spoke to them both again.

It was well past midnight when I finally had time to send a brief reply to Livy, who had emailed me after my father had rung her at work to tell her what had happened.

From: Emilia Morris
To: Olivia Taylor
Date: 20 July 2016

Subject: Re: Oh my god!

Hi Livy,

I'm so sorry I haven't had time to reply to your email until now. I'm fine but, yes, Casey was caught in the blast. There's a plane on its way from the UK now with a doctor on board. They'll assess her, and if it's safe, they'll fly her straight home. I spoke to the surgeon in Goma about half an hour ago and he's had to amputate her leg. It's fucking awful. Also, one of our drivers, Alain, was injured but all they'll tell me is that he's lost a hand. I feel absolutely terrible because I was supposed to have been in that clinic with Casey. I keep thinking maybe if I'd been there I might have seen something. I might have realised what was going to happen.

I'll email again later.

E xxx

Fortuné returned to Goma immediately and refused to let me out of his sight, and Dad went into meltdown, convinced I was going to end up like Casey, or worse. He begged me to come home, but for several weeks I tried to pretend to him and to myself that what had happened to Casey was a tragic one-off, a could-have-just-as-easily-been-hit-by-a-bus-in-Slough type of thing, and not something that should make me question whether it was safe for me to be in DRC.

Then, on 5 October 2016, I received an email from Alice Corbett (now Global Director of PR and Communications) and I could no longer pretend. Alice told me I was being 'transferred to London' because they were creating a 'publicity taskforce' of senior PR people 'to combat the negative publicity generated by anti-Community protests'. She said, 'You should view it as a promotion, Emilia, in recognition of everything that you have achieved for us in the Democratic Republic of the Congo. Well done!'

I knew I was supposed to be pleased. It would be wonderful see Dad and Livy, and of course it was nice to know that my bosses thought I had been doing a good job. I was being offered a hefty pay rise, maybe enough that I would eventually be able to buy a flat (and, wherever I ended up living, I was pretty much guaranteed my own flushing toilet). All that was great.

But, on the other hand, Fortuné was in DRC. Being apart for even a night was bad enough; the idea of getting on a plane and leaving him made me feel sick. I couldn't imagine my life without him next to me, calling me *mpenzi*, even as he reminded me to live in the moment. But that wasn't all. Being in Congo for three years had given me the time and space to become someone other than Rachel of Chalkham's daughter and I wasn't at all sure that I could keep my past at the same distance back in the UK.

For everything I had given to Congo, I had taken far more.

I talked to Alice and she made it clear that the Community considered that my time in DRC was over. If I didn't accept the relocation to London, there was no alternative job for me. I talked to my dad and he just said, 'Come home, Ems.' And, of course, I talked to Fortuné. Even now, five years later, I feel upset when I remember all our conversations as we desperately tried to figure out a way to stay together.

Of course I could leave the Community, but even assuming I was permitted to remain by the fickle Congolese immigration, Fortuné and I would have to move out of our room in the compound. The Community would probably fire him out of spite if I left, but even if it didn't, there was no way we could live on Fortuné's wages alone and how was I supposed to get a job? There wasn't exactly a queue of Congolese employers beating down the door for an English-speaking National Communications Manager. I had relied heavily on our translators at work, and because Fortuné's English was so good, I hadn't really made much of an effort to improve my French or to learn Swahili. But even if I *could* find a job, I would probably never again be able to visit the UK, because even with two salaries it would be impossible to afford the cost of the flight.

There was virtually no chance of Fortuné getting a visa to work in the UK, and even though returning to London on the money they were offering meant that I would be able to afford for us to travel to see each other, we had no idea how feasible it would be to maintain a long-distance relationship. Plus, there was no guarantee that we'd be granted tourist visas to each other's countries – and even if we were, I only had five weeks' holiday a year, and Fortuné was lucky if he got a day or two every now and again. I was trapped between two equally unacceptable options. I postponed my decision for as long as possible but in the end I had to choose. It was the most difficult decision I have ever made.

34.

Everyone has their own love stories, and mine is not the subject of this book, but from the moment at Goma airport when Fortuné turned away from me, knowing that if he didn't find the strength to leave I would never get on the plane, our separation was like a heavy nausea continually rolling around my stomach. In fact, the sickness was so real and so ever-present that I found myself taking a pregnancy test about a week after I returned to the UK (it was negative).

It is tempting to say that I came back from Congo full of doubts about the Community, but that simply isn't true. For one thing, I welcomed the distraction of work – at least there was the chance that entire minutes might pass without me thinking about Fortuné. But also, although I might have begun to question some of the more radical ideas, fundamentally I still trusted that the Community as a whole was travelling along a positive path. I believed the propaganda. I believed in the 'once in a generation' and 'never before undertaken' consultation. I believed in the importance of listening to people who had never been listened to before. Perhaps most importantly, I still believed our programmes were benefiting the people we were delivering them to.

I'd only been back for four days when I made my way to the repurposed Olympic Park in Stratford, east London. As you are probably aware, in the aftermath of the 2012 Olympics many of the buildings were leased to the Community for a peppercorn rent. Because there was no consensus about what to do with the place (handing it all over to sports teams and retail parks was mooted, but no agreement was ever reached), letting the Community move in for practically no money was a way for the government to acknowledge the huge swell of public support for the organisation in the wake of the Event. Plus, I have no doubt that *The Telegraph* hit the nail on the head when they reported, '*Traditional political parties are running scared. If the Community changes its stance on political neutrality, there is every reason to believe that pro-Community candidates could sweep the board at the next election.*'[18]

The Community has greater aspirations than muscling in on traditional political parties in the UK or anywhere else, but back then that hadn't yet become clear and so, in early 2013, despite the Olympic Park representing hundreds of millions of pounds of prime London real estate paid for by the taxpayer, the UK government decided that handing it over to the Community was a small price to pay to obtain a tacit agreement to keep out of politics.[19]

On Monday 16 January 2017, I arrived at the Olympic Park – by then renamed Silence Park – to start my new job in strategic communications. The contrast with where I had been living for the previous three years could not have been starker. The Community's global headquarters was eye-wateringly, embarrassingly ostentatious. It is the blueprint for national headquarters around the world, but none are as extravagant or as luxurious as Silence Park.

[18] *The Telegraph*, 29 January 2013.
[19] For anyone interested in further reading on the Community's approach to political power or the deal to occupy the Olympic Park, see *By Your Side: The Community's Seat in Politics* by Dr Angelica Lopez; *Silence and Power* by Dr Stephanie Mitchell; *Fanning the Flame: Corruption and Fraud at the Olympic Park* by Professor Ibram Brown; and *Theft! How a Government Robbed Its Citizens* by G.F. Larch.

Immediately in front of the main building was a square flanked by vegan food outlets and single-origin hand-roasted coffee stands. The square itself was dominated by a huge bronze representation of my mother's head and shoulders rising out of a shallow pool of water in the shape of the world. Rachel had one muscled arm flung out, embracing the globe, the other was held to her mouth, fist clenched, one finger brushing her pursed bronze lips. Everyone called it the Shculpture. Each day I had to walk past my enormous metal mother before passing under huge black letters spelling out the name of the building where I worked: The Rachel of Chalkham Central Office and Conference Suite.

The lobby walls were clad with 21,078 tiles, each one bearing the name of a woman who had died at the Event. In front of each wall, a white pillar was topped with an artificial flame which burned twenty-four hours a day. Every room in the building was named after an Event site and each one displayed a large map of the world with the name of that particular room identified by a dot of red light. So, for example, the four meeting rooms on the west side of the first floor were called Queenstown (New Zealand), Concepción (Chile), Třebíč (Czech Republic) and Moundou (Chad), although generally we just referred to them as 1, 2, 3 and 4. Unsurprisingly, the boardroom on the fifth floor was called Chalkham (UK).

I worked in Cairo (Egypt). Five of us had been brought together as a sort of task force to promote Community pro-grammes through a combination of social media strategies, traditional PR and leveraging the Community's connections (and funds) to persuade publications and websites to run op-ed pieces by us and, conversely, to quash anti-Community pieces.

On the morning of Wednesday 18 January 2017 – only two days after I had begun my new job – I received a message that I was required on the fifth floor for a meeting with Sophie Turrell.

There was a separate reception desk up there and after giving them my name I was shown into Goderich (Canada). The meeting rooms were luxurious: thickly padded leather seats, original art works on the walls by people I had actually heard of and a menu listing a bewildering range of teas, coffees, milk substitutes and dairy-free snacks.

After about ten minutes Sophie swept in. She shook my hand and said, 'So good to see you back in London, Emilia. I wanted to thank you *personally* for your service in the Democratic Republic of the Congo.'

It was always a bit of a shock seeing Sophie Turrell in person. I would forget how ordinary she is, and how utterly different from my mother. They may have both run the Community, but that's where the similarity ends. Despite Mum's silence (or perhaps because of it), she had a magnetism that you could practically see. People wanted to be close to my mother, even if they didn't know why exactly. Sophie Turrell is not the same. To look at, she is Ms Average personified. Average height, average weight, average length light-ish brown hair. On that particular day she was wearing a suit that was either very dark blue or light black – it was impossible to tell. To be honest, she looked like an accountant.

It is when Sophie starts talking that she morphs from Ms Average to Ms Anything-but-Average. It's difficult sometimes to know which is more powerful: Mum's silence or Sophie's words. People like Sophie always find a way to get to the top, and presumably if she hadn't joined the Community she would be wielding her malevolent influence and talent for persuasion somewhere else. Who knows what would have happened to the Community if Sophie hadn't jumped into the void left by my mother?

That morning, up there on the fifth floor, she asked about my work in Congo and it quickly became apparent that not only had

Sophie read every report I'd written during my time there, but she appeared to have instant recall of every detail. The woman was a machine. Not long after I'd arrived in Goma I'd sent Laura a report about objections to our programme which had been raised by a church group. Sophie wanted to know exactly what they had said and how I had dealt with it. But I couldn't even remember writing the report, let alone the complaint or what I'd done about it.

I met with Sophie several times in London and on each occasion our conversations were more like cross-examinations. It always seemed to me that she behaved differently with me than she did with others. With hindsight, I assume that as some-one who had actually known Rachel – being her daughter, no less – I was probably one of the few people Sophie felt threatened by, which translated into her being terse at best and downright rude to me at worst. If I couldn't tell her what she wanted to know, she'd just cut me off and move on to something else, which is probably why I responded badly to a patronising little homily she decided to give me after we'd finished talking about my time in Congo.

'So, Emilia,' she said, refilling her cup from the pot of oolong tea that had been brought in for her by one of the serving staff. 'I hope you realise that you are valuable to our Community. The work you're doing is vital to help us honour your mother's legacy. Rachel left us a roadmap which I am doing my best to navigate further, faster. Our destination is a place where every person in the world is listened to, heard, respected and their needs are met but, as you've seen for yourself out in the field, there are barriers – roadblocks – along the way. As we clear these obstacles, I'm sure I can rely on you to reassure any doubters that we are doing your mother's work. After all, you owe it to Rachel to make their sacrifice count.'

Roadmap? Roadblocks? Casey had had her leg blown off, for goodness' sake. Surely that was more than a 'roadblock'? In any case, who was this woman to tell me what I owed my own mother?

I distinctly remember looking out of the huge glass window at the monstrous Shculpture of my mother and Sophie was already on her way out of the room when I said, 'Why aren't we listening or hearing?'

She turned back to face me and said, 'What do you mean?'

'Isn't that what we're supposed to be doing? Aren't Rachel's Goals about mending the world? And shouldn't listening and hearing come before everything else? That's what I've always understood, but since I've been back, I haven't seen anyone listen. Not really, properly listen.'

'But that's exactly what we're doing all the time, Emilia. What on earth makes you think we're not?'

'Well, for one thing, no one mentions *Shhhh…* any more. I've not heard anything about the four steps since I got back here. You know… listen to people, hear their problems, understand their needs, deliver solutions. I know we've got all these symbolic Hearing Places and campfires, but is anyone actually doing any real listening and hearing?'

There was a knock on the door and a young woman poked her head round. 'Sorry, Sophie. Your eleven o'clock is in five minutes.' The head disappeared.

Sophie looked at her watch, then at me. 'That rather proves my point, Emilia,' she said. 'I'm about to have a call with a senior government official in India.'

I failed to see how that proved her point, or any other point for that matter.

'I am talking to people,' she continued, sounding impatient. 'I am listening to them. Our programmes are evolving in response to those conversations.'

'But are you still listening to the people that no one else is listening to?'

She looked at her watch again. 'Of course I am, but I don't have time for this now, I'm afraid.'

'Who?' I said. 'Who are you listening to?'

She reached for the door and looked over her shoulder at me. 'Well, you, for one. I'm listening to you.'

With that, she walked out of the room, leaving me alone in Goderich (Canada).

35.

I had been working at Silence Park for almost a fortnight when I got the call from the reception desk to say that I had a visitor. I made my way to Paso de Carrasco (Uruguay) on the east side of the second floor and there, standing by the window, crutches propped against the wall, was Casey.

She had lost weight and strands of grey threaded her hair, but she looked in considerably better shape than I'd expected.

'Hello, stranger,' she said.

We hugged for a long time.

'I didn't know you were here,' I said.

'I came for a meeting on the fifth floor and I couldn't leave without saying hi.'

'Hi. It's so good to see you.' Even as I said the words they sounded desperately inadequate and my eyes filled with tears.

She pulled me in for another hug, put her lips to my ear and said, quietly, 'It's OK, Emilia. Really, it's OK.' She pushed me gently away. 'I've had the best possible care. The Community's been amazing. It's paid for everything. And now I've got Letitia.'

'Letitia?'

Casey pointed at her leg. 'Letitia. My left leg.'

I stared at her, frozen. Was she joking? Should I laugh?

In the end, it was Casey who laughed, and the sound was so familiar: generous, infectious and just so Casey.

She hitched up her trouser leg and I stared at the slim prosthesis.

'You look horrified,' she said.

'No... it's just different to the pictures you sent.'

'The first leg was temporary. Letitia was made especially for me. Since I've had her, I've been doing better. Things are OK. Really.'

I thought of the sporadic emails I'd sent Casey after she'd been flown home from Congo, this woman who had flung her warm, funny self into my room in Slough and hauled me out of my pit of anger and grief, patiently holding the pieces while I put myself back together. And how had I repaid her when she had nearly died? A few emails.

'I'm so sorry, Casey,' I said. 'If I had travelled with you to Kalehe that day, I'd have been there. Maybe I'd have seen something...'

'No,' she said sharply. 'The sick bastards who did this to me, they are the ones who should apologise. I'm furious, but not with you. Those anti-progressive fuckers took my leg, but they will not stop me. I'm making things happen, Ems. Everything is changing. Remember Rachel's mantra: "If you're not with us, you're against us".'

Rachel's mantra? Where had Casey got that from? I let it pass. It was not the day to pick a fight.

I have thought long and hard about whether I should include what I'm going to write about next. It isn't easy to separate my gratitude for Casey's support in the aftermath of the Event, and my guilt that I wasn't there when she lost her leg, from the frustration I felt with her during our time in DRC and the fact that for several years now she has allowed the Community to engage her intellect for the specific purpose of desensitising people to its toxic programmes.

Dad doesn't agree with my decision to write about Casey, but my overriding loyalty is to the truth, no matter where it takes me; and the truth is that what follows is one of the clearest examples of the schism between Rachel's original idea of a 'Listening, Hearing' Community and the aims of the radical and radicalised Further, Faster arm that now dominates the organisation.

In October 2016, Casey became the first recipient of the Rachel of Chalkham Research Fellowship at the University of Central London. Funded by the Community, the purpose of the fellowships, which are awarded at universities around the world, is to create a body of academic research which can be used as both justification and validation for radical Community programmes. Casey was an obvious candidate: intelligent, with experience in the field, and completely committed to the Community's cause. Plus, she had lost a leg in service, so you could say it owed her. In any case, there was no surprise when she was awarded the inaugural fellowship.

She was a prolific writer of papers and articles during her research year, and you can find most of them in the usual academic sources. But there was one which received an extraordinary amount of publicity. I'm sure you know what I'm referring to. *That* article.

I had the opportunity to read Casey's article several weeks before it was published in the first edition of *The Future Human*. The title was 'Population Longevity Aspirations: A Fatal Orthodoxy of Collective Amnesia', which at first glance just sounded like a collection of unnecessarily long academic words. One might very well have been tempted to flick past it and move on to something more interesting (much of the rest of the magazine focused on the use of AI in cancer diagnosis, a far more engaging topic).

However, it is no exaggeration to say that the title of Casey's article masked one of the most inflammatory pieces ever published.

It might have seemed a strange choice for an editorial team issuing their first ever publication to include an article written by a research fellow best known for having had her leg blown off in Congo, but they were gambling on the resulting publicity they would receive from its inclusion. And they were right.

Casey's article had been circulated to the Strategic Communications team in advance so we could make plans for both publicising and defending it against the resulting controversy, which is why I read it in advance of publication. It is also how I know for a fact that the publicity campaign that flooded cities in several countries with billboards displaying *The Future Human* magazine cover was entirely funded by the Community. Anyone who saw that picture will remember it. The pope is sitting on the Chair of Saint Peter. At first glance, nothing is amiss, but when you look closely, you realise that the whole picture is a collage made up of thousands upon thousands of images of the word 'liar'. Once you've seen it, you can't unsee it. It was simple, powerful and extraordinarily controversial – an image as iconoclastic as the article inside.

The Future Human was (and still is) available for free online, but so many people wanted to own a physical copy of the magazine that, despite multiple print runs, it was impossible to keep up with demand[20]. It was undoubtedly the most successful magazine launch in history, and the Community's PR team made sure that Casey appeared on major news and current affairs broadcasts around the world. The public was drawn to this courageous young woman whose crutches were always conspicuously resting against her chair, although I knew for a fact that she no longer had need of them. She was photogenic, engaging and likeable, even as she enthusiastically defended her 'evidence' for the introduction of programmes to encourage mass suicide.

One of Casey's most talked about appearances, certainly in the UK, was on *Our Country/Our Voice*. It is impossible to overstate the controversy that exploded after she appeared on an early evening, light entertainment, mainstream television programme and made a case for encouraging perfectly healthy people over a certain age to consider euthanasia.

I first watched the show when it was broadcast in February 2018 and I recently watched it again online. The two interviewers, Ben Gold and Lily Hutchins, sit side by side on an orange sofa opposite Casey, who is on a matching yellow sofa, looking beautiful with her immaculate afro, bright red lipstick and a tailored white silk shirt tucked into a red skirt that falls just below her knees. Several times during the interview, the camera pans down to linger briefly on the sleek rose-gold contours of Letitia. A pair of crutches are propped next to Casey and every now and again she reaches out to touch them.

I am grateful to the *Our Country/Our Voice* production company for giving me permission to reproduce a transcript of the interview.

> Ben Gold (BG): *And now we welcome Casey Banza from the Community, author of the article that everyone is talking about. Hello, Casey, and thank you for being here.*
>
> Casey Banza (CB): *Hi. Thank you for having me.*
>
> BG: *Before we start, I should warn viewers that we are about to talk about material that some people might find upsetting. If you're watching with small children, you might want to consider changing the channel for the next few minutes.* [Pause]

Lily Hutchins (LH): *So, Casey, you're here to talk about an article you wrote which was published in* The Future Human *magazine. For any viewers not familiar with it, and I have to say, parts of it are really shocking, perhaps you could start by giving us a flavour of what your article says.*

CB: *Sure. My article presents evidence of how, until the last few hundred years, senicide was a key tool used by humans in population management.*

LH: *Senicide?*

CB: *Sorry, yes, senicide is the practice of encouraging elderly people to choose voluntary euthanasia.*

LH: *Wow. OK. My goodness. So did this happen a lot?*

CB: *Absolutely. All the time. In fact, it was commonplace in cultures right across the world. It's only in recent times that we've come to see it as something to be discouraged or wrong in some way.*

BG: *Can you explain to our viewers why it was so popular?*

CB: *It was considered a generous and selfless gift which allowed elders to show how much they cared for the generations that followed them, freeing up resources, particularly food, and enabling their communities not only to continue but also to thrive. In my research—*

BG: *You were a research fellow at the University of Central London, is that right?*

CB: *Yes, that's right, and in my research I focused on uncovering evidence of how senicide used to be considered as natural a part of life as, say, giving birth. I also investigated the reasons why it's fallen out of favour in recent times.*

LH: *You say recent times...?*

CB: *Well, in the context of how long humans have been around, I'd say the last four hundred years or so is most definitely recent times [laughs].*

BG: *Can you give us some examples of how senicide used to be, um... practised... if that's the right word?*

CB: *Sure. Well, the Egyptians and Mayans underwent ritual mass poisonings. The Inuit have a tradition of the elderly taking themselves out to the ice to die. Then there were a whole variety of creative suicide solutions [laughs] on offer in Ancient Greece and the Roman Empire. There were the Heruli, a Germanic tribe around in the time of Attila the Hun, who used to set fire to themselves, and of course many people are familiar with the Hindu practice of sati, when a widow immolates herself on a funeral pyre. Then there's—*

LH: *That all sounds pretty horrific, particularly those last two methods you mentioned. Do you think they influenced Rachel of Chalkham's decision to use fire at the Event?*

CB: *I think there's every likelihood that they did, yes.*

BG: *Many of your critics say you're trying to promote a mass euthanasia programme and you're glamorising suicide. What do you say to that?*

CB: *Let me be clear. I am not and nor is the Community glamorising suicide. And there's no question of a mass euthanasia programme. All I am doing is presenting research to demonstrate that senicide should be considered as a valid option to tackle the world's population crisis.*

LH: *Let's unpack that a little. The figures in your article around what you call the population crisis look quite scary.*

CB: *I'm not calling it a population crisis. It is a population crisis. And, yes, the numbers are scary. We should all be scared. In 2016, more than 815 million people did not have enough food to eat. A similar number did not have access to a reliable source of clean water. That's 11 per cent of the world's population. I don't know about you, but I find that terrifying.*

LH: *And the link with senicide...?*

CB: *So many resources are expended nowadays to ensure that people live as long as possible. The average age of citizens at death is one of the key measures of whether or not a country is what we like to call developed. Take the UK, for example. In the last 100 years, life expectancy for women has increased from forty-eight to eighty-one years.*

BG: *That's got to be a good thing, right?*

CB: *Well, this is the point. Is it? Is it a good thing? The human race is so fixated on keeping everyone alive for as long as possible that it takes priority over absolutely everything else. But while we're expending all this energy and effort to keep everyone alive, often far beyond when people have outgrown their usefulness to society, we ignore the fact that we only have limited resources. We have completely abandoned the tools we used to use to make sure there was a fair and equitable allocation.*

BG: *And you're saying one of these tools was senicide, right?*

CB: *Yes, certainly that was one of them.*

BG: *What you're suggesting is really controversial...*

LH: *And shocking...*

BG: *Quite right. Shocking. Aren't you worried that this might turn people against the Community?*

CB: *[laughs] I think the Community will survive. And in any case, I know better than most what can happen if you annoy people...*

LH: *You're referring to the bomb.*

CB: *Yes, my leg was blown off when someone decided they hated what the Community stood for and bombed one of our clinics in DRC.*

LH: *How are you doing now?*

CB: *I'm good. I'm extremely fortunate to be part of the Community – I've had fantastic support.*

BG: *How do you feel now about what happened to you?*

CB: *It's made me even more determined not to be intimidated. I refuse to worry about people's selfish sensitivities when the population crisis facing our world is so urgent.*

LH: *Your passion about this subject is obvious, but how would you answer the accusation that what you're suggesting unfairly targets our elder citizens?*

CB: *Well, you remember that I said 11 per cent of the world's population don't have enough food to eat, yes?*

BG and LH: *Yes…*

CB: *In 2016, the same year that that study was published, 901 million people in the world were aged sixty or over. Do you know what percentage of the world's population that is?*

LH: *Six per cent?*

BG: *Eight per cent?*

CB: *It's 12.3 per cent. In 2016, 11 per cent of the world's population didn't have enough food to eat and 12 per cent were over sixty years of age. It's no coincidence. In the past we understood there was a vital link between age of death and scarcity of resources. That's why we need to reconsider senicide. Many older people want to do their bit to help the younger generations. This fixation that the human race has about keeping people alive as long as possible denies our elder generation their right to choose to die at a time appropriate to their wishes and circumstances. Rachel of Chalkham showed us that silence is the key to solving the problems of our world. Choosing death is simply another form of silence, just as Rachel herself demonstrated.*

BG: *Surely you aren't saying that when people reach the age of sixty they should consider whether it's time for them to die?*

LH: *We'd lose half our audience!*

CB: *Look, I am not suggesting that senicide is appropriate for everyone over sixty. All I'm doing is highlighting the relevant facts and the statistics and explaining what my research revealed about how humans used to manage population numbers in order to ensure sufficient resources. What I would say, though, is that the older people become the more they should be encouraged to consider whether they are still making a positive contribution to society, and if they feel they are not, then maybe they should have other options available to enable them to show how much they care about the people that come after them.*

LH: *We're almost out of time here, so I'd like to thank Casey for coming along today.*

CB: *My pleasure, thank you for having me.*

LH: *For anyone who would like to read Casey's article, it's available in* The Future Human *magazine and online at* www.thefuturehuman.org.

BG: *If you've been distressed by anything we've been discussing, details of organisations that can help will be broadcast at the end of the programme.*

LH: *In the meantime, we look forward to seeing you again tomorrow, when we'll be showing you how to make vegetarian haggis, taking a look at another of the finalists in the High Street of the Year Competition and enjoying a performance by chart-topping band, The Twinsets.*

BG: *But for now, from all of us here at* Our Country / Our Voice, *from our sofa to yours, enjoy the rest of your evening and, until tomorrow, bye-bye* [waves].

LH: *Bye-bye, everyone* [waves].

[Credits]

Before anything else, I would like to point out that I completely refute Casey's idea that an ancient tribe from Germany or the Hindu custom of widow immolation somehow played a part in my mother's decision to burn herself to death at the Event. Nothing in the notebooks suggests there is any truth in this whatsoever. I do not believe Rachel was 'inspired' by such things or, for that matter, that she was remotely aware of any historical tradition of senicide. This is a clear example of the Community seeking to twist every last action of my mother's in order to justify its devastating policies.

Although the subject matter of this interview was undoubtedly controversial, perhaps what is most notable about it is what they *didn't* discuss. By the time Casey appeared on *Our Country/Our Voice* – three months after the magazine's publication – *The Future Human* was already embroiled in a number of court cases. The magazine's legal team was entirely funded by the Community, and it needed to be, because the organisation which mounted the most public attack against Casey's article was, as everyone knows, the Catholic Church. The lawsuits were the reason why that part of her article wasn't mentioned by the interviewers.

In the article, Casey claims to have 'uncovered evidence' proving that the original reason the Catholic Church introduced celibacy was as a 'population-management tool'. Famines and plagues were rife in the first few centuries of the existence of the Church and there was a constant fear of a lack of resources. For every priest or nun who did not have a child, countless other children would also never be conceived and within only a few generations tens of thousands of people would never be born. Casey says that, although celibacy was the Church's contribution to managing population levels, in more recent centuries it has been complicit in 'covering up the origins of clerical celibacy'. This is the 'lie' which Casey accuses the Church of perpetuating.

I don't know if Casey genuinely believes that the Catholic

Church is involved in some sort of mass cover-up – what her article refers to as the 'collective amnesia that humanity labours under, in its efforts to promote longevity at all costs' – but such a shocking accusation guaranteed her article an enormous amount of publicity, and the only thing that appears to have been achieved by the Catholic Church's various legal cases has been a raising of public awareness about the issues around overpopulation.

I vividly remember watching Casey on the original broadcast of *Our Country/Our Voice*, sounding as unemotional as if she was demonstrating the following day's vegetarian haggis recipe rather than promoting the concept of mass euthanasia as a method of managing the world's population. I remember the horror I felt when it dawned on me that these ideas of hers – of theirs – were at genuine risk of becoming acceptable because, no matter what word Casey used for it, or how she dressed it up as a 'choice' and a 'generous and selfless gift', what she was talking about was suicide.

The Community was once again encouraging people to take their own lives.

36.

Even after Casey's appearance on *Our Country/Our Voice*, I ended up staying in the Community for a further twenty-one months.

Part of me still hoped that the radical Further, Faster ideology she had aligned herself with would remain marginal, that the ideas would never actually become official Community policy, but if I'm being completely honest, I had a far more selfish reason for not walking away until late 2019, and to explain, I must return to the contraceptive-implant programme.

I will carry the shame of my involvement in that programme for the rest of my life. It's not enough, but it is the truth. Until relatively recently, I justified my actions by claiming I was simply doing the job I had been given, that I couldn't possibly anticipate the consequences of what we. were doing in Congo (and elsewhere), and I genuinely believed we were doing the right thing. All of that happens to be true.

But it is also true that, right from the beginning, multiple charities and other organisations had flagged concerns, and I would like to apologise specifically to those individuals who repeatedly tried to bring their concerns to my attention while I was in Congo. I did not hear you. Also, my father, who sent me all those articles warning of the dangers of the programme, and Scholar, who tried to explain – I did not hear them either.

By the time I finally began to listen, it was too late. I was already back in London. Countless women had been harmed and, to this day, terrible violence is still being perpetrated around the world on women who have had the implant. Although the programme has been quietly dropped from the Community's annual reports and publicity campaigns, I am absolutely certain that it continues and every day women are still being bribed to accept the implant.

In the end, it was thanks to my insomnia that I finally came to understand the terrible consequences of the Community's implant programme. After I returned to London, in any free moment I had, I would obsessively search the internet for a job, any job, in the UK that would consider an application from a Congolese man. Each day after work, I would rush home and begin scrolling through job sites, convinced that if I didn't, I would miss that one opportunity which would provide a visa for Fortuné. Eventually, in the early hours of each morning, when I found myself scrolling back through websites I'd been looking at three or four hours earlier, looking at the same jobs, jobs for which he was completely unqualified, I would force myself to stop.

It was impossible to guarantee a time when Fortuné and I could speak on the phone or Skype. Either he had a shift starting, or I was in a meeting, or he had run out of data on his phone, or the electricity was down in the compound. I never wanted to go to the pub, or the cinema, or travel on the underground, because what if he rang and I missed his call? By the end of 2017, I had emailed applications for literally hundreds of jobs on his behalf, and not one employer had even replied. No one, it seemed, could find a place in their organisation to employ a multilingual, intelligent, talented man from Congo.

So it was usually around 2 a.m., when I'd exhausted the job sites but still couldn't sleep, that I would search out blogs and news articles about DRC and wider sub-Saharan Africa. Reading about the place I loved, coming across mentions of places I knew, food I'd eaten, even looking at travelogues complaining about long-drop toilets and mosquitoes made me feel just a little better, albeit briefly.

At first, the implant programme was mentioned only in passing, in reports buried among other more newsworthy items, and initially I dismissed them. But I kept coming across reports here, articles there, until I eventually began to take notice[21].

NCCW reports that a woman who has had the Community's contraceptive implant is 70 per cent more likely to suffer domestic abuse and 24 per cent more likely to be killed by her spouse[22].

Regional offices have recorded an increase in brutality towards women in every country where the Community has rolled out its implant programme, according to testimonies from multiple women including from the sister of a twenty-six-year-old woman in Malawi who died of sepsis after gouging a chunk out of her own arm to try and get rid of the implant[23].

[21] Although I have included links to the websites where I found the following articles, most of them no longer exist and/or the articles have been deleted.

[22] https://NCCW/8dec17/Community/implant/abuse. NCCW was a Ugandan-based women's rights charity. It is now defunct, principally because of pressure brought to bear by the Community on the Ugandan government to ban it. In return for the authorities shutting down this highly vocal, highly Community-critical organisation, the Community sponsored the construction of a state-of-the-art conference centre in Kampala.

[23] https://LevellingUP/04022017/Malawifocus. LevellingUP is a Canadian charity, which is still in existence, although the scope of its work has significantly reduced since 2017, when it produced a series of reports focusing on countries where the implant programme had been rolled out.

*Woman in Burundi dies after her husband hacked off
her arm with an axe to get rid of her implant[24].*

The day after I read about the death of the woman in Burundi,
I went to speak to a friend of mine who worked at the Silence Park
in the department responsible for taking down online sites which
had even a hint of negativity about the Community. She has asked
me not to identify her. She told me that the team of twenty – all
qualified lawyers – spent all day, every day, working to remove
material from the internet as fast as it was put up, which explained
why I often couldn't find articles that I had only read a few days
before, and is also why I began copying pages from websites,
jotting down statistics, printing out articles.

The Community must have known it had something to hide,
I decided, or else why would they need a whole team of lawyers
to get this stuff removed? I was finally beginning to grasp how
catastrophic the programme's consequences were, and I felt
horribly guilty. How could I have completely failed to realise that
convincing women to make themselves infertile for years might
not be in their best interests? Why hadn't I heard what Scholar
was trying to tell me when she left the Community? She
understood the damage being done to the women of her country.

I was ashamed. Deeply, unreservedly ashamed. However,
my shame was of no use to the women being hurt by the programme. I didn't know what to do. I was Rachel's daughter, but
the Community had decided long ago that that afforded me
no special treatment whatsoever. So I kept digging. And awful
reports kept being published, fleetingly, before being removed
from the internet.

[24] www.tanzaniatimes.com/news/Burundi-Community-wife-killed-by-axe-
attack

A report from WADV says that 34 per cent of all women in Africa and the Middle East who have had the implant suffer domestic abuse and/or societal ostracisation within eighteen months[25].

A woman in Afghanistan was brutally raped and left for dead by eight men on her way home from a Community clinic. The men told her that as she'd had an implant fitted it was their right to have sex with her because there was no risk of pregnancy[26].

Five women found hanging from tree with Community 'reward bags' tied around their necks[27].

I'm not proud of how long it took me to accept the truth, but it was this report, the one about these women murdered in Burundi with the bribes that they had received from the Community tied around their throats, which finally persuaded me to act.

It wasn't easy to get a meeting with Sophie Turrell. Her assistant kept telling me how busy Sophie was and how she had no time until, in the end, I resorted to the 'I'm Rachel's daughter and I think she'll want to see me' line. I didn't expect that to work, but I was granted an audience.

I prepared more thoroughly for that meeting than for any

---

[25] WADV stands for Women Against Domestic Violence, a South African based charity, which, like NCCW, has long since been forced to close.
[26] https://RapeWatch.org.uk/daily-update/Afghanistan-implant-rape/
[27] https://www.dailyrecord.co.ug/News/international/5-Burundi-women-die-after-receiving-implant/573976-032718/index.html

meeting I've ever had. I put together a one-page summary of the main points, prepared slides with the key bullet points, collated bundles of all the relevant reports I could get my hands on and copied the key documents onto a flash drive to give to Sophie. I practised what I was going to say over and over again in front of the bathroom mirror.

On my way into work on the day of the meeting – 12 April 2018 – I bought a large coffee from the coffee bar near the Shculpture and walked over to stand in front of it. Before confronting Sophie, I wanted to confront my mother – or, at least, an oversized image of her. It sounds rather ridiculous, but it wasn't until that morning that I realised what an uncannily good job the artist – Naomi de Witt – had done of rendering my mother's features in bronze. Her combative expression reminded me of the countless times I'd gone to see Rachel, stalking down to the camp spoiling for a fight for some reason or other. Then, as now, Mum's silence made an argument impossible.

It is only while writing this book that I have come to understand that what I heard in my mother's silence depended entirely on my own mood. For example, if Dad told me to go tell her about a bad result in a school test, Mum's silence was palpably disappointed. If I was feeling sad, there was sympathetic silence. When I got my A-level results and my place at Bristol University was confirmed, Mum's silence was her most joyful silence for years.

Perhaps this was the entire point of Rachel's silence: it reflected whatever was directed towards it. If you recognise yourself in someone's silence you will, perhaps, be more receptive to them and their struggles and fears and aspirations. In any case, take it from me, it's impossible to have an argument with someone who is silent. You end up just arguing with yourself. I think Mum instinctively understood these things. In fact, I am certain she knew that if we learned to use silence as well as we use words, then not only would we hear ourselves more clearly, but others would hear us more clearly too.

But standing in front of the Shculpture before my meeting with Sophie, this insight into my mother's silence had yet to arrive and I, spoiling for a fight, saw a reflection of my own mood in my mother's grotesquely huge bronze face. Women were suffering because of what we were doing. Women were literally *dying* because of us and *she* was responsible. Rachel of Chalkham was responsible for it all. Other people might be in charge now, but my mother had begun the whole thing. I threw the cup of coffee at my mother's head. It hit her right eye, and although the cup dropped to the floor, the coffee rolled down her face. Hot tears. Good. She deserved to cry.

Fabrication.

Spin.

Exaggeration.

The reports were full of them, according to Sophie.

She was inscrutable while she listened to my presentation, so I had no idea what she was thinking. When I had finished, she didn't say anything, just sat there, spinning the memory stick I'd given her round and round on the table between us. The silence stretched for what felt like minutes before she finally spoke.

'We had an agreement, Emilia. We're at a critical point in the implementation of the roadmap towards achieving Rachel's Goals. Obstacles will appear and we must all work together to overcome them.'

'These aren't just obstacles...' She held up a hand and my voice trailed off.

'I listened to what you had to say, Emilia. I listened and I heard you. That is what we do in our Community, so please extend me the same courtesy.'

She stared at me, waiting, until I nodded reluctantly.

'As we move along the roadmap to our destination, there will be obstacles. I thought you understood this. After all, if you're not with us, you're against us. We've only just started the journey, and no doubt there will be greater roadblocks, but we must all stay focused on our destination. Eyes on the prize, Emilia, eyes on the prize.'

She laughed a little laugh, but it didn't reach her eyes. Her next words were stern. 'When we spoke last time, we agreed that you were ready to clear obstacles and reassure doubters.'

I didn't recall agreeing to anything. As I remembered it, Sophie had waltzed into the meeting room, told me what I should be doing and waltzed out to speak to the prime minister of India or some such.

She had a lot more to say about my presentation, not just that the reports were exaggerated, misleading, full of spin and fabrication. She trotted out statistics from Community-sponsored reports that contradicted the ones I had given her, she repeated endorsements by political leaders, she gave me details of the latest eye-watering donations from corporate sponsors, she quoted from books I hadn't read and websites I hadn't seen, but the whole time I was becoming more and more frustrated. Where was her empathy, let alone responsibility or culpability, for the situation that women around the world were finding themselves in?

I wasn't naïve enough to think she was just going to accept what I'd put together and immediately pull the plug on the whole programme, but I had hoped that when she heard what I had to say and saw the reports she would at least take it seriously. I didn't expect instant change – the Community was too big, too corporate for that – but I expected something other than a flat denial of the facts.

Eventually, Sophie changed tack and, leaning towards me, she said, 'Even if there *is* a scintilla of truth behind all this, Emilia, you must understand that it's just collateral damage.'

Collateral damage? She was talking about women who were being beaten, ostracised, mutilated and murdered.

I wanted to get to my feet, to run away from her as fast as possible, but I didn't. Eventually I managed to say, 'These are real people, and they're being hurt, or worse, because of us.'

'All progress carries a price,' Sophie said, picking up her mobile and flicking through messages. 'Nobody said our journey would be easy.'

'So you don't care about what's happening to these women?' I asked.

She looked up from her phone. 'Haven't you been listening to anything I've said, Emilia? I care deeply for them and for all women, all people. That's why we must strive to go further, faster along the roadmap to achieve Rachel's Goals.'

It was blindingly clear to me that everything that came out of her mouth was nonsense. Her words meant absolutely nothing.

This, then, was the beginning of the end of my time with the Community. This is what it took for me to finally see the hypocrisy of this Community of my mother's, an organisation built on the promise of listening that now only heard what it wanted to hear. I am deeply ashamed it took me so long to understand this.

Sophie had put her phone down and was looking at me, steadily, waiting for me to speak.

'You don't care about these women,' I said. 'How can you? What's happening to them is because of what *we're* doing. It's our fault.'

I paused for a moment, giving her an opportunity to agree, but when she said nothing, I continued, 'If you won't do anything about it—'

'What, Emilia? If I won't do anything about it, then what?'

'I'll resign. I'll find someone who *will* listen to me. I'll talk to the press.'

'If that's what you feel you must do, then of course I can't stop you, but it would be such a shame, Emilia. Such a shame. And just when we had some really good news for you.' She did another no-eyes laugh. I had no idea what she was talking about and my confusion must have shown on my face, because she said, 'Hasn't HR told you?'

I shook my head, expecting her to offer me a promotion or a pay rise or something. There was absolutely nothing she could say that would persuade me to remain in the Community for a moment longer.

'We're cutting back on security out in Congo, and although we haven't told Fortuné yet, he's going to lose his job next week. However, we have been considering offering him a consultancy role here in London. It's a great job with a substantial salary, and of course we'll fast-track his visa.'

37.

I am writing these words in the same hotel room where I've been for the last three days. I was alone for the first night, but now Fortuné is with me.

Three days ago, someone calling themselves @SlaughterThe Daughter posted the address of our supposedly 'safe' flat on social media. I do not know how they found out where we were staying. They said I was 'hating on Rachel' by writing a book 'full of filthy lies', and so they were going to come to our flat to 'smash some sense' into me and that anyone who believed in 'keeping Rachel's legacy pure' should join them.

The first we knew about it was the sound of hammering on our front door. Judging by the shouting, several people were outside. I was terrified. It took me straight back to when those thugs from The52 stormed our pub, except this time the person they were after was me. For the second time in my life, I rang 999.

They were either hurling themselves or something really heavy against our front door. Fortuné grabbed a knife from the kitchen and I prayed the door would hold until the police arrived. My husband would do anything to protect me. If they broke the door down and Fortuné stabbed someone, what would happen to him?

Where the flat faces the street, there is a big bay with three windows. Because Fortuné and I were both in the hallway, we didn't know someone was swinging a hammer at the window until we heard two thuds, followed by the sound of smashing glass. Fortuné reacted first, running into the living room. I followed. In the distance I heard police sirens. Outside the window, a woman was holding a hammer. She was wearing a retro Community T-shirt, the neon-pink one with the finger against the lips. Her make-up was immaculate and I remember thinking how incongruous it looked on a face distorted by hatred.

The window had not fallen out completely, but on the floor jagged shards of glass were surrounded by a carpet of tiny pieces. The woman continued to swing the hammer, bashing through the rest of the glass and bellowing words I couldn't make out. Fortuné moved towards the window. He didn't seem to feel the glass slicing his bare soles. The sirens were ear-piercing, and still the woman swung her hammer, screaming, spitting saliva. Fortuné raised the knife. He jabbed his hand through the window and thrust the blade into the woman's arm. She howled and dropped the hammer.

The police arrived just in time to see him stab the woman in the arm and Fortuné was detained. Of course he was. No matter that this was an unprovoked attack on us. No matter that we were the victims, that Fortuné was defending our home, me, himself. No matter that he has a legitimate visa, he was kept in jail overnight before being released without charge.

There is surprisingly little about my husband that annoys me, which is a good thing considering how most of the rest of my life seems to have been mired in anger. But one of the few things that I do find intensely irritating is that he refuses to believe in coincidence. He is a fatalist. According to him, everything is predestined. Everything happens for a reason and is part of some grand playbook. For example, he believes we were destined to meet. He genuinely thinks that every decision I took in my life right up to the actual moment that he came to pick Scholar and me up from the compound in Goma that Christmas Eve was leading me towards our meeting.

I do not believe this. In so many ways my husband is a wonderful man, but on this point I think he is deluded. In fact, his view is completely ridiculous because if he was right, that would mean we would have no free will. We would have no agency over our own lives; if everything is preordained then nothing we do will ever make a difference one way or the other.

For a man who is otherwise not egotistical, Fortuné's belief in fate can also have the effect of making him sound astonishingly egocentric, as if he is at the centre of the universe, and the purpose of absolutely everything is to deliver his destiny to him. It's one of a very small number of triggers that cause arguments between us, and we'd been heading towards one of those arguments when the women arrived outside our flat.

Before they came, while we were drinking coffee from arabica beans grown on Gloria's – Fortuné's sister's – fledgling coffee plantation, he opened a letter from the Home Office. His visa was being reviewed, it said, because it had 'come to their attention' that 'there may have been irregularities in the original application'. The Community is so concerned about me writing a book about my mother that it is prepared to enlist civil servants to threaten us, and although Fortuné's visa was legitimate – every criterion met; every box ticked – it would be foolish for us to underestimate how far its influence stretches.

For Fortuné, the letter was not simply a letter, it was our destiny writ large on a piece of paper topped by the Home Office shield because, according to him, the review of his visa is a clear sign that we should return to Congo. My husband has had enough of the Community's games and threats. He is tired of living in the UK where he so often feels unwelcome. His sister Gloria has offered us both jobs. Her coffee-bean business is doing well and she needs help. She has asked Fortuné to return home and become her general manager. She has just signed a substantial contract to sell her beans directly to a large American coffee chain and there's the potential for many more such contracts. My PR experience and my English would help. Fortuné wants us to go – in fact, he's convinced we should. He thinks Gloria has offered us jobs because now is the time we are meant to leave the UK and return to Congo. For him, the letter from the Home Office was just further confirmation.

But what about my father? How can I pick up my life and leave him for a second time?

When those awful women arrived outside our flat, I was in the middle of working myself up over what I saw as Fortuné's thoughtless assumption that I would be happy to move so far away from Dad again.

Now, three days later, as he hobbles around this hotel room on his poor sliced-up feet, Fortuné is telling me the attack on our home was a sign. In his mind the reason those people came to our flat was to prove to me conclusively that it is our destiny to return to Congo.

38.

By the middle of 2018, I knew what the Community was and I loathed it, but when I was faced with a choice between continuing to work for an organisation that was doing terrible damage around the world and the chance of a visa for the man I loved, I did not hesitate to abandon any principles I might have had. I allowed Sophie to buy my silence.

She delivered on her promise, or bribe, whatever you want to call it, and the Community offered Fortuné a job in the Security Sector in London and sponsored his work visa. They even paid for his flight to the UK. Everything happened surprisingly quickly – only a matter of weeks – and I wish I could say that I felt at least some vestige of guilt as I waited for him to walk through the Arrivals door at Heathrow Airport, but I would be lying. Despite everything I had come to understand about the Community and my part in what the organisation had done, on that particular day there was no room in my mind for anything except Fortuné.

Even after he had arrived, and we were finally together, I refused to do anything that might risk him losing his Community-sponsored visa and so I continued to work for them. I did not feel able to walk away until we were married (in February 2019 at Winchester registry office, just the two of us with Dad and Livy as witnesses; I wore a beautiful *pagne* patterned with lemon-yellow leaves and flamboyant pink bougainvillea that Andréa had given Fortuné when he left Congo with the hope that I would one day wear it to marry her son). Even then I didn't leave. I hung on, waiting until we had gone through months of submitting paperwork and attending interviews to prove our relationship was genuine and Fortuné was finally granted his spouse visa.

In the fifteen months between 14 July 2018, when Fortuné arrived in the UK, and 17 November 2019, when we collected his passport with the long-awaited visa and our dependence on the Community finally came to an end, I kept my head down, avoided confrontation, and hated every minute of every day that I spent at Silence Park. I put my needs ahead of everything else, and having spent the last eight years of my mother's life hating her silence, for my remaining time at the Community I hated myself for my silence, too.

39.

Dad came to the hotel this morning.

My publishers are obviously feeling guilty about our address being leaked because they have upgraded us to a *very* nice hotel. In fact, we have a suite, no less. Dad phoned to say he was in the lobby. Fortuné answered, then immediately announced he was going for a walk, grabbed his coat and left. It took some time for Dad to come up and it crossed my mind that he and Fortuné were probably having a chat downstairs.

While Dad admired the view of London from the dizzy heights of the fourteenth floor, I looked at him closely. He has healed remarkably well considering how badly he was beaten up. His arm is still in a cast, but other than that you would never know what had happened. Like me, my father carries many invisible scars, but despite everything I think he's finally doing OK.

After he came out of hospital, his trademark 'Howard Jones' hair finally succumbed to the lure of the clippers. The baldness makes him look older, I think, but more handsome. I wonder if he will ever want to be with someone else. His relationship with my mother, which wasn't straightforward, even at the beginning, was so complicated and although I've often told him that I'd love for him to find a new partner, I really don't know if Dad will ever feel ready for that.

He turned from the view and I could tell by the way he was looking at me that something was on his mind.

'I've got something to tell you,' he said, but then, 'hang on a sec…'

He crossed the room to the mini-bar (which is more *full* bar than *mini*) and brought a bottle of red wine and two glasses back, putting them on the table between us. He unscrewed the cap, half-filled a glass and held it out. I shook my head.

'Fair enough,' he said. He took a sip, and another. 'Dutch courage.'

Then, looking out of the window, rather than at me, he said, 'I think you should move back to Congo.'

Fortuné had been talking to Dad behind my back. The pair of them ganging up on me. Anger surged through me. Nothing new there, then. 'I can't believe he's asked you to persuade me to leave. How dare he?'

'Don't get all worked up,' Dad said. 'We only talked about it because I'd called him to discuss something else. It's what I've come here to tell you.'

Now I was scared. Was Dad ill? Was that it? He finished the wine and poured some more.

'What's going on, Dad? Is something wrong?'

He put down his wine glass, reached across and patted my hand. 'Nothing's wrong, Ems. Stop worrying. Look, can we talk about you and Fortuné in a minute? Let me tell you my news first.'

'What is it? Are you ill?'

'God, no, Ems. Is that what you're worrying about? No, darling. I'm perfectly fine. I'm sorry, it's nothing like that. No, it's a good thing.'

'So what is it?'

'I've been offered a visiting fellowship at a university in New Zealand.'

It took a few seconds for me to switch my emotions, replace

fear with joy, but I got there in the end and I gave him a hug. 'Oh my god, Dad, that's just fantastic.'

And it was. I was so immensely proud of this man, my father, who had struggled for so long to make a life for himself that didn't revolve around Rachel's life, and her death. He almost hadn't made it, but now look at him.

'Seriously, Dad, that's just brilliant. I'm so proud of you. Where exactly is it? When do you leave?'

'Dunedin, on the South Island. The thing is, though, Ems. I haven't decided yet if I'm going to accept.'

'What? Why not?'

'How I can leave you here with everything that's going on?' He waved a hand at the window, as if it was London itself that was threatening me.

'That's crazy, Dad. This is an amazing opportunity. You have to go. You can't stay here just because of me.'

'Really? Fortuné told me that's exactly the reason you don't want to go back to Congo. *You* want to stay here because of *me*.' He took a sip of wine then smiled at me.

'He shouldn't have told you that,' I said. 'In any case, there's Livy as well…'

'Come on, Ems. Be honest with me now. You've always said that if you and Fortuné could find decent jobs you'd go back to Congo in a flash. He told me about Gloria's offer. What's stopping you?'

I didn't know what to say so I just shook my head.

'Think about it, Ems. You don't want to go because you don't want to leave me. I don't want to go because I don't want to leave you. But I think, if we're really honest, we have to admit that neither of us is doing so well here in the UK at the moment, are we?'

I shook my head again.

'And there's Fortuné,' he said. 'It's what he wants. And you've nearly finished the book. I think there's a lot to be said for us all being as far away from here as possible once it's published. I know that's what Fortuné thinks.'

'So the two of you have decided everything behind my back?' I said, cranking up my righteous indignation, but then Dad said something that stopped me dead in my tracks.

'Sometimes you remind me so much of your mother.'

I'm aware that this is the sort of thing people say to each other all the time: *you remind me of your mum*; *you're just like your mother*; *like mother, like daughter.* When I first joined the Community, when it was still a novelty for Rachel's daughter to be a Member, people often said something similar to me, but they were only ever referring to my physical resemblance to Rachel and I knew that wasn't what Dad was talking about.

'What the hell does that mean? How can I possibly remind you of her?' I asked.

He took his time. He poured more wine. He took a sip. He put his glass down. He took a deep breath and let it out slowly. 'Your mother was opinionated. She was stubborn. She stood up for herself and her views. She would cling to a point of principle long past the point when she should have abandoned it and walked away.'

'What are you saying? That I have all Mum's bad traits?' Even to myself I sounded like a petulant teenager.

'Darling, stop looking for the negatives in everything. I'm saying you are strong and independent. I'm saying you stand up for what you believe in. I'm saying you don't often admit you might be wrong. Just like your mother.'

'They don't really sound like compliments, Dad.'

'Emilia. Listen to me. What I'm trying to say is that I believe you will be OK wherever you are. You will make a good life for yourself. You and Fortuné. You will thrive. But you'll be able to do that so much more easily if you aren't living here, in the long shadow of your mother's legacy.'

He gestured out of the window again and this time I followed the sweep of his hand and we both stared out of the window in silence.

Dad has left and Fortuné isn't back yet, so I'm alone with my laptop, trying to summon up the few words that remain to be written, but the conversation with Dad keeps going round and round in my head and all I can see is the face of that woman outside our flat, swinging her hammer. She really hated me. I mean, really, really hated me, just because I'm writing a book about my own mother. It's ridiculous. What on earth do these people think I'm going to say? What are they so scared of? It's not like anything I've written is going to bring down the Community, however much I wish that it would.

What Dad said also got me thinking about why it is that what the Community has already achieved isn't enough. I mean, where does it come from, this terrible urge to go further, faster?

I can't speak for the Community, but I do have a theory.

I think what my mother did at the Event stopped the entire world, just for a moment, and in that moment we considered how it might feel to really listen and to really be heard. Many of us found that we liked the idea very much and we liked the organisation that was offering to listen to us. The enormous popularity of the Community attracted very wealthy individuals and companies who donated money and resources so they could align themselves with the Community and claim that they too were striving for a more peaceful, fairer, contented society. This unique combination of mass popularity plus extraordinary wealth propelled its astonishing growth.

And, for a while, the Community did listen, but in time it no longer heard the voices of other people and began to listen only to itself. And what it heard was that it wanted what every other rich and powerful organisation in history has ever wanted: more money and more power.

And how do these organisations get more money and more power?

Having been part of the Community, having seen how it works, here is my answer to that question: they implement policies that destabilise and divide. They create schisms. They set people arguing among themselves, and while people are distracted they take their power and they take their money. Most importantly, they hide in plain sight the solutions that will deliver what they desire.

And, of course, there is a solution which achieves all of that: a programme that destabilises and divides while delivering money, and vast amounts of it.

From the moment of Rachel's death, the Community's plan was to convince the world that it was listening. That it had the world's best interests at heart, that it could deliver what the world needed, priming millions, perhaps billions, of ordinary people to believe that the Community could achieve all of Rachel's Goals and in doing so solve the greatest issues facing humanity.

The plan was to build trust in the Community and its programmes.

The plan was staggeringly successful, and the Community's ambition grew. It wanted more money, more power, more, more, more… Until on the eighth anniversary of the Event – 31 October 2019 – the Community finally revealed the true extent of its devastating ambition.

40.

Concerned that the Event site would be turned into a shrine, Natural England blocked all attempts made by the Community to buy the Chalkham Boar hill. However, the farmer who owned the adjacent fields had no such scruples and gladly sold them sixty-five acres. In early 2020, planning permission was granted for the Rachel of Chalkham Interactive Visitor Centre, but the place was still a field on 31 October 2019 when around eight hundred Members and high-profile supporters were invited to gather for the annual Celebration of Silence.

Dad and I were invited – we were sometimes asked to turn up to these sorts of things – but he said (and I quote) that he would rather run naked down Winchester High Street than stand around in a field with a bunch of Members. I didn't want to go either, but Fortuné convinced me that I should. As it turned out, his spouse visa would finally come through less than three weeks later, but at that point we were both anxious that something might still go wrong with the application. He said he would come with me to the commemoration. We would just show our faces – there was no need for us to talk to anyone, just make sure I was seen to be toeing the party line. I said fine, if he felt that strongly that I should be there, and if he promised not to leave my side, we could go, provided we did not go to the village of Chalkham itself, not under any circumstances. Just the idea of standing in that street where Steven Trent had killed those people made me feel sick.

As with everything the Community does, the anniversary was planned like a military operation. Fortuné had been involved in the logistics for the day and security was tight: miles of fencing had been erected around the entire area, various forms of ID were required and everyone had to pass through a body scanner before entering.

Once in the field itself, the scale of the commemorations became clear. Everything was oversized. There was an enormous stage, topped by a huge pair of inflatable neon-pink lips with a disembodied finger pressed against them, tethered to the ground by thick steel ropes. The backdrop of the stage was made up of multiple video screens, which themselves were surrounded by stacks of speakers. On the right-hand side, one of the video screens displayed the time, the second hand sweeping round a clock face, while the minute hand ticked inexorably towards the exact time on that morning eight years ago when my mother had lit her pyre. All around the stage inflatable Shellys bobbed up and down. The whole effect was riotous, raucous and as far from being a sombre commemoration of mass suicide as it was possible to be.

To one side, there was a designated press area. Inevitably, it had been 'leaked' that the Community was about to announce a major new programme in its drive to tackle the population crisis. The press, who loved a Community announcement, had turned out in force.

Standing in this muddy field, on this damp, dank day – the sort of day that the south of England does so well – my attention was not held by the elaborate inflatables and over-the-top audio-visual displays; instead I couldn't tear my gaze away from what lay past the stage, beyond the perimeter fencing. I stared at the hill beyond which was dominated by the Chalkham Boar. I really didn't want to look at it, but I couldn't look at anything else. It was the first time I'd seen it in eight years. The first time I'd seen the Boar since I'd been there, on that hill, watching my mother burn to death.

Suddenly, from nowhere, I missed my mum with a grief so violent that I had to fight to contain it, to push it down, to press it back inside me, because if I did not, I was afraid it would overwhelm me. I forced myself to look away from the Boar and stepped to the side so Fortuné's back blocked my view of it. I swallowed noisily a couple of times and Fortuné looked at me. 'Ça va, mpenzi?' he asked. I tried and failed to smile, and he frowned and would have asked me again, but at that point a gong rang out around the field. The formal proceedings were about to begin.

The first item on the agenda was the small matter of remembering and commemorating the death of my mother and all 21,078 women who had died in the Event. Ceremonial firepits were lit around the field and as a huge *Shhhh…* banner was unfurled, Sophie and the other board members filed onto the stage while the video screens flashed up live footage of Members gathered at other Event sites around the world.

We began with a Guided Silence Session. That much was the same as it always had been. Sophie stepped up to a single microphone at the front of the stage. When the enormous clock on the video screen showed precisely 11.17, she took a deep breath and into the microphone said, 'Shhhh…' The second hand swept down the right-hand side of the clock face. When it reached the bottom Sophie fell silent, and the second-hand climbed back up the other side, sweeping inexorably past seven, eight, nine, ten, eleven. At the precise moment that it reached the top, the minute hand clicked forward and it was 11:18 and there, in that field in Hampshire, and in Event sites around the world, outside a shopping centre in Port Said in Egypt, on a rugby pitch alongside Lake Wakatipu in New Zealand, on a piece of waste ground on the outskirts of Concepción in Chile, in the foothills of the Ishpatina Ridge in Ontario and in so many other places where women had burned themselves to death in 2011, there was silence.

I can't know what anyone else heard in that silence, but I can tell you what I heard.

I heard the splutter of newly lit flames striving to take hold. I heard the roar of petrol-fed fire. I heard a raging heat killing everything it touched. I heard the screams of women unable to stay silent as their insides boiled. I heard the pleas of women begging for their implants to be removed. I heard the agonised cries of women beaten for failing to conceive. I heard the silence of women murdered because of what we had done to them.

Tears streamed down my face. Fortuné put his arm around me, but I shrugged it off. I didn't deserve his comfort.

Around the world the silence went on and on, but in my head the noise of suffering was deafening. Finally, after what felt like hours, although it was no more than ten minutes, Sophie spoke into the microphone. Her voice was quiet. 'Rachel taught us to listen and to hear, and by listening and hearing, we honour you, Rachel of Chalkham. We honour you and we honour the sacrifice of every single one of our Members who burned so that the world would listen. We honour you each time we hear the voice of someone whose voice has never been heard before.'

At that point she bowed her head slightly and nodded, like she was remembering all the countless occasions on which she herself had heard a previously unheard voice. It was rubbish: the woman was obsessed by only one voice, and she used it to continue talking.

'It was the privilege of my life to work with Rachel at her camp, just a mile away from here. Most of those who worked most closely with Rachel chose to embrace permanent silence in the Event, but I was chosen for a different task. I stood ready to grasp the opportunities that would come from the sacrifice of Rachel of Chalkham and the others, but every single day I wish I had been one of those who chose to sacrifice themselves.'

Fortuné looked at me sharply and I realised I'd actually snorted with laughter at the very idea that Sophie had ever spent so much as a minute wishing she had burned to death.

'For the eight years of her silence, Rachel exemplified how we should behave. And at 11.18 on 31 October 2011, Rachel's final act released the benefits that can be brought about by silence. Everything that we have achieved since that day was made possible by the sacrifice of so many at the Event.'

Sophie bowed her head. So did the others on the stage behind her. Who the hell were these people? I barely recognised any of them and I was certain that none of them had known my mother. I glanced at the Chalkham Boar. I remembered the day that Livy and I had seen Mum walking there alone, how distant she was from me even as she reached out to stroke my cheek. Surely that was Rachel's legacy: silence, solitude and, yes, listening to each other. Not this circus surrounding me.

I must have sighed or something, because Fortuné reached for my hand and this time I let him take it.

Sophie was still talking.

'Since the Event, for eight years now, we have been working tirelessly to deliver Rachel's Goals. Her actions illuminate the path along which we have been travelling. We all know that it's no coincidence that Rachel chose 31 October 2011 to be the date of the Event. It was the day the world's population reached seven billion. Overpopulation is the biggest crisis facing humanity. The numbers are reversing, but not fast enough. We need to travel further. We need to travel faster. We need to do more. We need to care more. I know some of you remain to be convinced. I know some of you are still asking "Why? Why must we do more?" But, if you are truly honest with yourselves, you know the reason why. We have only one world and our resources are insufficient. Despite all of our programmes, there is not enough food, there is not enough water, people are starving, resources are not shared fairly. These are problems we all face and every single one of us should care. Anyone who denies these things is not accepting the truth, because the truth is: there are too many people.'

And here it comes, I thought. *Here. It. Comes.*

Sophie turned towards the side of the stage, holding out her hand. Someone I didn't recognise scurried out and handed something to her. The camera zoomed in on it. It was a piece of A4 paper. She held it up but the camera was too far away for me to be able to read what was written on it.

'This is Rachel's final message to us all. She wrote the blueprint for our newest programme, which I am immensely proud and humbled to announce here, today, because this initiative, more than any other, truly honours the sacrifice of Rachel of Chalkham and all 21,078 Members who died in the Event. This programme is the culmination of everything that Rachel wanted her Community to achieve. It will deliver a fairer, happier world. It is the greatest honour of my life to present to you the fulfilment of Rachel's silence project.'

There was a drumroll and then fireworks exploded from the top of the stage and the giant screens behind Sophie flashed up 'Show euthCare'.

As other screens showed Members around the world jumping up and down, waving *Further, Faster*, banners, Sophie leaned close to the microphone. 'To explain the details of our revolutionary euthCare programme, I'd like to welcome to the stage one of our most talented rising stars. This Member is already known to many of you thanks to her bravery in the field and her courage in standing up for the truth. Please give a rousing Community welcome to... Casey Banza.'

It was not entirely unexpected, I suppose, although until that point I hadn't even realised that Casey was there. As she climbed the steps onto the stage, her limp was hardly noticeable. Sophie smiled and nodded and ceded her place at the microphone. Casey stood still, waiting for the applause to die down. Cameras picked out her face on the huge screens behind her. Beside me, Fortuné stiffened.

Then Casey began to speak, her words carrying to hundreds of Members in the field and thousands upon thousands more watching around the world. 'I care. Do you?' She paused, long enough for thousands of people to scream yes, they cared.

'EuthCare is a truly transformative programme, offering individuals a chance to sacrifice themselves for the benefit of their families, their society, humankind and our planet. We in the Community are providing you with a genuine opportunity to demonstrate how much you really do care. Just as Rachel made her death count, we are inviting you to make your death count, too. Just as Rachel chose permanent silence for the benefit of humanity, we are allowing you to choose a time to permanently silence yourself, too. Our euthCare programme offers the opportunity to show how much you care. It offers the opportunity for selfless silence. For transformative silence. For ultimate silence.'

Casey talked for a long time. She explained in great detail the things that, in the three years since that day, have become disturbingly familiar to us all. She described how, in return for transferring your assets to the Community and committing to a pre-agreed date for your death, you would receive the opportunity to spend the rest of your time in 'beautiful live-in facilities' with 'top-class chefs' responsible for preparing 'gourmet meals' (strictly Leaf not Beef compliant, of course) before people retired to 'luxury bedrooms' with beds complete with '2,000 thread-count Egyptian cotton sheets' to ensure 'a perfect night's sleep, every night'. With the aid of a slick video, Casey ran through how each participant would have access to leisure activities and sports complexes; to beauticians and hairdressers and yoga instructors; to classes in everything from flower arranging to ju-jitsu and creative writing, woodwork, painting and music lessons.

She shifted up a gear when she explained how medical professionals would ensure that the benefit of every single death would be 'maximised' because a planned death meant all useable organs, tissue and cells could be harvested and reused for the benefit of future generations.

She was at pains to point out that you didn't even have to become a Member to sign up – the euthCare programme would be open to all.

What Casey entirely failed to mention were the dozens of actuaries employed around the world whose job is to adjust and refine the algorithms which determine such matters as how the wealthier you are at the point you transfer ownership of your assets to the Community and enter a facility, the more luxurious that facility will be; or how the earlier your pre-agreed date of euthanasia, the greater the number of facilities that will be on offer to you; or how the older you are when you sign up to the programme, the less medical care you will be given once you forfeit your money, your home, your life as you knew it; or how the algorithms take into account the number of children you've had and shift your priority levels down accordingly to 'compensate the world' for your selfish decisions.

This, then, was the euthCare programme: stunning in ambition, diabolical in intention.

★

Of course, we had seen it coming, Fortuné and me. So had many others. Not the scale of it, perhaps, nor the specific details, but certainly the intention to persuade people to commit suicide 'for the good of humanity'. But what I don't think anyone properly understood until that day and that speech by Casey was how it would benefit the Community.

Driving home, we were silent at first. I think I was in shock. But, as you know, I can't bear silence for long.

'I feel like I'm living in a prequel to some terrible dystopian novel,' I said.

Fortuné glanced at me, puzzled.

'Most dystopian novels,' I continue, 'throw you right into whatever strange hell people are living in, but there's normally not much detail about how that hell came about. But here we are in the prequel. We're in pre-hell. This is how it begins. Trouble is, this is not a novel: it's real life and it's completely terrifying.'

Fortuné nodded. 'Adui wa mtu, ni mtu.'

'I know, I know, the enemy of man is man,' I said, not really in the mood for Fortuné's aphorisms, which he always preferred to deliver in Swahili. 'Although, right now it's probably more appropriate to say the enemy of man is the Community.'

'That too,' he said.

'Another thing,' I continued, 'there's no way that piece of paper Sophie was waving around was written by Mum. I just don't believe it. This is what I've been saying for years. How many "blueprints" for how many programmes is Mum supposed to have written, for god's sake? And all this stuff about how Sophie is speaking for Rachel, that *this* was what Rachel had intended her Community to become, *that* was why she chose the date for the Event, *this* is the culmination of my mother's silence project. That woman has no idea what Mum wanted her Community to achieve. How could she?'

'It's a shame your mother didn't write a diary, *mpenzi*,' said Fortuné, flicking the indicator and accelerating onto the motorway.

My husband couldn't possibly have anticipated the consequences of what he'd just said as we were speeding along a sliproad onto the M3 motorway because, throwaway though his comment was, *that* was the moment when I finally remembered Mum's notebooks.

The box they were kept in had been moved from place to place over the years until, at the beginning of 2019 when Fortuné and I moved into a larger flat, I finally reclaimed all the things I'd stored at Dad's. The plastic IKEA box had been in a van load of other belongings we had collected from Winchester.

I don't know why I hadn't thought of the notebooks before. Predictably, Fortuné says that after so many years of not giving them a second thought I remembered them at precisely the time when I was finally ready to do something with them. I don't believe that, and if I had to hazard a guess, I would say that the combination of seeing the Chalkham Boar, remembering the Event all over again, hearing all the lies spouted by Sophie and the horrors of Casey's euthCare programme was so completely overwhelming that it washed away the final barriers I had constructed around my memories of Mum.

Or maybe there is a simpler explanation. Perhaps I missed her so much that day that I needed to find a way to be close to her. I don't know.

Whatever the reason, when we arrived home I didn't even wait for Fortuné to turn off the engine before I threw myself out of the car, raced into our flat and up to the spare room. I knelt on the floor, peered under the bed and pulled out the box.

At first, I didn't take the lid off. It occurred to me that I might not be doing the right thing after all. I had never read Mum's notebooks. I hadn't even flicked through them. I had no idea what I'd find. What if Rachel's silence project wasn't as benign as it had appeared to be? What if Sophie was right and Rachel really had made plans for every awful thing the Community was doing? What if the notebooks laid out plans for all the population-management programmes, the implant programme, this horrific euthCare programme? What if Sophie and the others were just following Rachel's instructions?

What if my mum was a monster?

I don't know how long I sat on the floor running through all the 'what ifs' but it was long enough for Fortuné to bring me a cup of coffee and for it to go cold on the floor beside me.

In the end, of course, I made myself open the box.

I lifted out all of the notebooks and realised that Mum had numbered each one on their inside front covers. I laid them out in order. There were twenty-nine of them, all different sizes and colours.

Then I opened notebook #1 to page 1 and I began to read.

Afterword

Rachel's silence changed the world for ever.

Consider what the Community has helped to achieve. Quite aside from the hugely influential Conflict Resolution Academies, there are the breakthroughs announced earlier this year by the Community's Climate Health Sector: the reduction in carbon emissions to pre-1990 levels; the almost complete cessation of deforestation in Brazil and Indonesia; sixteen countries on target to achieve net reforestation within the next three years; the massive reduction in meat consumption; the generation of 49.8 per cent of the world's electricity using renewables in 2021.

The Community does not claim to have achieved these things alone, but there is no doubt that its money, influence and popularity have all played a huge part in the success of these initiatives. These things benefit us all so why, I keep wondering, isn't this enough?

Fractured World: Life without Community (eds Dr S. Thomas and Dr E. James, Tricornity Press, 2022) is a series of essays written by acknowledged experts in their fields who were asked to speculate what our world would be like if the Community had never come into existence. The picture they paint is bleak. They posit a world of rampant climate catastrophes. Without the unifying international coalescence that happened around the Community after the Event, at best they envisage political alliances fracturing, divisions deepening, opinions polarising and, at worst, devastating factional conflicts, genocides, a better-than-evens chance of nuclear war. They are adamant that without Community-driven curbs on meat production there would inevitably have been a proliferation of cross-species disease, likely leading to a global pandemic, although they also consider it possible that lithospheric frailty in the earth's crust created by fracking might have killed us first. These dark visions of where our pre-Event world was heading is purely speculative, of course, but according to the contributors to *Fractured World*, these were just some of the devastating futures awaiting humanity if Rachel had not founded the Community.

Of course, we can never know what would have happened to our world if my mother had not stopped talking. But I believe it is imperative that we ask ourselves: is what is happening a price worth paying for what *might have* happened?

From the outset the Community fixated on solving what it calls the 'population crisis'. It was the third of what they declared to be Rachel's Goals and positioned as something both reasonable and necessary. However, their absolute focus on it has led them to conclude that certain people are expendable. They are following a contemptible tradition of drawing an arbitrary line and labelling one side of it 'us' and the other side 'them', and for the Community, older people have become 'them'.

In many parts of the world now, suicide is no longer seen as something to be avoided. Suicide is encouraged as a generous act. There is increasing pressure on anyone over the age of sixty-five to commit to a date on which they will enter Community facilities, and in a growing number of countries, a failure to agree a date for one's suicide is considered supremely selfish. It is well documented that those who refuse to do so are often shunned and deprived of social and/or medical care. The 'Choose euthCare' marches on the first Saturday of each month have become a global phenomenon, as young people 'remind' the elderly to 'do their duty', 'show you care' and 'choose euthanasia'.

Meanwhile, the actuaries who work out the euthCare projections continue to do an outstanding job: the Community has accumulated unimaginable sums of money by persuading people to exchange everything they own in return for the promise of a 'life of luxury' for a limited period before dying on a contractually agreed date.

I cannot atone for what my mother created; all I can do is say that I am certain Rachel did not intend her legacy to become what it has. My mother sincerely hoped that her silence project would persuade people to listen to each other and by so doing bring about a more peaceful, more understanding, kinder society. I do not believe she intended her Community to do more than that. Dad and I agreed to publish the notebooks in order to return Rachel's voice to her, and we believe they demonstrate that Rachel did not and could not anticipate what the Community has become. She would not have wanted this.

However, there is another reason why Dad and I decided to make the notebooks public. Even the most conservative estimates predict that the royalties from their publication will run into the hundreds of millions, and Dad and I are united in our view that we should not receive a single penny of it. Money cannot prevent all the harm that is being done. Money alone will probably not stop the Community. But money might at least be able to help, and so all royalties from the sale of Mum's notebooks will go to charities offering assistance to the victims of the Community's cruel and self-interested programmes and to organisations working tirelessly to weaken the Community's stranglehold on public consciousness around the world.

I cannot honestly say whether my mother would approve, but I like to think she would.

Then there is this book that you have just read, a companion piece to the notebooks, an account of my life as Rachel of Chalkham's daughter and my years as both a willing and an unwilling Member of the Community.

I did not expect to find writing this book so difficult. I did not expect to feel such conflicting emotions about my relationship with my mother or to find it so painful to re-examine her silence. I am grateful for the opportunity that writing this book has given me to hold my anger up to the light, to examine it, to understand it, and in doing so allow it to begin to dissolve. It is with a considerable amount of pleasure and relief that, as I write this today, I realise I am no longer angry with my mother.

I have informed my publishers that I will not be undertaking any press or marketing activities. My account will be read, or it won't. It will be taken at face value, or it won't. For me, the important thing was to tell the truth about Rachel and her Community, and that I have done.

Dad has taken up his new lecturing post. He emails me regularly about his visits to see nesting albatrosses and glimpses of the aurora australis. He is a big fan of the wineries in New Zealand. He sounds happy.

Fortuné and I have returned to the Democratic Republic of the Congo. When the plane landed in Goma, I burst into tears. We had come home.

Thankfully, the Community's interest in Congo has waned and their presence is limited to a handful of largely benign Climate Sector programmes. That is not to say they won't decide to trial another solution out here, but for the moment they are focused on establishing euthCare facilities in countries with high numbers of wealthy older individuals. The implant programme was dismantled nearly three years ago, and one of the charities that will benefit from the royalties from Mum's notebooks offers a free no-strings-attached implant-removal service. Scholar is co-chair of the charity, which operates in six African countries.

Andréa has come to live with Fortuné and me, for which I am immensely grateful because I will need her help when the baby arrives. The pregnancy was a surprise and Fortuné and his whole family are delighted, as is Dad. I am too, except a little part of me can't help worrying that, having spent so much of my life living with the label 'daughter', I will not know how to add 'mother' to my identity. Andréa says I'm getting myself worked up about nothing, that being a mother will come as naturally to me as breathing. I wish I could be as certain.

Andréa is a strong woman. She lost her husband to war and raised nine babies before her youngest, Nicolas, was killed by poachers. And yet, even though Fortuné is a grown man, it is clear to me that when they are together Andréa is simultaneously seeing not only Fortuné her adult son but her baby boy, too. In her gaze, as she watches my husband making a crib for our child, Andréa is remembering his new-born-baby smell, his cries, his arms reaching for her. He may be my husband, he may be about to become a father, but Fortuné will always be her baby, and the more time I spend with Andréa, the more I understand that, before anything, she is a mother.

I cannot say the same about Rachel.

How will I know how to do what Rachel did not?

And yet, finally, I am able to say that I am proud of my mother. She was an ordinary woman who did an extraordinary thing, and in a world where so few people believe in anything, she believed in her silence project. She believed she was doing something important. Perhaps that is all anyone can do. Perhaps it is enough.

**Emilia Morris, Democratic Republic of the Congo
December 2022**

Author's note

I was supposed to visit the Democratic Republic of the Congo in March 2020 but as a result of the pandemic, the trip was put on hold. I have spent time in both Rwanda and Uganda, which helped inform my descriptions of the wildlife and landscape (the Virunga mountains where the gorillas live span all three countries). The research I undertook to try and imagine what it might be like for a young woman from Hampshire arriving for a new job in Goma highlighted the lack of Democratic Republic of the Congo authors published in English. I am indebted to the authors and publishers of the following and highly recommend them: Fiston Mwanza Mujila's *The River in the Belly* (translated by J. Bret Maney) is a stunning collection of poems, rivalled only by his novel *Tram 83* (translated by Roland Glasser); and *Congo Inc. Bismarck's Testament* by In Koli Jean Bofane (translated by Marjolijn de Jager) is a searing indictment of the legacy of the colonisation of Congo. Although Alain Mabanckou hails from the Republic of the Congo, his many wonderful novels allowed me to peer over the border into its much larger neighbour. English-speaking monoglots could only benefit from greater access to voices from the Democratic Republic of the Congo.

I am deeply grateful to the London Library for the year I spent as a 2020/21 Emerging Writer, during which I had access to the most incredible resources. In particular, Mbadu Fidèle Muanda, Gahungu Parfait Ndongo, Lauren J. Messina & Jane T. Bertrand

(2017) "Barriers to modern contraceptive use in rural areas in DRC" in *Culture, Health & Sexuality*, 19:9, 1011–1023 and Anatole Romaniuk, "Persistence of High Fertility in Tropical Africa: The Case of the Democratic Republic of the Congo" in *Population and Development Review*, vol. 37, no. 1, 2011, pp. 1–28 provided the statistics quoted in the novel with regards to the low use of contraceptives in DRC, as well as the reluctance to use contraceptives as discussed by the character Professor Ruth Ngoy.

This novel is a deliberate blending of fact and fiction, reality and unreality, and although, generally, it is for the reader to decide for themselves where one ends and the other begins, I would like to make it clear that the church in Kibuye in Rwanda with its display of skulls and its message of 'Never Again' is a real place and one of many locations in Rwanda which remembers the estimated million people killed during the Rwandan genocide in 1994.